FLIGHTWISE

PRINCIPLES OF AIRCRAFT FLIGHT

CHRIS CARPENTER

Airlife
England

Copyright © 1996 Christopher Carpenter

First published in the UK in 1996
by Airlife Publishing Ltd

British Library Cataloguing in Publication Data
A catalogue record for this book
is available from the British Library

ISBN 1 85310 719 0

Typeset by Wearset, Boldon, Tyne and Wear
Printed and bound in Great Britain by
Biddles Ltd, Guildford and King's Lynn

Airlife Publishing Ltd
101 Longden Road, Shrewsbury SY3 9EB

Foreword

For many of us flight still has a magical quality. To see a modern airliner weighing hundreds of tons lumbering along a runway, then suddenly rising majestically into the air, always seems somewhat amazing.
The phenomenal performance of birds that can hover, twist, dart,
glide and land almost vertically, is a constant source of wonderment.
At some point in our lives we all ask the question, how do they do
that?

Chris Carpenter has set out to explain in mainly non-mathematical
terms just how an aeroplane flies. He is not the first person to undertake the difficult task of explaining in simple terms, the branch of
applied mathematics, called aerodynamics, which lies at the heart of
everything to do with flight.

Chris himself refers to Air Commodore Kermode's books *The
Mechanics of Flight* and *Flight without Formulae* which first appeared
in the 1930s. Penguin Books published a splendid paperback by
Professor O. G. Sutton in 1948 called *The Science of Flight*, but this
text has long since been out of print.

Aerodynamics is full of subtlety, sophistication, complexity and
beauty. None of these things are easy to explain but explanation is
possible given some interest and enthusiasm on the part of the reader.
Aerodynamics is also full of ideas and concepts which, whilst no doubt
clear to their originators, need 'translation' for a wider audience.
Anyone who has tried to read the early papers by Newton or
Lanchester will see how hard it is to explain something entirely new.
Often the vocabulary has to be invented and vague analogies resorted
to. Then over the years with use and application, new ideas are clari-
fied and made more understandable.

Flightwise, like its predecessors, is to be welcomed. Chris Carpenter
has shirked nothing. He tackles all the ideas, the concepts, the difficulties with careful determination. The result is a book which represents
another excellent step forward in the adventure of understanding
aerodynamics.

Professor J. L. Stollery, CBE, DSc(Eng), FEng

Contents

Preface

This book might alternatively (if dryly) have been entitled 'The Physiology of the Aeroplane'. Physiology is defined in Chambers Dictionary as 'the science of the processes of life in animals and plants'. Like the birds which the early aviators wished to imitate, the aeroplane in its three-dimensional world of freedom has a 'life', a *modus operandi*, which is the source of fascination to many. For the amateur enthusiast and the professional aviator or engineer alike, an understanding of the principles on which flight depends and by which it is controlled is at least highly desirable, and for many it is absolutely essential.

To understand these principles requires of the reader only the degree of intelligence which most people possess combined with an enquiring mind which incessantly asks 'why?', and is not satisfied with the trite (and frequently incomplete or fallacious) explanations so often offered in popular literature on the subject. A facility with advanced mathematics is demonstrably not required, unless one needs to pursue the subject further for some specific purpose. Mathematics is a tool for analysts and designers, and is scarcely ever intended as an aid to understanding. Despite the use of the term 'mathematical modelling', mathematics does not provide the reassurance of a scale model, or a tangible representation of a physical system, and it is not (for most people) a visual aid to understanding. Rather, to understand the mathematical model involves delving to a second, deeper level of comprehension, a tier beneath that of the physical system itself. The upper tier should and can be understood very fully first of all, and the mathematics tackled afterwards or alongside if needed.

Through my experience of teaching the aerodynamic principles of flight over a number of years, I have become very aware of the need for a book based on the above principles. *Flightwise* has therefore been written in the hope that it will fill this gap in aeronautical literature.

On one side of this gap there is the essential and mainly excellent range of aerodynamics text books, some targeted at engineering undergraduates, some at graduates, some of broad coverage and some highly specialised. These books are almost invariably very heavily weighted towards the analytical aspects of the subject, and are hence inevitably packed full of mathematics, much of which is very advanced by any standards. Some also offer substantial textual explanations of the principles being dealt with, but these explanations may not appear to the reader to stand alone but rather to be an integral part of the related analytical procedure. Whilst this is no doubt intellectually justifiable, my experience of students is that they tend to gloss over any difficulties that they may have in understanding the principles properly, so long as they can master the tricks needed to produce the required answers. Such an approach is perhaps well geared to our existing higher education teaching and examination system. Sadly the student is under great pressure to pass examinations, where questions tend to be mainly mathematical in content since such are easier to set and to mark 'objectively' than questions designed to reveal the student's understanding of the material.

Two specific examples from my experience vividly illustrate the problem resulting from such an approach. At a lecture more than halfway through an advanced course being given to well qualified and motivated graduates, a gasp of exclamation spontaneously arose from almost the entire class, when for the first time they suddenly realised what a boundary layer was, and that it had physical significance for an aircraft. The subject of the course was Boundary Layers!

The second example occurred in one of my aerodynamics classes of Royal Air Force Engineer Officers under training at the Royal Air Force College at Cranwell. The course would have been better named 'principles of flight', since to many people the word 'aerodynamics' implies 'lots of very difficult, scarcely relevant mathematics'. In fact the course was deliberately non-mathematical, but it sought rather to explain qualitatively, in considerable intellectual depth, the relationship between an aircraft's shape and features and the aerodynamic forces on it. At the start of each course, I explained this to the students, who were mostly engineering graduates, and offered any aeronautical graduates the opportunity to opt out of the course and to do some individual project work instead, this option almost invariably being taken. On one such occasion, an honours aeronautical engineering graduate chose rather to continue with the course. The classes were small, and there was plenty of opportunity for interaction between myself and the students, so that by the use of directed questions each student's grasp of the subject matter quickly became apparent. I was astonished to discover that this particular student, who had satisfied his examiners in the (no doubt mathematical and analytical) questions he had been set at university, was probably the slowest on the uptake and the least well informed on aeronautical principles that I had ever taught on one of these courses. He had never been encouraged to ask 'why?'

On the other side of the literary gap, there is very much less literature available. There have been various simple manuals and notes produced to introduce *ab initio* pilots and aircraft tradesmen to the barest rudiments of the subject, and the occasional item in popular socalled 'encyclopaedias', but these are often peppered with crude and erroneous over-simplifications which can be thoroughly misleading.

On the other hand, an excellent pair of books, *The Mechanics of Flight* and *Flight without Formulae*, both by the late Air Commodore A. C. Kermode CBE MA FRAeS, have since their first appearance in the 1930s been the most noteworthy authoritative works attempting to fill the said gap. Kermode's books have provided part of the inspiration for writing *Flightwise*, in which I have attempted to do a similar job.

Flightwise is composed largely around a compilation of my own teaching thoughts and notes produced for courses which I have taught within the Royal Air Force and at the University of Warwick. I have also used similar teaching material with amateur enthusiasts in an Adult Education evening class and a flying club, and in all cases the response of the audience to the style adopted has been enthusiastic and heartening, making me confident in the hope that most readers will find reading *Flightwise* a rewarding and enjoyable experience. For those who require a mathematical treatment in order to be able to produce numerical results, the book does not claim to be a total text, but it is hoped that it will provide such people with valuable introductory and supporting material, answering those questions which are so often annoyingly glossed over in the deeper texts.

I should like to thank all those who have contributed towards the creation of this book: to all the staff of the College of Aeronautics at Cranfield University, for presenting me with an excellent grounding in the subject of aerodynamics and flight mechanics, and in particular to Professor John Spillman, the style and substance of whose lecturing at Cranfield has had a strong influence on all of my own teaching and writing; to Ian Sturgess, Malcolm Wilkes and the late Alastair Jackson for volunteering to read the draft of the book, and for their highly valued advice; to my colleagues in the Engineering Department of the University of Warwick for freeing me to take sabbatical leave to write this book; and to all of the students whom I have had the privilege of teaching, who are without doubt the greatest source of inspiration of all.

Chris Carpenter
Weston on Avon
1996

Author's Introduction

Starting from the premise that the reader is intelligent but has no scientific, technical or advanced mathematical training or knowledge, this book has a two-fold aim. Firstly it attempts to provide a thorough insight and depth of understanding into the subject of the principles of aircraft aerodynamics and flight, (hence the title). Secondly it is hoped that the reader will be left with a deep sense of satisfaction at having got thoroughly to grips with a subject that most people, through ignorance and a misguided sense of the difficulty associated with anything scientific, (especially aerodynamics!), prefer to leave in the hands of the experts. Combining both of these aims, it is hoped that *Flightwise* will provide you with enjoyable reading, rather than an exercise in academic drudgery.

If you are concerned about the level and amount of mathematics to be encountered, rest assured that advanced mathematics is emphatically not needed to achieve the objectives of the previous paragraph. A certain amount of mathematical terminology (e.g. the meaning of direct and inverse proportion, the sine and cosine of an angle, and the elementary geometrical handling of vector quantities) makes the task of explanation very much simpler, but such concepts will be introduced *ab initio* when required for those unfamiliar with them. Beyond this, the use and manipulation of very simple algebraic formulae (such as one quantity being expressed as the product or quotient of two or three others), will be the limit of the mathematical treatment. The laws of indices will be called upon in a couple of places, but guidance will be provided in the text as to where the reader may skip to if he or she is unfamiliar with these. Where ideas based on elementary calculus emerge, these will be treated in such a way that those unversed in calculus will be able to follow the arguments fully without recourse to the small amount of differential notation used.

This is not to imply that the subject of aerodynamics is devoid of mathematics – far from it! Indeed, a full analytical study of most of the concepts covered in this book involves in-depth use of mathematics, much of which is very advanced by any standards. However, this mathematics is not designed and does not serve to *explain* the subject, but rather to take it through to its full analytical conclusion, for the sake of those whose work requires them to produce quantitative answers.

For the serious student of aerodynamics with professional aims, this book is not intended and will not serve as a complete text. Its aim for you is rather to provide support, either before or alongside your analytical studies, and to add some flesh to the often necessarily skeletal explanatory sections sandwiched between the mathematical developments in your aerodynamics textbook. A student who only learns to do sums and exam questions (however well) without having a good grasp of the physical principles underlying them has his development potential severely stifled.

This book deals with the 'why?' and the 'how?' of the principles of aircraft flight. If you have an enquiring mind and are interested in fixed-wing aeroplanes, the book is meant for you. Enjoy it!

CHAPTER 1
The Requirements of a Flying Machine

INTRODUCTION

Ever since man first took to the air, his flying machines have taken on a plethora of different forms. At first his determination to fly was motivated simply by the desire to prove his mastery over the last of the elements, and to achieve the three-dimensional freedom envied of the birds and for so many centuries denied to him.

Once the initial challenge had been met, it gradually became apparent that this new-found ability had opened up a tremendous range of practical possibilities, both peaceful and warlike. Having discovered how to construct a machine that could carry a pilot aloft, the quest was now on to perfect the machine for each of its possible roles, and thus the development of the aeroplane's shape and equipment branched out into the many ramifications that we have seen between those early days and today.

A total classification of all flying machines would include lighter-than-air craft, fixed-wing aircraft, rotary-wing craft, space-craft and hovercraft. This basic subdivision, and the many uses made of vehicles in each, immediately illustrates the vast scope of practical possibilities which have been opened up by the achievement of flight. It also shows dramatically how the form of the flying machine has evolved very differently according to the demands being made of it.

Because of this great diversity, we will restrict our attention in this book to fixed-wing aircraft. After a brief overview in this chapter of the uses to which fixed-wing aircraft have been put, and a discussion of the capabilities and features which these requirements have demanded of the design, we will go on in subsequent chapters to consider the means that the aeronautical engineer has discovered and developed of designing aircraft to meet these demands.

Of course there is very much more to a modern aircraft than simply the airframe. The sub-branch of engineering referred to as Aeronautical is often thought of as a specialisation, but in fact it might well be argued that the aeronautical engineer is the least specialised of any in the engineering profession. An aeronautical engineer needs to be well versed in very many branches of engineering science and technology including structures, aerodynamics and fluid mechanics, thermodynamics and propulsion systems, chemical engineering, power electrics, electronics, computer science, control systems, materials technology and other newer and more specialised subject areas. In the early days, his three basic needs were a knowledge of aerodynamics, of propulsion systems and of structures. The only one of these which needed to be developed uniquely for the purposes of flight was aero-dynamics, since the feature which distinguishes an aircraft from all other vehicles is that the only forces acting upon it (apart from gravi-ty) are those caused by the passage of air over its surface and through its propulsion system.

The aerodynamic forces on an aircraft depend mainly on its exter-nal shape. Fortunately for us, this is the feature of the aircraft which is most universally familiar and readily perceived. It is of course the shape of the aircraft which is captured in photographs, and so this is the first feature which tends to capture the imagination of the enthusi-ast, and which identifies the aircraft and specifies its role and capabili-ties to the expert. It is discussion of the shape of the aeroplane, together with the reasons for the evolution of this shape, that forms the substance of this book.

WHAT IS AN AEROPLANE?

Let us imagine an intelligent aspiring flying machine inventor in a world in which manned-flight had not been achieved. What are the basic requirements in getting aloft and travelling through the air? In the first place, he requires some form of box or platform to carry the pilot and perhaps (thinking ahead) some additional load. Then he requires some means of supplying an upward force to overcome the ubiquitous downward force of gravity. Since this can only be supplied by the air, and experience suggests that forces due to air flowing over objects like his box are generally small compared with the force of gravity, he realises he will probably need a surface with a considerable horizontal area. If the required upward force is not to over-balance the load box, it would seem necessary to distribute the area of this sur-face symmetrically about the box. The concept of a body (fuselage) and a pair of wings emerges, and the designer's observation of the birds would suggest that he had got it right so far!

The question then arises (so tiresome to the early aspiring aviators) as to how the wings are to produce the required upward force which we will for now call 'lift'. Observation of the birds suggests that this can only be achieved either by energetic flapping or by advancing steadily through the air. The experiences of his fore-runners with their ornithopter experiments make our designer wary of adopting the for-mer (flapping) approach, and so he decides to investigate the latter. This ties in well with his additional requirement of progressing through the air, and so it seems that he will also require some means of propulsion. Any push or pull from a ground-based object would be cheating, and would severely limit his scope, and so he requires something that will push or pull against the air. The concept of the fan or propeller is familiar to him, and so he decides on a propeller together with some power source to drive it round, which he will place in his load box. This also demands that he decide on a direction of travel, and hence a 'front' and a 'back' for his box. From this, together with the requirement for the wings to be symmetrically disposed, the conventional basic form of the fixed-wing aircraft familiar to us is beginning to emerge. Another glance at the birds suggests that he is on the right track, although they seem to prefer frantic wing flapping to the designer's choice of a propeller for propulsion.

In passing, it is interesting to note that nature abhors rotating parts. Not only do birds not sport propellers, but the idea of an animal with wheels appears equally absurd! This is because peripheral living tissue needs to be connected with the main body (the power house and control centre) by means of various ducts (e.g. veins and arteries), movement actuators (muscles, tendons) and signal-carrying leads (nerves). On one revolution of an organic wheel or propeller, all of these would get hopelessly twisted together! The invention of the wheel, (and of the propeller), required for its development beyond a simple roller the more fundamental invention of the rotating bearing, an idea not taken from the natural world. However, the bearing brings with it its own problems, such as transmitting any services or control-runs to the rotating equipment mounted on it. (Try unrolling a hose-pipe or electrical cable from a reel, with the centrally emerging connector or plug connected to the tap or mains!)

Returning to our aircraft, we will take a giant leap forward and assume that the designer has worked out how to shape his wings so that, with forward motion provided by the engine-driven propeller, they produce the required lift force to support the total weight. Having attached some wheels to facilitate the earth-borne acceleration needed to reach flying speed, he attempts to get airborne.

As he leaves the ground, he discovers that he loses the reassuring natural stability that firm contact with the earth had been providing, and that his craft immediately tends to pitch nose-down into the ground. Assuming that he and the craft survive this unnerving experience, he returns to the drawing-board to investigate how he might control his craft against this pitching effect. Once safely airborne, he will also require to adjust his craft according to whether he wishes to climb or descend, and he realises that the same control will be capable of serving this purpose. After considerable investigation he realises that he needs another symmetrical lifting surface, smaller than the wing, placed a good distance either in front of or behind the wing, whose lifting effect he can control manually. This will be capable of providing a pitching effect (a 'moment') by which he will be able both to compensate for the natural pitching effect which he experienced on leaving the ground, and also to control his aircraft upwards and downwards once airborne. He decides upon the aft position, and calls the surface a tailplane.

Aviation history has in fact provided us with two possible configurations for this pitching control surface. The Wright brothers put theirs at the front, but almost all later aircraft designers have found it preferable to mount the surface at the rear. However, this does not mean that the Wright brothers necessarily got it wrong, and today a number of modern aircraft, from light sporting types to ultra-sophisticated combat aircraft, have reverted to having this control mounted at the front. This is called the canard configuration, about which much more will be said in *Flightwise: Aircraft Stability and Control*.

To support the aft pitch control surface and provide it with a moment arm (effectively a lever), our designer realises that he must extend the load box, or fuselage, aft. By skinning the extension, this will provide additional space to increase the load-carrying capacity. But in order to maintain fore-and-aft weight balance, the fuselage must also be extended in the forward direction. Thus the familiar long, thin fuselage is a natural development. This is doubly fortuitous since the long narrow shape enables the size of the fuselage to be increased without any increase, and even possibly a reduction, in air resistance, so that more forward speed can be achieved with the same powerplant. Again the birds seem to have got the idea first! Furthermore, since our designer has opted for an aft tailplane, he is able to mount his engine and propeller centrally in the space now available at the front of the fuselage.

Safely airborne at last! The up-and-down (pitch) control proves difficult and demanding to handle, but the designer decides to return to that problem later on. In the meantime, to cut a very long story short for now, in order to have total control over the motion of the aircraft both in the air and during take-off and landing, he develops means of rotating the aircraft about both the fore-and-aft axis (rolling) using wing-tip control surfaces known as ailerons, and also about the axis perpendicular to the plane of the wings and fuselage (yawing). The latter is achieved by means of a fin and rudder above the tailplane, and works in a similar fashion to the tailplane but sideways. The extended fuselage proves useful again for this purpose.

So by an almost inevitable logical development, the aircraft has taken on the basic form of most aircraft with which we are familiar – a cruciform of fuselage and wings, with small horizontal and vertical flying surfaces at the rear. The needs of airborne load-carrying under control have been met.

It was mentioned that the controls were demanding to handle. The solution to this problem necessitated ensuring that the aircraft possessed natural stability during flight. This means that, if the aircraft deviates vertically or horizontally from the required direction in any untoward fashion, it should be so designed that it naturally, without pilot intervention, tends to recover from the deviation smoothly and quickly. This does not usually require the use of additional flying surfaces or other components to those already incorporated, but merely very careful attention to the precise shape and relative positioning of these components.

Complete stability is not an essential attribute of an aircraft. However, just as our designer's initial attempt at taking-off could have proved disastrous for lack of stability, very many aircraft have met catastrophic ends through the same short-coming. It may be possible for the pilot to take rapid recovery action, but if his reactions are not quick enough or if he is otherwise busily occupied, such action might not be attempted until it is too late and recovery is impossible. A reasonable degree of stability is virtually essential in the interests both of flight safety and also of minimising the pilot's work-load.

Thus we have developed the basic form of a powered, load-carrying, controllable, stable, fixed-wing aircraft, by means of considering the barest essentials of flight. The aircraft development tree now branches, and we look at some of the additional requirements which have been made of the fixed-wing aircraft, and the influences that these have had on aircraft development.

WHAT MAKES A BETTER AEROPLANE?

Speed

It was not long before the aircraft's potential for speeds substantially higher than could be obtained by earth-bound vehicles was realised and exploited. Initially the motivation was purely for sport and the challenge presented, but very quickly thoughts turned to high-speed transportation of people and goods. Although speed was not at first needed for military applications, once fighter aircraft design became competitive to the death it was realised that speed (amongst other things) was a major contributor to dominance in combat and escape. In another scenario, as represented by the retired American SR71 Blackbird reconnaissance aircraft (which is making a come-back), extreme speeds have proved their usefulness in rapid aerial surveying.

The air resistance (technically the drag) of an aircraft increases with the square of its speed. (Doubling the speed implies quadrupling the drag; trebling the speed increases the drag nine-fold.) Thus the quest for high speed implies the need to keep the dragginess of the aircraft as low as possible, or to provide more and more thrust from the propulsion system to overcome the increased drag, or both. We are here concerned with the drag, since the propulsion system, a very major factor in the development of modern high-speed aircraft, is not the concern of this book.

The search for low aircraft drag resulted in the enclosing and smoothing of the fuselage, in comparison with the very early aircraft in which a simple open framework sufficed. As mentioned earlier, the lengthening of the fuselage resulting from the need for pitch control was fortuitous in that drag was thus reduced.

As for the wings, the early biplane configuration, which was ubiquitous on account of its very strong structure with its spars and bracing wires, was superseded by the monoplane as a result of the quest for less drag. This was a vast improvement, since the spars and bracing wires tended to produce a contribution to the total drag very much greater than is suggested by their relative thin-ness and small frontal area. With the monoplane also came the retractable undercarriage, an enormous advance when it is appreciated that the drag of an aircraft's undercarriage may be as much as the drag of the whole of the rest of the aircraft. Beyond these quantum steps in drag reduction, there has been (and continues to be) continual improvement in the design of low-drag wing cross-sections (aerofoils) and wing planforms.

As speed increased, a 'new' phenomenon was encountered as aircraft approached the speed of sound, and an apparently impenetrable speed barrier (the so-called 'sound barrier') presented an obstacle for a long time. Not only had thrust systems using propellers reached the limit of development, but aircraft drag was found to become suddenly very much greater. Shock waves were encountered, resulting in a new type of drag (wave drag) not met in lower speed aircraft. However, the aerodynamic challenges were met, the propeller gave way to the newly invented jet engine, and the 'sound barrier' became merely a hiccup in the drive towards higher and higher speeds.

Manoeuvrability

When aeroplane began to engage aeroplane in dog-fights, it soon became apparent that, although speed could give a pilot a major advantage, an equally important feature enabling him to dominate the engagement was the ability to make very tight turns in any direction. Surprisingly, as we shall see later, it was not so much the effectiveness of the control surfaces which was critical in achieving tight turns, but rather the ability of the wings to produce very large amounts of lift. This in turn necessitated a very high degree of structural strength in the wings, which is undoubtedly why the biplane played such an enduring role in the scene of early fighter aircraft, its natural ruggedness and strength outweighing the drawback of its high drag.

The compromise between high drag and high structural strength to sustain large lift forces is still a reality facing the designer of the modern combat aircraft. For monoplane wings to be strong enough they must be relatively short, which is not a favourable feature for low drag. Thus to maintain speed in a tight turn, a large amount of thrust is required, and so the need for good manoeuvrability makes demands not only of high lift and structural strength of the airframe, but also of high thrust from the propulsion system.

Far more extreme manoeuvrability demands are made of missiles designed to home-in on and to hit fast-moving aircraft which may be attempting to take evasive action, and thus many times greater lift forces must be generated by missiles than by aircraft. The limit for aircraft manoeuvrability is usually dictated by the amount of 'g' force that the pilot can sustain without blacking out, (typically around 8 'g', which means that the lift being produced by the wings is eight times the weight of the aircraft). However, the missile having no human pilot may be designed for much higher 'g' loads, typically around 30 to 50 'g', or even higher. Clearly great demands are made of the same features as before, namely the aerodynamic lifting capacity, the structural strength and the thrust to overcome the high drag.

From one extreme to another: a completely different type of aircraft requiring high manoeuvrability is the glider or sailplane. The reason for this is that it uses narrow chimneys of warm, ascending air (thermals) to gain height, having no power of its own, and to keep inside a narrow thermal often necessitates flying in very small circles, and hence turning very tightly. However, in this case the compromise between the requirements of high strength and low drag has to be approached from a different perspective, since there is no engine to provide thrust to overcome high drag. Thus the glider is given very long, narrow wings in order to minimise the drag, and the lift force will normally be limited to only about 3 or 4 'g', in order to keep the structural loads in these long wings within manageable bounds.

Range and Payload

The possibility of long-distance aerial transport, especially across the sea, has provided the aircraft designer with another motivation to make improvements, in this case to the range and the load-carrying capacity of the aircraft. In most cases the proposed journey is a single one, but in the case of a bomber the payload is released at the destination whilst the aircraft must be capable of making the return trip before landing.

The two concepts of range and payload are mentioned together since, uniquely with aircraft, they are closely related. This is because the range depends upon the quantity, and hence weight, of fuel carried. Since the aircraft actually has to support its total weight (rather than just move it horizontally like ground vehicles), the more fuel it carries the less payload capacity there is left for passengers or cargo. Weight is a crucial issue in aircraft design, a feature which distinguishes the art sharply from the design of most other forms of transport.

Apart from considerations of overall aircraft size, the crucial factor to be considered, termed the 'specific air range', is the amount of fuel required per unit distance covered. In British units this is typically quoted in gallons (or pounds) of fuel per nautical mile flown in still air (air nautical mile); compare this with the typical expression of a road vehicle's economy characteristics in terms of miles per gallon, ostensibly the reciprocal of the former quantity (although a slightly different definition of distance has been used).

The ratio termed specific air range must be minimised, which may be achieved by a combination of measures aimed at both minimising the numerator (fuel burnt by the engines) or maximising the denominator (distance). The former makes requirements on the propulsion system designer to ensure both that the engine converts the fuel efficiently into mechanical work, and also that this mechanical work is converted as efficiently as possible into thrust between the aircraft and the passing air, the rôle of the propeller or jet pipe ducting system.

The aspect of the problem concerning us is the maximising of distance travelled for each unit of fuel burned in the engine(s). Since the thrust required for straight level flight equals the drag, this once again makes demands on our ability to keep the aircraft's drag to a minimum, and in particular that part of the drag which depends directly on the lift being produced. In straight level flight the lift is equal to the weight, and so the lift-dependent drag depends directly on the weight. Thus the greater the weight (other things being equal), the greater the thrust required and the fuel burnt per unit of distance. Airline captains have to be very acutely aware of this relationship when flight planning, since the addition of extra passengers means either that less fuel can be carried (within the same overall weight) resulting in a reduced range, or that if the same amount of fuel is carried the total weight will be increased and so the total range will be reduced. Compensating for this by increasing the fuel load carried will further increase the all-up weight and so may in fact reduce the overall range further.

The main aircraft design feature having a strong direct bearing on its range characteristics is the slenderness (technically the aspect ratio) of its wings for a given total wing area, the same feature that we have seen is used to minimise lift-dependent drag on a sailplane. A glance at the planforms of most large airliners and bombers today clearly demonstrates the use of this feature, and in fact the trend has been for aspect ratios to increase in recent years as a benefit derived from other wing design improvements.

Economy

In the modern world of commercial competition, the need for economical operation of civil transport has become paramount. In this context time becomes a crucial factor. The less time a particular journey takes, the sooner that aircraft can be released to pick up a new load and start its next revenue-earning journey. Furthermore, any period during which the aircraft is on the ground (for whatever reason) may be thought of as time when it is being a net drain on financial resources – effectively the aircraft is only earning revenue when it is actually flying.

On long routes, the proportion of time during which an aircraft is actually airborne is the major part of the total time for which it is allocated to that particular flight. In comparison, when flying short legs, say of less than an hour, a much larger proportion of the time will be spent loading, unloading, fuelling, taxi-ing, awaiting air traffic clearance and suchlike non-productive activities.

So for long-haul airliners, flying speed is of the essence, not so much for customer appeal (although shorter flying times are clearly an important point), but for increasing aircraft utilisation. The design features discussed earlier for the achievement of high speed are therefore important, although as the speed of sound is approached, with the accompanying large increase in drag and hence thrust, a pay-off is reached between the economic savings of speed and the additional cost (and weight) of more fuel. This has resulted in a new design aim, that of pushing up the speed as much as possible without running into the high drag regime associated with approaching the speed of sound. The most noticeable aircraft shape development that has resulted from this is that of swept wings, and in addition, (although unnoticed by the casual observer,) a different shape of aerofoil section in the wings.

The maximisation of range and payload also contributes significantly to economical commercial operations. The direct effect is a reduction in fuel consumption for a given flight distance, which results not only in lower fuel costs but also the capacity to carry more fare-paying passengers without increasing the all-up weight. But a further major advantage is that aircraft down-time is greatly reduced if a journey can be accomplished in a single hop without the need for a refuelling stop en route. Fortunately the design features which enable high flight speeds tend to be the same as those needed for maximum range, so that no compromise is needed.

Height

Flying at high altitudes for its own sake is today probably only a requirement of reconnaissance aircraft, wishing to see down without being seen. However, even this function has now been substantially taken over by satellites. Before the full development of radar tracking, height was a requirement of bombers, (typified by the British V-bomber fleet) which used it as a means of concealment from ground observation.

Today the main reasons for flying at high altitude are more indirect, and arise from the fact that the air density reduces with increasing altitude. The drag of an aircraft varies in direct proportion with the air density, and so flying at altitude is another means of reducing drag. Furthermore, whereas propellers are more effective in the higher density air at low altitude, jet engines obtain on balance an overall advantage with a lower air density.

Endurance

Endurance is a measure of the time for which an aircraft can remain airborne, regardless of speed. It is not a primary requirement of transport aircraft, although good endurance characteristics can be useful in the event of an aircraft being held in the circuit before landing, in the case for example of the runway being temporarily blocked. It may also be a consideration if a diversion to another airfield is necessitated, in which case the speed is of little importance. Cases arise where a diversion may be necessitated due to bad weather at the original destination, although the forecast is for the unfavourable conditions to have lifted in a relatively short time. In this case a diversion may in fact be obviated by the pilot flying at maximum endurance speed (lower than normal cruising speed) before reaching the original destination, thus delaying his arrival until the weather has lifted.

There are other important functions of flight in which flying for maximum endurance is the primary concern. Some examples are the aerial patrolling of shipping lanes or road traffic, inspection of cross-country power and pipelines, and localised aerial photography. Airborne Early Warning Aircraft (AEWACs) require to stay-put ideally in the same spot for long periods, using their altitude as a platform for 'eyes' which can see over the horizon and thus warn of impending attack. For many of these applications forward speed is in fact a necessary evil rather than a requirement, and there is much to be said in favour of lighter-than-air craft fulfilling these rôles rather than fixed-wing aircraft. Unfortunately, airships have fallen so far behind in their development compared with fixed-wing aircraft that they are expensive and insufficiently well tried and tested, so that their use would involve a costly risk at first. Furthermore, an aircraft is multi-rôle, whereas the uses of an airship are severely limited by comparison. Despite these considerations, airships are once again being reassessed for the radar and surveillance rôle. One alternative vehicle that suggests itself is the helicopter with its stationary hovering capability. However, this is quickly ruled out in most cases by its high operating costs both in terms of fuel consumption in the hover and of ground maintenance.

The aircraft design-features which are favourable to good endurance characteristics are on the whole the same as those which benefit high speed, range and economy, namely low drag and efficient propulsion systems. However, endurance flying does demand a slightly different flying technique from flying for maximum range, in that the aircraft has to be flown at a lower speed, and this in fact leads to an instability in the speed which greatly increases the pilot's workload.

Because of the diversity of demands made on combat aircraft compared with the fairly well defined specific rôle of most other aircraft, great strides have been made in designing efficient multi-rôle aircraft. The Pan-Avia Tornado is an excellent example of this, with its facility for varying the wing sweep. In the context of endurance flying, the ability to extend the wings wide apart provides it with a very high aspect ratio (compared with most combat aircraft), and thus low drag. As a result, the aircraft is able to fly out to a likely combat zone and then to loiter in the air at low speed for long periods, in readiness for instant combat action as and when required, at which time the wings may be swept back for high speed and combat effectiveness. The loiter may be extended by the use of air-to-air refuelling. Without this loitering facility, combat aircraft tend to be very limited in terms of the range at which they can operate and of the length of time for which they can engage an enemy.

Short Take-off and Landing (STOL)
From the earliest days of flight, one of the bugbears of the fixed-wing aircraft has been its dependence on a fairly long strip of level ground (or smooth water) on which to accelerate up to flying speed before taking off and on which to land and decelerate to rest. The problem has been exacerbated by the development of ever larger and, in particular, ever faster aircraft. The problem is intrinsic to the basic concept of a fixed-wing aircraft, in that such a craft depends for its lift on forward speed.

Although on the whole the problem has had to be lived with, there are situations such as flight from and into short city airports and decks of aircraft carriers where solutions have had to be found if such operations were to become a reality. This has led to the development of the Short Take-off and Landing, or STOL, aircraft.

There are also variations to the theme, such as V/STOL and STOVL (the V standing for Vertical as an alternative to Short), and of course there has been the parallel development of the helicopter and (to a lesser extent) that of the airship. Although by no means unimportant in the overall picture of aviation development, such concepts are outside the scope of the pure fixed-wing aircraft with which we are concerned in this book.

STOL aircraft require wing forms which provide a much larger than usual lifting effect, so as to provide a lift force equal to the weight at much lower speed. The necessary development to achieve this has essentially been to the aerofoil cross-section of the wings rather than the planform, along with the occasional use of engine power to enhance the performance of this modified aerofoil section. High-lift wings are usually notable for the various secondary-wing-like appendages attached close to the leading and trailing edges of the wings, tending to give the impression of a rather precarious and flimsy construction. Sometimes air compressed by the engines or blown by the propeller is used to augment the natural flow of air over these surfaces.

The penalty for the use of such devices is that they inevitably increase the drag in normal flight. Therefore a STOL aircraft which is required also to have good conventional flight characteristics usually has these appendages retractable in flight, with the accompanying weight penalty that the retraction mechanisms and actuators necessitate.

A similar philosophy is employed in most non-STOL aircraft, in order that landing speeds and hence runway lengths may be kept within reasonable bounds. Many an uninitiated airliner passenger, seated with a view of the rear portion of a wing, has been alarmed by the apparent falling apart of the aircraft as these 'flap' mechanisms have been deployed shortly before landing!

Good Handling Qualities

We mentioned at the start that good handling qualities in terms of controllability and stability are not only an essential safety feature but are desirable for easing the pilot's workload and perhaps freeing him for other essential tasks. This of course is true for aircraft in all the rôles that we have considered. Some of the features found to be desirable for providing certain characteristics, most notably the use of sweep-back for achieving high subsonic speeds without excessive drag, bring in their wake very serious handling problems which have demanded considerable ingenuity for their solution.

Combat aircraft without doubt make the heaviest demands on their aircrew, since not only is the pilot frequently having to alter his speed, height and direction of flying, sometimes performing rapid and stressful manoeuvres, but also he (together with the second crew member if carried) has a substantial additional work load in managing the weaponry and all the aircraft systems, whilst also navigating and updating the mission plan. It was implied earlier that the use of high altitude for concealment became useless with the development of radar, and today there are only two ways that a pilot may fly unobserved into hostile territory. One is to keep in the shadows beneath the radar coverage, which necessitates flying at heights considerably less than the height of many ground features such as trees, tall buildings and power transmission lines. The other is by using a 'stealth' aircraft, as discussed in the next section.

High-speed low-level flight demands rapid and hard manoeuvring to avoid obstacles. Under these conditions the aircraft's ride through the air can become extremely hard, akin to driving a small fast boat over a choppy sea. Apart from the discomfort to the aircrew, weapon aiming and control handling under such conditions may become difficult or impossible. Perhaps surprisingly a considerable easing of this problem is available by appropriate planform shaping of the aircraft. Short, stocky (low aspect ratio) wings give a gentler ride than long slender ones. Also, swept-back wings are considerably better than straight ones.

Although such design features can be of assistance, the chief means by which pilot tasking can be and has been increased without unduly increasing his workload is undoubtedly the digital computer. A computer cannot itself provide the forces and moments necessary for manoeuvring, since only the airflow over the surfaces can do that. But the use of the computer has allowed the designer to adopt many departures from the conventional use of aircraft control surfaces, and this has given rise to new aerodynamic configurations becoming practicable which had hitherto been theoretically possible and advantageous but not realistic for the aircrew to handle without assistance. It is likely that the most noticeable development in this category will be the ubiquitous use in next-generation combat aircraft of canard foreplanes, at which Wilbur and Orville Wright might have said 'I told you so!'

Stealth

We have seen that the quest for effective shielding from being sighted by an enemy was at first met by flying at high altitude, and now by flying very close to the ground. Against ground-based radar the first is ineffective and the second is and will always be highly dangerous. But neither gives any protection against observation by an airborne radar search, and so the search for methods of concealment has moved into a new phase.

The answer adopted was to attempt to make the aircraft 'invisible' to radar. After investigating which features of an aircraft reflect the searching radar waves most strongly and which features most weakly (or not at all), together with what materials are least reflective, a new generation of 'stealth' aircraft has been developed. The shape of stealth aircraft is substantially different from what we have become used to as perceived wisdom. However, it is interesting to note that this is the first time in the history of the fixed-wing aircraft that aerodynamic considerations will have been ousted from their position of dominance by other factors in determining the shape of an aeroplane.

We have seen in this chapter some of the ways in which the aeroplane has evolved in order to meet the very diverse requirements made of it. No (or very little) explanation has been offered to show *how* each feature referred to actually produces the desired effect, and it is hoped that this introduction will have left you wanting to know and understand the answers to a number of fascinating questions. Let us now set off on our journey of exploration.

CHAPTER 2
Forces and Aeroplanes

INTRODUCTION

Before we can start to look in any detail at the way in which aerodynamic effects are produced and manipulated on an aircraft, we must first set the scene by investigating some very fundamental questions. Perhaps the most basic question, which arises as soon as the idea of a flying machine is considered, is 'How can it keep itself up?' A cursory thought might invoke the idea that it has something to do with forward movement, and so some additional basic questions about the relationship between the motive force provided by the engines, the prevailing force of gravity and other forces are likely to arise.

There is a recurring theme in such questions, and it is the concept of a *force*. In fact, throughout our study of flight, we will never be far removed from the idea of force, since it is the production, reduction and manipulation of forces which is at the heart of all aspects of making an aircraft stay up, move along, change direction when required, and desist from changing direction or orientation when not required. We therefore begin with an examination of the meaning of this word.

The more we know about forces (as with so many other things in life), the harder it tends to be to give a simple and accurate answer to the question 'What is a force?' Many graduate engineers in my experience immediately start groping for a formulation of an answer to this question by invoking technical words such as energy, pressure and momentum. However, all of these words (as defined in science and engineering) are composite concepts involving a relationship between at least two simpler concepts, and all of them have been invented for the sake of facilitating analysis of the behaviour of a force. They all beg the more basic question 'What is a force?' Before reading on, try to think how *you* would answer this basic question in such a way that a 10-year-old child would have a good understanding of the meaning of the word 'force'.

A force is simply *a push or a pull*. The word says nothing at all about the means by which the force is being applied. A toy truck may be pulled along by a string; a stopper may be pushed into a bottle by direct contact; an apple hanging on a tree, and likewise the same apple when falling, is pulled by an invisible force called gravity. A nut is pushed from both sides by a nutcracker. Furthermore, the word 'force' says nothing at all about the *effect* that the force is producing. There may be movement resulting, as in all the above examples; there may not, as in the case of the apple still attached to its tree, or a person pushing against a rigid building; and there may be other effects such as something breaking, or something getting hot. Within the word 'force' nothing is said about the effect of the force – just that it is a push or a pull.

Of course we are very interested in the effect (particularly movement) produced by the force, as well as in the force itself, which is the cause. In order to take the matter further, we can do no better than to examine Newton's three classic but often misunderstood Laws of Motion.

NEWTON'S LAWS OF MOTION

Imagine that Esther Rantzen, of BBC Television's 'That's Life!' fame, were to take her camera crew out onto a city pavement to do one of her light-hearted popular surveys, and were to stop passers-by and ask them whether they could remember and state any scientific law or principle. Mixed with a number of nil responses, I would expect that she might be regaled with Archimedes leaping from the bath in the all-together shouting 'Eureka!' – 'I've found it!' – though what he had suddenly found would probably be left to the imagination! Or she might come across a smart-Alec presenting her with Einstein's '$e = mc^2$', although again an explanation would probably not be forthcoming. But I venture to suggest that, if she persisted, the 'law' most likely to be forthcoming from the dim recesses of memory might be 'Action and reaction are equal and opposite', perhaps associated with a falling apple and . . was it Newton or William Tell?

Sir Isaac Newton was undoubtedly the father of all modern mechanical technology. The principles established by him and summarised in his three fundamental 'laws of motion' are the starting point for all theoretical analysis and design work which has led to all the mechanical developments of the technological age of today, not least the principles of flight. It is astonishing that such a benefactor of mankind should today be commonly regarded as a rather quaint eccentric who saw an apple fall from a tree and reached the unremarkable conclusion that things fall downwards!

Newton's Third Law

Almost everybody is familiar with Newton's Third Law 'Action and reaction are equal and opposite', sometimes alternatively quoted as 'To every action there is an equal and opposite reaction', but what does it mean? Living in a largely pre-technological age, Newton did not have at his disposal the very specialised technical vocabulary that has now been developed, and so he was forced to use everyday words that were most suited to expressing the concepts that he was dealing with. Thus the word 'action' probably meant nothing more precise (before Newton's adoption of the word) than 'the exertion of energy or influence', as it is defined in the Shorter Oxford Dictionary. Comparing the word as used in Newton's context with today's technical vocabulary, we find that 'action' here means force, and so Newton's First Law states that *forces* always occur in equal and opposite pairs and not singly. The simplest example of Newton's Third Law is that of an object resting on the floor. Its *weight* is the name we give to one force of the force pair, that which acts downwards. The 'equal and opposite' force is the passive resistance (the 'reaction') of the floor, acting upwards, exactly balancing the weight. Although not obvious, this reaction force must exist, or else the object would be freely falling under the action of its weight. In the case of the toy truck being pulled, the equal and opposite force is the force on the hand of the person pulling it. At each clamping face of the nutcracker on the nut, there is a force pair consisting of the force towards the centre of the nut produced by the nutcracker, and an outward force resisting this provided by the strength of the nut shell.

But that's easy to understand when the force agent (e.g. the string) is obvious and the motion is steady. Consider now the case of a sack of ballast just after being dropped from the basket of a high-flying hot-air balloon. Under the action of gravity it immediately starts to accelerate (get faster) downwards. For the time being we can ignore air resistance, since its speed starts from zero and so it is at first going slowly. The only force on the ballast is its weight (gravity) acting downwards, and the ballast is out of contact with the balloon basket and the Earth. Where is the 'equal and opposite force' of Newton's Third Law? Does it exist? Or should the law be qualified in some way to suit this situation?

Yes, there *is* an equal and opposite force. The force on the sack of ballast is a gravitational force of attraction, and as such it is the attraction between *two* objects. One is the ballast, the other is the Earth itself, and the reaction is an upward force acting on the Earth. Surprisingly the force on the Earth has exactly the same magnitude as the ballast's weight, although it seems to have no effect on the Earth. The reason for this will become apparent in the following section, when we consider Newton's Second Law.

Newton's Second and First Laws

Newton's Second Law is by far the most important and powerful of the set of three. By comparison, the Third Law effectively sets the scene (despite being the last of the set), and as we shall see the First is simply a special case of the Second. Newton's Second Law is the one which provides us with the answer to the vital question 'What is the relationship between a *force* (a *cause*) and its *effect* in terms of movement produced by the force?' It provides us with the basic (and fortunately a very simple) mathematical formula from which all design and analysis work involving forces and movements (i.e. almost everything conceived of under the generic title of Mechanical Science) starts. Although the ideas encapsulated in the Second Law formula are actually simple and can be precisely stated in a very few words, they often prove difficult to grasp on account of previously formed misconceptions. These misconceptions sometimes spring from misunderstanding or misuse of the specialist technical vocabulary that is used to express the Law. But they can also arise more naturally and instinctively due to the fact that the central concept of Newton's Second (and thus First) Law appears to run counter to our human experience of the way nature appears to work.

Newton's Second Law tells us firstly that a force on an object causes that object to *accelerate* (i.e. move progressively faster[1]) in the direction of the force. The First Law, which as we have mentioned is simply a special case of the Second Law, deals with the case when the force is of zero magnitude. It tells us that if there is no force acting on the object, then there will be no resulting acceleration or change in speed; the speed will remain unchanged, but it does *not* say that the object's speed will be zero.

Herein lies our first hurdle to comprehension and acceptance, since this conclusion does not conform with our natural experience. We *know,* don't we?, that you need an engine in a car to keep the car going at a steady speed (on a level road), and that if you run out of petrol the driving force disappears and the car will slow down and stop. We also know from experience that any unpowered system moving under residual motion (such as a spinning top, a pendulum, or our car free-wheeling) does not carry on indefinitely, as Newton's Second Law seems to suggest, but comes to rest after a certain amount of time. But Newton appears to be saying that the top, the pendulum and the car will in the same circumstances carry on doing their thing for ever! How can this be?

A BRIEF HISTORICAL DIVERSION

Before discussing this question, it is interesting to reflect on the historical development of the now accepted principles governing forces and motion. In the late 16th Century, following centuries of the intertwining of the philosophy of Aristotle with the doctrines of Christianity,

---

[1]In fact a fuller definition of 'accelerate' will later be needed in order to take account also of motion which is not in a straight line, but the simplification is satisfactory at this stage in our journey.

there was an upsurge in philosophical and mathematical thought, most notably spear-headed by the Italian Galileo Galilei (1564-1642), largely inspired by an interest in astronomy. Galileo was the first to dispel the Aristotelian ideas of motion, and by bringing the power of mathematics to bear on his experimental work he was probably the founder of what we now know as the scientific method. Legend has it that his inspiration came from seeing a lamp swinging in Pisa cathedral, and that he observed that the time taken for one complete swing (the 'period') was independent of the angle through which it was swinging. His greatest contribution to science was discovering the principle, stated above to be the First Law of Newton, that an object with no external force acting on it continues to move in a fixed direction without its speed changing, and that a force applied to the body has the effect of producing an acceleration. However, he did not have an understanding of the force of gravitation, and so was not able to develop his ideas to the full. This was left to his successor, Newton.

The far-sighted scientific work of Galileo brought him into sharp conflict with the Church of Rome, since (rather like Charles Darwin of a more recent era) his ideas were thought to be contrary to the teaching of the Holy Scriptures. For example, accepted (Scripturally based) wisdom maintained that it was the hand of God that kept the heavenly bodies circling in their orbits, and by extension kept life moving on Earth. But here was someone who believed and was claiming to demonstrate that, once set in motion, the heavenly bodies did not need any divine intervention to keep them going, but would continue indefinitely on their way *unless* any intervening force should occur to *change* that motion! Galileo thus appeared to be denying any rôle for God in the universe, and thus inevitably he was persecuted for blasphemy. Believing adamantly in his scientific proof of his new ideas, he appealed to Rome, but the church authorities, fearful that the repercussions of accepting these ideas might undermine Catholicity in its fight with Protestantism, refused to accept him and his ideas. The Jesuits declared him more dangerous than Luther and Calvin put together! He was tried for and convicted of heresy, but his sentence of imprisonment was commuted by the Pope to house arrest, in which he remained for the last eight years of his life.

Isaac Newton was born in the year that Galileo died, and lived until 1727. By building on the theory of Galileo, and most importantly arriving at the theory of gravitation which was lacking from Galileo's work, he was able to develop the work into a thoroughly well structured, mathematically based treatise which he published in 1687 under the title *Philosophiae Naturalis Principia Mathematica*. The ideas of this work have been the key to the development of all mechanical science ever since, and have only been found to be lacking in accuracy when it comes to very large scale (extra-terrestrial) considerations, where Einstein's Theory of Relativity has come to the rescue, and very small scale (nuclear) considerations, which are dealt with in the subject of Quantum Mechanics.

RETURNING TO NEWTON'S FIRST AND SECOND LAWS

We must now return to the matter in hand, and formalise Newton's Second Law, which we recall provides the relationship between a force acting on an object (the cause) and the resulting movement of the object (the effect). The relationship, which is, conveniently, of the most simple possible form, is:

> **A force causes an object to accelerate in the direction of the force with an acceleration which is directly proportional to the force.**

For the moment we will consider simply rectilinear (straight line) movement, with the force acting directly along this line. (Shortly we will introduce the additional concept of the directionality of the force, which will allow us to broaden the application to much more general situations.) The phrase 'directly proportional' has a very precise mathematical meaning, and makes two essential statements about the relationship. The first is that, when one of the quantities is zero, then the other quantity is also zero. This is, of course, nothing other than Newton's First Law, and so that law need not strictly have been stated independently by Newton. However, it is so important (and unexpected) that we are indebted to Newton for stating it separately, if only for emphasis, and we will examine its implications later. The second statement implied by the phrase 'directly proportional' is that if one of the quantities is changed by a given factor, (e.g. doubled, quartered, or trebled,) then the other quantity also changes by exactly the same multiplier. In other words, the *ratio* of one quantity to the other remains constant as the quantities themselves change. Expressing this second statement in mathematical notation, using F for force and a for acceleration, we have:

$$F/a = (\text{Constant})$$

or

$$F = (\text{Constant}) \times a$$

To investigate the implications of this, we must devise a system in which no force other than our test force F applies to our test object. Unfortunately this is not actually possible, since gravity is always present, but by placing the object on a flat horizontal surface and apply-

ing the test force horizontally, the effect of gravity is conveniently cancelled out by the 'equal and opposite reaction' from the surface,
according to Newton's Third Law. But there still remains a problem,
in that any horizontal motion will be resisted by an opposing force,
even if small, due to friction. It is precisely this force which makes us
tend to the opinion that, without a motion-maintaining force, things
always eventually come to rest. We must therefore do all that we can
to reduce this friction force to a minimum, so that it is negligibly small
in comparison with the applied force, either by making the surfaces
ultra-smooth, or by use of freely-running wheels or rollers, or by supporting the object on an air cushion using the hovercraft principle.

Having devised a suitable system, it is necessary to be able to apply
a steady force which does not alter in magnitude as the object begins
to move, and which we can measure. We also need some accurate system for measuring the speed of the object repeatedly at very short
intervals of time, from which we will be able to evaluate the acceleration. All of these practical problems will be found to be dealt with
fully in any basic text-book on practical Physics or Mechanics, and
need not be our concern here.

We can now use our experimental set-up to verify Newton's Second
Law, that a force produces an acceleration proportional to the force.
We simply apply a number of different known forces to the object and
measure the resulting acceleration in each case. Dividing each force
by the corresponding acceleration, we discover that the numerical
answers are all the same (within the accuracy limitations of our experiment). We have thus verified that the force and the acceleration are
proportional to each other, and we refer to the resulting constant
number as the 'constant of proportionality'.

The questions then arise: what is the significance or meaning of this
constant number? In what circumstances is it constant? Are there any
circumstances under which it ceases to be constant? If so, how could
we change it? To answer these, we observe that the one thing that we
have not varied in our experiment is the object itself. We could repeat
the same experiment with a different object. If we do so and the new
object is heavier than the first, we will find that the constant number
we get on dividing force by acceleration is larger. If we repeat this several times with a range of objects of different heaviness, we will discover that the constant of proportionality is directly related to what
we have loosely called the heaviness of the object. Thus this constant
number provides us with a measure of a certain property of the object,
which appears to be related to heaviness.

This property is called *inertia*, a noun based on the adjective 'inert',
from the Latin word '*iners*', meaning idle, inactive or 'without art' (*iners*). It will be found that the heavier the object, the greater the

constant of proportionality, i.e. the greater the inertia. If the same size force is applied to a heavy (high inertia) object as to a light (low inertia) object, it is found that the heavy object experiences less acceleration than the light one, the accelerations being in inverse proportion to the inertias. The meaning of two quantities being in inverse proportion is simply that their *product* (not their ratio, as in direct proportion) is constant. So, as one gets bigger, the other gets smaller. Inertia is thus a measure of the resistance of an object to being accelerated, or of its sluggishness or tendency to remain inactive.

An understanding of inertia allows us now to solve the conundrum posed earlier of how it can be that, according to Newton's Third Law, the downward force of gravity on the sack of ballast dropped from the balloon is equalled by an upward force of gravity acting on the Earth, although the Earth appears to be unaffected. The truth is that the Earth *is* accelerated upwards a little bit, towards the sack of ballast. However, the inertia ('heaviness') of the Earth is so very much greater than that of the ballast, that the Earth's acceleration is correspondingly smaller – in fact so small that it is imperceptible.

We have used the word 'heavy' without precise definition in introducing the concept of inertia. By heaviness we do not mean quite the same thing as weight, although the difference is not easy to observe. An alternative word *mass* is introduced by scientists to refer to the property of an object which gives it inertia. Unfortunately, however, the term mass does not have a simple, yet satisfactory, definition, but is usually merely defined as 'quantity of matter', which is really not much more meaningful than the word mass itself! Even Sir Isaac never mastered the relationship between mass and inertia, and so we are in good company if we accept the important principles on trust. For all work involving Newton's Second Law, we may simply take it that inertia and mass are synonymous, and that the word mass (and hence the symbol m) is invariably used in preference to the word inertia.

We should note and understand that mass is *not* synonymous with weight. If I require to buy, let us say, ten kilograms (or 22 pounds) of groceries, it is the mass (i.e. the number of kilograms, or pounds,) of food that I am buying that is important. Its weight is merely a nuisance if I am on foot and carrying it home. If my home and the shop were on the Moon, I would be grateful that the same amount of food would weigh (i.e. be pulled downwards by the Moon's gravity) only about one-sixth as much, and therefore that it would be very much easier to carry home. The weight is less, but the mass is the same. I would not be justified in expecting the shopkeeper on the Moon to charge me only one-sixth of the Earth price, since it is the mass, and not the weight, which corresponds to the food value. On the Moon my car, a version of my Earth saloon car with exactly the same mass and propulsion force available from the engine, weighs only one-sixth of its Earth weight. Unfortunately, however, I cannot expect to get six times as much acceleration out of it as on Earth, since the inertia, its resistance to being accelerated, depends on the mass and not on the weight.

UNITS

Since the Second Law constant of proportionality is the mass m, the previous equation $F = (constant) \times a$ may now be written

$$F = ma$$

which is its normal form. We have so far said nothing about what units any of these quantities are measured or specified in. There are many systems which could be used, but each of them is based on the same principle: out of the three quantities, we choose two to which we can assign independently defined units, and then use the relationship to define a corresponding unit for the third quantity.

In all systems acceleration is taken as one of the two chosen quantities, since its unit may be defined in terms of just distance and time, which are independent of any mechanical considerations[2]. As we have said, acceleration is the measure of how quickly the speed is changing. If at a particular moment an object's speed is, say, 3 metres-per-second, and one second later it is 7 metres-per-second, and it continues to get 4 metres-per-second faster in each subsequent second, then its speed is seen to be increasing at a rate of 4 metres-per-second in every second. We say that its acceleration is 4 metres-per-second-per-second. Since second appears twice as a divisor, we sometimes say 4 metres-per-second-squared, and in abbreviated form we write 4 m/s^2. (You may sometimes see 4 ms^{-2}, which means exactly the same thing.) In British units we would have feet-per-second-squared (ft/s^2), and a foot being about a third of a metre the number will be about three times as big as it would be in m/s^2.

The choice of the second unit to be pre-defined varies between mass or force according to the system of units we are using. Neither is intrinsically better nor more fundamental than the other, so that the choice is largely arbitrary and historic. In the System International, (abbreviated SI,) the most commonly used metric system in use today, we pre-define the unit of mass as the kilogram (1000 grammes, abbreviated kg). In the British Engineering units, we first define our unit of

---

[2]Quantities such as speed, velocity and acceleration are called *kinematic* quantities. Kinematics is the name given to time-dependent geometry, and so kinematic quantities always contain just units of distance (geometry) and time.

force, but in fact this is rather a devious process, since we pre-suppose the existence of a standard mass, the pound, and define a force of one 'pound force' (abbreviated lbf) as the force of gravity acting on this one pound mass (i.e. its weight) at a specific agreed place on the Earth. (The specifying of a place is necessary since the gravitational pull of the Earth varies slightly from place to place.) Note that in this case we can no longer use the pound as our unit of mass as well, since we would then have pre-defined all three of the quantities in the Law, and there is then no chance whatsoever of the law holding numerically true.

Let us first of all consider the process of defining the remaining unit, the force unit, in the SI system. We simply carry out our previous experiment using an object whose mass is exactly one kilogram, and vary the force that we apply to it until the resulting acceleration is exactly one metre-per-second-squared. Substituting 1 for m and 1 for a in the equation, the force F is equal to $m \times a$, i.e. 1×1, or 1. But one *what?* One new unit of force to make our set of units work together when used in Newton's Law. We must give it a new name – what better than calling it the newton (abbreviated N) in honour of Sir Isaac? (Note that the name of the unit is written with a small letter, as with all units in the SI system which are named after people, but that its abbreviation takes the capital initial letter.)

You may be worried that you are unfamiliar with forces measured in units of newtons. Although you have a good feel for the weight of a 1-kilogram mass and that of a 1-pound mass, you may be wondering how big a force or weight one newton is. Is it, for example, nearer to the weight of a bus, a bicycle, a cricket ball or a match-stick?

The best way (as we have just seen) of conceptualising forces is to think of them in terms of weight of, or the force of gravity on, a known object. A major discovery of Galileo and Newton was that, under the effect of gravity at any fixed place on the Earth, provided that no other forces interfere, *every* object experiences exactly the *same* acceleration downwards. Thus a brick and a coin, if dropped simultaneously side by side from a height, will fall side by side as if they were attached to each other. If a coin and a feather were used, the feather would quite clearly lag behind, but this is because the additional force of air resistance is of a similar order of magnitude to the gravity force, thus invalidating the experiment. However, experiment does show that, if both feather and coin are dropped together inside an evacuated vertical glass tube[3], then the feather does indeed reach the bottom at the same moment as the coin!

[3]A glass tube containing the coin and feather, having its ends sealed-up, and then all of the air pumped out. The tube is tipped from vertical one way up to vertical the other way up, and the coin and feather will be observed to fall side-by-side.

Experiment has shown that the acceleration with which everything falls towards the Earth is approximately 10 m/s^2 or 32 ft/s^2, (more precise figures being 9.81 m/s^2 and 32.2 ft/s^2). If we now apply this fact, through Newton's Second Law, to a one kilogram mass falling freely under gravity, and substitute $m = 1$ and $a = 10$ into the equation, we conclude that F is 10 units of force, or newtons. In other words, the weight of a one kilogram mass is approximately 10 newtons, and so a force of one newton is approximately the weight of 1/10 kg, or of 100 grams, which is typically the mass of an average eating apple. We thus have a convenient aide-mémoire in that a force of one newton is about the weight of the object of Newton's inspiration! (Would it be facetious to point out furthermore that SI also stands for Sir Isaac?)

In practice the newton is too small for use in many engineering applications, and the practical unit of force is the kilonewton (kN) which is 1000N. The weight of 1000 apples is not an easy quantity to conceptualise, so an alternative would be useful. A normal builder's sack of cement has a mass of 50kg, and so its weight is approximately $50 \times 10 = 500$N. Thus a kilonewton is approximately the weight of two such sacks of cement.

Turning now to the British Engineering system of units, we remember that we are approaching the problem from a different angle, knowing units for acceleration and force. In this case we need to define a compatible unit of mass. We proceed roughly as before, but this time we apply a constant force of one pound-force (e.g. by hanging a one pound mass on the end of a string over a frictionless pulley). We measure the acceleration, and then, keeping the force constant, vary the mass of our object by adding bits to it or by taking bits away, and re-measure the acceleration until we achieve an acceleration of exactly one foot-per-second-squared. Substituting $F = 1$ and $a = 1$ into our equation, we find that $m = 1/1 = 1$, and we define this mass as our unit of mass. What would be a suitable name for a unit of mass? We have seen that inertia (which is synonymous with mass) imparts to an object an innate reluctance to change its velocity and a preference to maintain the status quo, which is the characteristic of sluggishness. What better name then for our new unit of mass than the slug!

How big is the British Engineering unit of mass, the slug? We may investigate this question in a similar way to that used earlier, by considering the effect of the force of gravity on it. If we take a mass of one slug (however big that may be – it doesn't matter), and allow it to fall under gravity, we know that it (like any other mass) will accelerate at about 32 ft/s^2. Substituting $m = 1$ and $a = 32$ into our equation, we find that $F = 1 \times 32$, or $F = 32$ pounds force (the corresponding unit of force). Thus the weight of our one-slug mass is about 32 pounds-force, and so a slug is about 32 pounds – quite a substantial mass!

BROADENING THE DISCUSSION

So far we have entirely restricted our discussion to the situation in which the object starts at rest and is acted upon by a force which gives the object an acceleration in the direction of the force. By implication we have also included the situation in which our object has an initial non-zero speed in a certain direction, and our force being applied to the object in the same direction has the effect of increasing this speed. We can now, with very little extra mental effort, expand the ideas to the situation in which the object is moving in a given direction, and a force is applied to it in exactly the opposite direction. What happens then is simply that the acceleration is negative, and the speed steadily reduces.

Clearly the same force-mass-acceleration relationship applies here, and so a much greater force (hence larger brakes) will be required to bring a motor car to rest from 20 miles-per-hour in a given short period of time than to bring a 20 mph cyclist to rest in the same time. A large airliner slowing down to rest after landing at 100 miles-per-hour would require a really colossal braking effect to bring it to rest as quickly as a light motorcar slowing down from the same speed. However, in this case the solution adopted is to allow the aircraft to decelerate much more gently, over a longer distance and period of time. Whilst limiting the performance requirements of the brakes and hence keeping their size within reasonable bounds, this does of course necessitate having very long straight runways.

But even with this simple extension to our original concepts, we are still constrained to motion in a straight line and to considerations of the force applying along that straight line. In order to be able to cope even with simple variations such as the person pulling his toy truck by a string, and certainly if we wish to examine what happens when objects move in curved paths, or forces act sideways on the objects, we must open the door to the topic of *vectors*. Although it is possible to build up the subject of vector analysis into an extremely advanced and complicated branch of applied mathematics, fortunately the fundamental ideas of vectors, what they are and how they behave, are simple and commonsense (honestly!), and only these fundamental ideas will be needed to enable us to become 'flightwise'.

VECTORS

The concept of a force contains two vital bits of information, one of which we have so far ignored or tacitly assumed. To specify a force, we must say *how big* a push or a pull it is, (its 'magnitude', usually in newtons or pounds-force), but in order for this information to be of any use to us we must also specify in what *direction* the force is acting. We will later see that velocity and acceleration are likewise quantities which require not just magnitude but also direction to be specified. Such quantities are known as *vector quantities,* or more commonly as vectors. (All quantities without direction, such as volume or your age, are known as *scalar quantities* or scalars.) The direction of a vector is given by means of specifying the angle(s) relative to fixed reference planes or directions. For instance, the weight of a certain man is a force of 600 newtons (600N) acting vertically downwards; a toy truck is pulled with a tension (a pulling force) of 5N in the string which is at 30° to the horizontal, at a compass bearing of, say, 270°. (We will return to this toy truck example in the next section.) Fortunately, however, for much of the time all the vectors being considered in a particular problem will be acting in one plane, making the specification of direction less cumbersome.

Diagrammatic Representation of Vectors

Since a vector has magnitude and direction, it is possible to represent it very conveniently in diagrammatic form on paper by means of a straight line segment in the appropriate direction. By a straight line segment we simply mean a finite part of a straight line between a start point and an end point, since without this limitation a straight line extends to infinity in both directions. For the sake of brevity we will from now on simply say 'a line' when we mean 'a straight line segment'. We must choose a suitable scale, so that a certain magnitude (e.g. force) is represented by a certain length. In our toy truck example, a suitable scale will be to use two centimetres to represent one newton (2cm : 1N). If considering a light aircraft we might for example choose 1cm to represent 1kN.

Before we can draw our diagram, we must first of all draw a reference line (direction) on the paper to correspond with an appropriate reference line in the real situation. In our example, we draw a straight line to represent the direction of the floor.

We can now draw our diagram as in Figure 2.1. The paper shown on the right of the figure will represent a vertical plane in which the force lies, and so we will not be concerned with the bearing of the force (270° clockwise from North), but only with its angle from the horizontal, which is 30°. We draw a line anywhere on the paper (not necessarily touching the reference line) at an angle of 30° to the reference line, and mark off two points on the line separated by the length which represents the magnitude of the force. In our chosen scale, the 5N force requires a distance of 10cm.

Finally we must consider the *sense* of our force, by which we mean in which of the two possible directions along the line it is acting. Thinking of the physical string, and recalling Newton's Third Law, we can see that in fact the tension acts in the string in *both* directions at once, pulling forward on the toy and backwards on the leprechaun. However, in any particular situation we are only concerned with *one* of these two equal and opposite forces, in this case the force on the toy. This force being upwards to the right, we must draw an arrow-head on the line to indicate this. (If we wished to analyse the force's effect on the leprechaun, we would have to put the arrow-head in the opposite direction.) It is customary to draw the arrowhead at the front-most point of the line, although it could be drawn at any point on the line between the ends. We now have a diagram looking like Figure 2.1, in which a physical drawing has been placed alongside a representation of a piece of paper bearing the vector diagram, to make clear that there is a difference between the physical drawing and the vector diagram. The paper could of course be turned round or taken somewhere else, but the vector diagram would still be valid.

Resolution of Vectors

It will be clear that a force acting on an object can have no effect on that object in a direction at right angles to that in which the force is acting. For example, if the leprechaun pulls on the toy truck exactly vertically upwards, the force will have no effect at all in moving the toy along the ground, although it may lift the toy up. We can also see that, when the string is at an angle of 30° to the ground as in the example, then *part* of its effect will be to move the toy along, and *part* will be trying to lift it up. Similarly, in the days of horse-drawn barges, the horse cannot pull the barge from directly in front (unless he swims or wades), but must walk on the towpath, so that part of his effort moves the barge forwards, whilst another part pulls the barge towards the

Figure 2.1 Real Vector and Vector Diagram

bank (and the horse towards the canal), and must be compensated for by the bargee with tiller and rudder. The further off-centre the horse pulls, (if, for example, the tow-path deviates temporarily from the canal-side,) the less of his effort propels the barge forwards and the more of his effort tries to pull it towards the bank.

In order to analyse what is going on in either of these examples, it would be very convenient if we could find out how much of the force's effect is in the direction of motion, and how much is acting non-productively at right angles. If we can do this, we can then treat the two parts of the problem entirely independently from each other, using only the forward part of the force to examine the motion, knowing that the sideways part has no effect on the motion at all. This procedure is referred to as *resolving a vector into components,* and the effective magnitude in each direction is called the *component* of the force in the stated direction.

The components can very easily be found once we have represented the vector in a vector diagram. Referring to Figure 2.2 which represents the same vector as in Figure 2.1, the horizontal component of the vector, i.e. the part of the force making the toy move along the ground, is given simply by the *projection* of the vector line in the reference line (the horizontal line) – or, if you prefer, the shadow of the vector in the reference line, cast by light shining straight down from very high up above the vector. (Can you see why the light source must be very high up?) To find the vertical component of the force, we must draw a line anywhere on the paper at right angles to the horizontal reference line, and the vertical component will be the projection of the vector in this line – or the shadow of the line cast by a light source far off to one side (the right in the figure). The lengths of these projections (when scaled back to force units) give the magnitudes of the effective parts of the force in these two directions.

Fortunately this process can be greatly simplified further, as shown

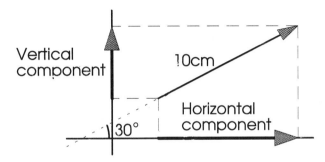

Figure 2.2   Resolving a Vector into Components

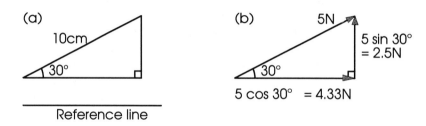

Figure 2.3   **Solving a Vector Triangle**

in Figure 2.3(a). All that is required is to draw in the vertical and horizontal sides of the right-angled triangle of which the vector forms the hypotenuse.[4]

If you are familiar with the method of solving a right-angled triangle by trigonometry, then the components can simply be calculated and a scale drawing is not necessary. The force magnitudes can be used directly as the lengths of the sides of the triangle, as in Figure 2.3(b). The horizontal component of the force is $5 \times \cos(30°)$ or about 4.33N, and the vertical component is $5 \times \sin(30°)$, or 2.5N. But without knowing anything about trigonometry, the right-angled triangle may be drawn to scale. The scale drawing method is very satisfactory for understanding what is going on, and also for working out answers, although rather tedious and less accurate and versatile than using trigonometry.

So, by resolving the force in the string into vertical and horizontal components, we now know that the effective force pulling the toy *along* is 4.33N, and the effective force pulling it *up* is 2.5N. When considering the horizontal motion of the toy, we may now completely ignore the vertical component of 2.5N as it has no horizontal effect; and vice versa.

Combining Vectors

It is also very useful to be able to carry out the process which is the reverse of resolving a vector into its components. Let us suppose in the toy example that it is *required* to apply a forward force of 4.33N to the toy to provide it with horizontal motion, and also that it is *required* to pull vertically upwards on the toy with a force of 2.5N. At what angle must the person pull on the string, and how hard must he pull? (This is clearly a very contrived example, simply to make the principle

---

[4]A hypotenuse is the side of a right-angled triangle which is opposite to, or remote from, the right angle, whereas the other two sides together *form* the right angle. The hypotenuse is also the longest side of the triangle.

clear, but we will shortly see important applications of the principle when dealing with the forces on aircraft.)

The problem can be readily solved by reference to Figure 2.3(b). We simply draw a scaled vector line representing one of the required forces first, say the horizontal one, and then, *starting from the end point of the first vector,* draw another vector line representing the other force. To find the combined effect, which is called the *resultant,* we simply draw a straight line from the start of the first vector to the end of the second vector. Measuring its angle to the first (the horizontal) gives the direction in which to pull the string, and measuring the length of the line gives the magnitude of the required force (to scale). Again the process can be carried out by means of trigonometry if preferred.

Why did we choose to draw the two vectors in this particular order? The answer is that it does not matter. If we had started with the vertical vector, AD in Figure 2.4, and then from its finishing point D drawn the horizontal vector DC, we would have reached exactly the same solution as by drawing AB and then BC. Of course, although not necessary, we could have included *both* constructions, and if they both started from the same point (A) then they would both finish at the same point (C), thus giving the entire rectangle of Figure 2.4. Notice that the resultant is then the diagonal of the rectangle, and clearly the diagonal of a rectangle must be longer than any one side of the rectangle, showing that the resultant of two vectors which are at right angles to each other must always be greater than either of the two vectors.

Perhaps the relationship between a force and a vector line on paper seems a little abstract to you. If so, it will be helpful to think of the vector diagrams in Figures 2.3 and 2.4 as if they represented another, much simpler, type of vector, called a *displacement.* A displacement simply means a straight line movement (e.g. a walk, or a roll of a ball) from one point to another. The movement starts at one point, and finishes at another point, and so can be represented by a vector line with magnitude (this time distance), direction, and sense, just as we did

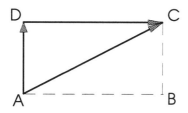

Figure 2.4   The Alternative Vector Triangle

with a force. Of course, in this case, the scale will be a ratio of distance to distance, and could even be 1 : 1 if suitable, in which case the vector drawing would be exactly the same as the physical representation.

Referring to Figure 2.4, let us suppose we wish to do a 'journey' from point A to point C. By a journey we mean any collection of displacements linked together nose-to-tail which result in us getting from A to C. Sticking to the figure, the three choices are A→D→C, A→B→C, or A→C direct. Whichever route we take, the overall effect, or resultant, is the displacement vector A→C.

So far we have combined two vectors which are at right-angles, because we started by reversing the procedure of resolving a vector into two perpendicular components. To extend this combining idea further, we might ask what other 'journeys' we might make in Figure 2.4 in order to get from A to C. The answer is that we can invent any route we choose, and apply exactly the same method as before.

Figure 2.5 reproduces Figure 2.4 exactly, but shows one additional random journey from A to C. Again, the resultant of the vectors along the path A→E→F→G→H→I→C is the single vector A→C. We could even do the same combining process (at least approximately) if our path from A to C were curved and tortuous, simply by breaking down the curve into a large number of short straight lengths which closely approximated to the curve.

Thus to combine any two or more vectors (or to *add* vectors, as it is often called, although it has little similarity to adding numbers,) we simply draw the vectors in any order, one after another, making sure that each new one begins at the ending point of the one before (like circus elephants, trunks-to-tails), so that all of the arrows continue in sequence. The resultant is simply the vector from the tail end of the first of the sequence to the arrow-head of the last of the sequence. This applies to any number of vectors in any directions at all. They need not even be confined to lying in the same plane, although we will

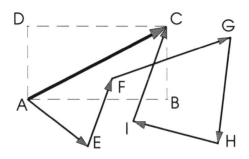

Figure 2.5   Addition of More than Two Vectors

not normally need to bother ourselves with the additional complication of three dimensional vectors.

We have considered here both forces and displacements as examples of vectors. But any quantity which has both magnitude and direction is a vector, and may be treated by exactly the same methods. Thus when required we can use these ideas of resolving and combining vectors with velocities and accelerations, as well as with forces and displacements. However, any one vector diagram must only contain one kind of vector, and we must be careful not to try to combine, for example, velocities and accelerations in the same vector diagram.

THE FORCES ACTING ON AN AIRCRAFT

The effects of the forces acting on an aircraft are basically of two types: effects on its overall motion through the sky, and effects of rotating the aircraft structure. The latter are very important and significant, and will be dealt with in detail in the sister *Flightwise* volume, which considers Aircraft Stability and Flight Control. For a great deal of our purpose, however, we can forget about the rotating effects of forces on aircraft, and we will treat the entire aircraft as if it were a *point mass*, just as we might treat a ball, without any specified orientation (front and back etc.). However, it will prove convenient in the diagrams to see aircraft as aircraft rather than as blobs, in order to bring out important features such as direction of motion and orientation of fuselage and wings. Bear in mind at all times in this and the next chapter that we are treating the aircraft simply as a point mass.

Aircraft in Straight and Level Flight

Figure 2.6 represents an aircraft flying at a steady (i.e. constant) speed in straight and level flight, and shows the forces which will be acting on the aircraft. First of all, there is the ubiquitous force of gravity producing the weight of the aircraft, acting straight downwards. Its magnitude is effectively constant, since we can ignore the slow reduction in weight due to fuel being burnt for our present purposes. Although the weight is in fact a distributed load contributed to by all parts of the aircraft, yet it is convenient to think of it as being a single concentrated force acting at the centre of gravity. As we are going to treat the entire aircraft as if it were a point mass, this centre of gravity is a convenient point to choose, and we will take it (for now) that all other forces also act through this point.

There will be a *lift* force (to be defined more precisely, along with drag, in Chapter 3), acting at right angles to the flight path, and in the present case this implies vertically since the flight path is horizontal. Lift is, loosely, the force created by the wings as a result of their motion through the air, in order to keep the aircraft up in the air.

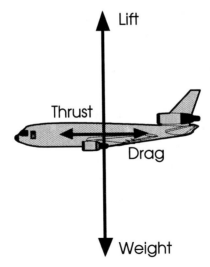

Figure 2.6   The Forces on an Aircraft in Steady, Straight and Level Flight

There will be a *thrust* force produced by the engine(s), acting forward in the direction of motion (i.e. horizontally).

Finally there will be some force of resistance to forward motion, caused by the aircraft's interaction with the air around it. This is called *drag,* and it is in the direction of the flight path, but in the sense *opposite* to the motion, since it opposes motion.

Since all the forces are either horizontal or vertical, we may conveniently analyse the horizontal and vertical motions totally independently of each other, by the principle established earlier when considering the resolution of vectors. We first note that the aircraft is in level flight, which means that it has no velocity vertically, either up or down, and no acceleration vertically. It follows directly from Newton's First Law that there must be no resultant vertical force, and so our two vertical forces, being opposite in direction, must be equal in magnitude so that they cancel each other out. We thus conclude that *Lift equals Weight*[5]. For straight level flight, then, an aircraft must be provided with wings that will give an upward force equal to the aircraft's weight.

Looking now at the purely horizontal forces and motion, we note that the aircraft is in *steady* flight, which means that its speed is not changing, and so there is no *acceleration* horizontally either. By Newton's First Law, no acceleration implies no resultant force in the

---

[5]The *vectors* lift and weight are not identical to each other, since their directions are not the same but opposite. It is only the *magnitudes* of lift and weight that are equal to each other. The same applies to thrust and drag in the next paragraph.

direction of motion, and so once again, since they are opposite in direction, thrust and drag must cancel each other out, and we conclude that *Thrust equals Drag.*

To many people, this is a far more difficult conclusion to come to terms with than the first, since we know, don't we?, that without a motion-sustaining force things come to rest! Surely the thrust must be somewhat *greater* than the drag? However, you will recall that it was precisely this gut feeling that brought about Galileo's persecution, and which makes Newton's First Law difficult to accept. The fallacy lies in the fact that we easily tend to overlook the resistance (friction) force which is opposing motion, and so are aware only of the propelling force in the direction of motion. In the case of the aircraft in Figure 2.6, we *have* drawn attention to the force of air resistance or drag, but still instinctively we may feel that it must be smaller than the thrust. After all, a well streamlined aircraft is carefully designed to have very low drag, whilst at the same time it may be provided with a number of very large engines which produce a tremendous total thrust, apparently quite out of proportion to the small aerodynamic drag force to be expected.

But in fact, and in accordance with Newton's First Law, this is not the case. Typically the total thrust produced by the four engines of a Boeing 747 when cruising may be of the order of 50 to 60 tonnes (and considerably more is available for accelerating and for climbing), which means that the drag in cruising flight is also 50 to 60 tonnes – a surprisingly large force for such a well streamlined object moving through air! (A tonne is a metric ton, or 1000 kg, which is approximately equal to a British ton. Of course, since we are talking about a force, strictly we mean a 'tonne force', or the force of gravity acting on a tonne, which is about 10 kilonewtons. In those units the total drag will be about 500 to 600 kilonewtons, more than half a million newtons. But we tend to be lazy with such words provided that the meaning is clear.)

It was mentioned above that the engines of an aircraft are capable of producing considerably more thrust than drag, and that this is needed in certain situations other than in straight and level flight at steady speed. It was also pointed out that, *in straight and level flight at steady speed,* the lift is equal to the weight. Before reading on, try to answer for yourself the following intriguing and to many people bewildering question, (to which graduate engineers in my experience almost invariably give one or another incorrect answer): Is there any phase in an aircraft's flight, (if so, which phase?) during which the wings are required to produce *more* lift than the weight of the aircraft? In other words, is it safe to design wings capable of just supporting the weight of an aircraft, plus a reasonable factor of safety, or should there be some greater design criterion?

Aircraft in Steady Climbing or Descending Flight

If you thought that by spotting the title of this section through the corner of your eye you had hit on the answer to the question at the end of the previous paragraph, then be prepared for a surprise. The fact is that during climbing flight an aircraft actually experiences *less* lift from its wings than its total weight, and not more!

To examine this claim, consider Figure 2.7(a), which shows the same aircraft as before, but this time in a steady speed climb along a straight but inclined flight path. The thrust must now be greater than the drag in order to climb, (just as a car or a cyclist needs more driving force to go up a hill than along the level). Since thrust and drag are collinear (i.e. acting in the same straight line), it is convenient to combine them into their resultant force, which will be [thrust minus drag] in the direction of forward flight. Lift is defined (as we shall see in Chapter 3) as being at right angles to the flight path, and hence to the [thrust minus drag] vector, as shown in the Figure. Having combined the thrust and drag forces into one, we finish up with a total of three forces acting on the aircraft.

Although the aircraft is climbing, it is moving along a straight line at a steady speed, and thus there are no *accelerations* in any direction – we say that the aircraft is in *equilibrium,* just as it was in the straight and level case earlier. Therefore Newton's First Law must apply in any direction we care to choose, be it vertically, horizontally, or along the thrust line or the lift line (or any other direction). If we apply the First Law principle in the vertical direction, there must be a total upwards force on the aircraft exactly equal to the weight acting downwards. Now the only forces with any upward effect are [thrust minus drag] and lift. Since they are at right angles to each other, their resultant will be the diagonal of the rectangle they form, as in the toy truck example as illustrated in Figure 2.4. The rectangle has been completed with dotted lines in Figure 2.7(b), and the resultant upward force shown as a dashed line. Effectively the resultant *replaces* the two aerodynamic forces. This resultant must be exactly equal and opposite to the weight, as we have shown.

It is clear from the diagram that the resultant is greater than the lift, since the resultant is a diagonal of the rectangle of which the lift forms one of the sides. Since the resultant equals the weight, the *lift must be less than the weight!*

Unfortunately a book cannot provide animated diagrams, but by considering Figure 2.7(b) and applying a little imagination, it is possible to see how the lift and [thrust minus drag] forces would be changed if the flight path were made steeper. (Note that for each steepness we are still considering the aircraft to be climbing at a steady speed along a straight path. We are *not* referring to a curved

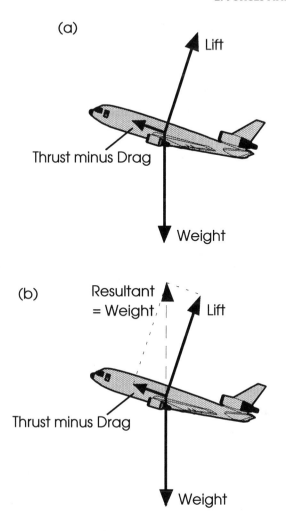

Figure 2.7 Forces on an Aircraft in Steady Straight Climbing Flight

flight path of steadily increasing steepness.) As the aircraft drawing is rotated (about the point representing the centre of gravity) to steeper flight paths, the weight vector will remain unchanged, and so the upward resultant will also remain unchanged, being equal to the weight. However, the proportions of the rectangle will change, [thrust minus drag] will become greater, and lift will become *smaller!* At 45° the rectangle will be a square, and the two forces will be equal to each other. At greater angles, [thrust minus drag] continues to increase, and lift continues to decrease.

Extending this process steadily all the way until the flight path is at 90° to the horizontal and the aircraft is climbing vertically, it will be clear that the lift force dwindles right down to zero, and that the [thrust minus drag] force, the only aerodynamic one left, becomes equal to the resultant, and so in turn becomes equal and opposite to the weight. Thus we see that in vertical flight there is *no lift*, but that the entire weight of the aircraft, together with the drag (now down-wards, adding to weight) must be handled by the thrust of the engine(s). We thus require considerably more thrust than weight, (i.e. a thrust-to-weight ratio greater than l, in the usual jargon,) if we wish to be able to fly vertically upwards, and even more still to be able to accelerate upwards.

The total disappearance of the lift force is perhaps a little surpris-ing. The reason for it is that lift is defined as being at right angles to the flight path. If in vertical flight there were *any* force at right angles to the flight path such as lift, then there would be an overall unbal-anced force on the aircraft at right angles to its flight direction, and this would give the aircraft an *acceleration out of its flight path*. The effect of this would in fact be to cause the aircraft to fly in a curved path rather than the intended straight path, and so it would no longer be flying straight upwards. But this introduces some very important new concepts which we will consider fully in the next section.

Let us return to the conundrum posed at the end of the preceding section. Since an aircraft in steady climbing flight has a lift force less than its drag, maybe an aircraft in steady *descending* flight will have more lift than drag? We leave this as a simple exercise to investigate for yourself. If you wish to do so, consider Figure 2.7(a) or (b), and imagine that the aircraft fuselage is turned round nose-to-tail, so that it is descending to the right. By thinking about what alterations, if any, should be made to the magnitudes, directions and names of the forces in the figure, you should be able to show that in fact the lift is still less than the weight, even in steady descending flight. What happens in a vertical dive?

FORCES IN CURVED MOTION

We have still not answered the question as to whether the lift provid-ed by the wings ever needs to be greater than the weight of the air-craft. All we have so far gleaned is that, when flying in a straight line (either level or inclined) the lift is always equal to or less than, but never greater than, the weight. The answer to the question in fact aris-es not under conditions of straight line flight, but of curved flight, and so it is to considerations of curved motion that we must now turn.

Consider an object moving along a circular path, such that there is no force either speeding up the motion or slowing it down *along* the

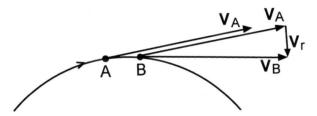

Figure 2.8 Velocity Diagram of an Object Moving Along a Circular Path

path. The direction of the object's motion is continually changing. Figure 2.8 shows two 'snapshots' of the object at two fairly close together points A and B during its motion from left to right along the circular path. At A the velocity vector $\mathbf{V}_A$[6] is tangential to the curve because there is no component of velocity in any direction other than along the curve. At B the magnitude of the velocity vector $\mathbf{V}_B$ is the same as that of $\mathbf{V}_A$ since there is no force speeding up or slowing down the object along the path of motion, and its direction is tangential to the curve at B.

Although $\mathbf{V}_B$ has the same magnitude as $\mathbf{V}_A$, it is not the same vector since its direction has changed. In other words, the *velocity* of the object has changed in going from A to B, even though its *speed* is unchanged. It is this change in the velocity that is of particular interest to us in the present context.

At B, the actual velocity of the object $\mathbf{V}_B$ must be the resultant of the velocity that the object possessed before the change from A to B ($\mathbf{V}_A$) together with another velocity vector representing the velocity change itself, which we will call $\mathbf{V}_r$ for reasons that will shortly become apparent. In other words, using the notation of adding vectors to imply combining them in the way discussed earlier, we have

$$\mathbf{V}_A + \mathbf{V}_r = \mathbf{V}_B$$

Since $\mathbf{V}_A$ and $\mathbf{V}_B$ are equal in magnitude, the vector triangle must be isosceles, and $\mathbf{V}_r$ must form the third side as shown in Figure 2.8. Note that the 'circus elephants' rule of combining vectors is correctly followed, in that the arrow $\mathbf{V}_r$ follows $\mathbf{V}_A$ sequentially, giving $\mathbf{V}_B$ as resultant.

Since we chose A and B to be nearby points on the circle, the isosceles triangle is very slender, and its base $\mathbf{V}_r$ is approximately

---

[6]It is common practice to use bold print (as $\mathbf{V}$ here) to denote a vector quantity. It implies that the letter signifies not only the magnitude of the quantity but also its direction.

perpendicular to $\mathbf{V_B}$[7]. Thus, since $\mathbf{V_B}$'s direction is tangential to the circle, it follows that the direction of $\mathbf{V_r}$ is perpendicular to the circle at B. In other words $\mathbf{V_r}$ is radial, and hence the use of the subscript r.

Thus $\mathbf{V_r}$, which represents the *change* in velocity in going from A to B, is a velocity component at right angles to the direction of motion at B. At A it does not exist (or is zero), but at B it has increased to a finite amount $\mathbf{V_r}$. We could repeat the entire procedure represented by Figure 2.8 for the next small step in the motion, replacing A with B, and B with a new point C. If we do, we find that we have to keep adding new radial velocities $\mathbf{V_r}$ always towards the centre of the circle, in order to constrain the object to its circular path. The velocity is therefore continuously increasing towards the centre, which means that there is an *acceleration* towards the centre of the circle. By Newton's Second Law this means that there must be a continuous *force* acting on the object towards the centre of the circle.

This force is called *centripetal force,* which means 'centre-seeking' (from the Latin *petare*, 'to seek', from which we also get the English word 'petition'). On a road vehicle it is provided by sideways friction between tyres and road. In the case of a weight being whirled around your head on the end of a piece of string, the force is provided by the tension in the string. If the road vehicle can't get enough friction on a patch of oil or ice, or if the string is suddenly cut or released, then by Newton's First Law the vehicle or weight will carry on as it was moving at the moment the centripetal force ceased to apply, that is, in a straight line tangential to the circle.

In passing, it is instructive to note the meaning of the other force which is often confused with centripetal force – *centrifugal force,* derived from the Latin verb *fugare*, which means to flee or run away. This is the equal and opposite force, the other one of the pair of which Newton's Third Law speaks, and since centripetal force acts radially inwards, so centrifugal force must act radially outwards – but *not* on the object moving in the circular path. If that were so, then the two forces would cancel each other out, and the object would be moving in a straight line rather than in a circle. No, the centrifugal force acts on the agent which is supplying the centripetal force. In the case of the weight on a string, it pulls *outwards* on the person doing the whirling, as anyone having tried his hand at the athletics event of hammer-throwing will be very aware. In the case of the road vehicle, the centrifugal force acts via friction on the Earth itself, in a horizontal direction, with unobservable effect because of the large mass of the

---

[7]To be exactly true, the distance between A and B would have to shrink to zero. But then we come into the realms of differential calculus. We are not here attempting to be mathematically rigorous, but rather to explain a phenomenon.

Earth. But consider for yourself what happens to some loose gravel if it happens to be under the tyres of the cornering vehicle.

When you are turning a corner reasonably fast in a car or a bus, you *feel* as if you are being pulled, or thrown, *outwards,* and so your physical experience might lead you to the conclusion that there is a centri*fugal* force acting on you. Actually, this is exactly the opposite of what is happening, since there is really an inward (centri*petal*) force acting on you, transmitted by friction through the seat and perhaps via the side supports on the back of the seat, and restraining your body to move in the same circular path as the vehicle. If the seat is too slippery and you are not constrained in any other way such as by a seat belt, the force will be insufficient and you will tend to slide 'outwards'. In fact what is happening is that *you* are carrying on in a straight line whilst the *seat* continues to travel in a circular path.

If you need further convincing that the force on an object moving in a circle is inwards rather than outwards, consider again a weight being whirled around on the end of a string. A string can *only* apply tension, and not compression, (have you ever tried pushing your dog on its lead?), and so the force cannot possibly be outwards.

Incidentally, the apparent conflict between the force you appear to experience when cornering in a car and the actual force on your body is nothing new to you, and is not confined to circular motion. If you are in a powerful car accelerating very hard straight forward, what do you feel? A rearward force pushing you back into the seat. What is actually happening to your body? It is being accelerated *forwards* (along with the car), and this acceleration is produced by the *forward* force of the seat-back pushing on your body. If the car then brakes very suddenly, the rearwards force on you required to decelerate your body (provided by your legs and seat-belt) makes it feel as if there were a force 'throwing you forward'. Actually these apparent conflicts in experience are nothing more than another example of Newton's Third Law of Action and Reaction, but it is very important for us to be quite clear which part of any force pair we are actually dealing with in any situation, or else we are likely to come up with some ridiculous answers.

Back to aeroplanes! If our aircraft is flying along a level circular path, there is no contact between it and the ground, and no string between it and the centre of the circle. So what agency provides the centripetal force to maintain the circular path? We will shortly see that we are not here talking about small, insignificant forces but very large ones, often the largest of all the aircraft forces, and often several times as great as the weight of the aircraft.

Without the caveat at the end of the last paragraph, we might have been inclined to answer that the agency which provides the centripetal force is some combination of the control surfaces on the back edges of the tail and wingtips of the aircraft (rudder, elevators and ailerons). However, these control surfaces are very much smaller than the wings, and so can only produce very much smaller aerodynamic forces. Furthermore, it will be observed that the control surfaces on an aircraft are nearly always attached to parts of the aircraft as far away as possible from the centre of gravity. This is deliberate, since the effect of the control surfaces is to cause the aircraft to *rotate about its own centre of gravity,* which does not require any centripetal force acting on the aircraft. The forces produced by the control surfaces apply *moments*, or turning effects, about the centre of gravity. As may be seen in detail in *Flightwise: Aircraft Stability and Control*, the purpose of the control surfaces is to re-orientate the aircraft in order for it to be able to produce the large centripetal force required. They do not provide that force themselves.

The centripetal force required must be produced by aerodynamic means, since there is no other possible agent such as string or contact with *terra firma* available. Clearly the only agents capable of producing these very large aerodynamic forces are the wings themselves. Thus it is *during a turn* that the wings must produce more lift than the weight of an aircraft, and so we have solved the conundrum.

We can conveniently examine the way the various aircraft forces interact in level circular flight by viewing an aircraft from either the front or the rear, thus eliminating from our mind irrelevancies such as thrust and drag.

It is common knowledge that an aircraft is usually banked when it is doing a turn (i.e. flying along a circular flight path). Consider an aircraft banked at 60° to the vertical as in Figure 2.9(a). The forces on the aircraft are its weight acting straight downwards and the lift force produced by the wings which will act perpendicular to the wings. We may resolve the lift force into two perpendicular components, one vertical and the other horizontal, which are shown using dashed lines. (Note that the lift force is *replaced* by its components – they do not act in addition to the lift.) For the aircraft not to start climbing or descending, the vertical component of the lift must exactly equal the weight, (Newton's First Law,) whilst the horizontal component of the lift provides the required centripetal force to produce the acceleration towards the centre and so maintain the circular flight path. (The centre of the circle is somewhere off the paper to the right.)

It is immediately clear that the lift, being the diagonal of the vector rectangle, must be greater than either of its components. By scale drawing of the vector diagram or by simple trigonometry it may easily be shown that, for Figure 2.9(a) with a 60° angle of bank, the lift is exactly twice the weight. The aircraft is said to be 'pulling 2g', and the

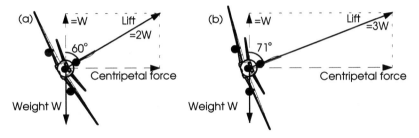

Figure 2.9   Forces on an Aircraft in a Banked Turn

reaction between pilot (or passenger) and seat is twice his weight, so that he feels pinned down into his seat. Another way of expressing this is that the ratio of lift to weight, the 'load factor', is 2.

If more centripetal force is required in order to achieve a tighter turn, i.e. to move along a circle of smaller radius without flying any slower, a greater horizontal component of wing lift is required whilst the vertical component must remain as before, exactly equal to the weight. Thus a steeper bank angle is required, and increased wing lift. This is illustrated in Figure 2.9(b) where the bank angle is 71° and the lift force equals three times the weight. The aircraft is 'pulling 3g', and the load factor is 3.

Airline passengers would not generally be happy to be subjected to a load factor much greater than one, although it must be slightly greater than one in order to turn the aircraft at all without losing height. Furthermore, if the wings only need to be designed for low load factors, they do not need to be as strong as for high load factors, and can consequently be designed much lighter and more aerodynamically efficient, by being long and slender as discussed in Chapter 12. Airliners are typically designed for a maximum load factor of 2, which corresponds to a bank angle in level flight of 60° as we have seen, but the normal operating load factor will remain well below 2.

If we wish to design an aircraft to be highly manoeuvrable, it will have to be capable of turning very tightly, which means increasing the design load factor. What is the limit of this process? Technologically, the limit will depend either on how much aerodynamic lift force the wings are capable of producing, or on the force that the wings can withstand before they break, which in turn depends on the structural strength of the wings. However, on combat aircraft the upper limit is usually imposed by physiological considerations. It is found that if pilots are subjected to more than about 7g (in which condition a twelve stone pilot 'weighs' over half a ton!) they experience a black-out, and although this tolerance level can be somewhat increased by equipping them with pressurised 'g-suits', there is little point in designing any manned aircraft for load factors exceeding around 9g.

Unmanned missiles, on the other hand, are not restricted by physiological considerations, and will often be designed to pull 30g or 40g (or even very much more) when performing tight manoeuvres in order to hit an evading aircraft.

Thus the idea that the rule for designing wings is 'lift = weight' is far from being the case, and aircraft wings must be capable of producing lift of several or many times the weight of the aircraft.

TRANSITIONAL FLIGHT

Before closing this chapter, for completeness we should consider very briefly another answer that is sometimes given correctly to the conundrum about when is lift greater than weight. In straight flight (whether level or climbing or descending) lift is never greater than weight. Yet there *is* a phase of the climb during which lift has to be temporarily increased. Whenever a change in flight path is made from level flight to climbing flight, or from descending flight to level flight, the change in direction cannot occur instantaneously, but the two straight paths must be linked by a short curved transition path. Just as in a horizontal circle, so in a vertical circle, there must be a centripetal force to constrain the aircraft to move in this circular path. The centre of the circle is above the flight-path, and so the centripetal force needed is upwards. It must be provided by creating more lift than weight during the transition, and its magnitude will be the difference between the lift and the weight.

This flying manoeuvre is referred to as a 'pull-up', and it is required in order to get airborne at the end of the take-off run on the runway, and just before touching down on landing, in order to make contact with the runway as gently as possible after descending along an inclined flight path. In the latter case, the manoeuvre is called the 'round-out' or 'flare'.

There is another essential flying manoeuvre called a 'bunt' or 'push-over', and this is the exact opposite of a pull-up. It is required at the top of a climb when adjusting to level flight, and also when entering a descending flight path from level flight. Naturally the centre of the short circular transition path in this case is *below* the flight path, and so *less* lift than weight is required, and the force [weight minus lift] provides the centripetal force.

In many cases the transition phases referred to above are so slight or gentle that they scarcely even need to be considered as separate manoeuvres. However, a salutary lesson was learnt by one RAF pilot I knew of who had recently come from flying 'fast jet' combat aircraft to flying the Dominie, a twin-jet executive-type aircraft used in the Royal Air Force for training navigators. On one occasion, after climbing quite rapidly to the required height, and forgetting he had passengers in the cabin, he bunted the aircraft somewhat over-enthusiastically. Just as a pull-up increases the load factor (or 'g'), so a push-over reduces it. The load factor being plus one in straight level flight, it doesn't take much of a bunt to reduce it by more than one, to a 'negative-g' value, and then un-fixed items and crew will rise off tables, floor and seats. Although the half-full chemical toilet was secured to the floor, its contents naturally were not, with very unpleasant consequences for the entire crew!

CHAPTER 3
Aerodynamic Force

INTRODUCTION

Although we have examined the need of an aircraft to experience aerodynamic forces, we have not yet broached the subject of *how* such forces can be produced, further than saying that they result from an object moving through the air, which is really no more than saying that the forces are 'aero-dynamic'. In considering this basic question we will introduce the relevant physical properties of the air in the atmosphere, we will come across the concept and purpose of an aerofoil, and we will meet and formally define the key words lift and drag which we have met informally already. We will also introduce the concept of aerodynamic coefficients (applied here to lift and drag), which are used whenever one is talking seriously about aircraft flight.

The topics of pressure and of viscosity will be only very briefly met in this chapter, since a fuller discussion of them here would be disruptive to the flow of the argument. Be assured that, if you feel that you do not know enough about these two words, pressure will be dealt with thoroughly in Chapter 4, and viscosity will be introduced and discussed in Chapter 6.

THE FORCE AGENT

When discussing the question 'what is a force?' in Chapter 2, we frequently used the word *agent*, by which we meant the physical mechanism providing the push or the pull. In the case of a push or a squeeze, the agent was physical contact between the pushing and the pushed objects. Two other agents often referred to were the pull of a string and the pull of gravity, the intangible and very mysterious nature of the second being tacitly accepted without question. Despite much talk about the effects of aerodynamic force, we did not once refer to the agent through which this is applied. We must therefore now ask and investigate the fundamental question, what is (or are) the actual physical mechanism(s) by which a flow of the invisible and elusive fluid air exerts force on an object in its path.

Let us start from the most general possible starting point, and consider what happens when a randomly shaped object is placed in the way of a moving stream of air, as in Figure 3.1. We are not here concerned with the fact that the object must itself have weight, so that there will be a force of gravity on it which we are not showing; or furthermore that it would in practice need some means of suspension in

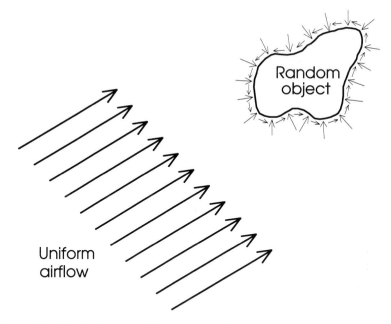

Figure 3.1 The Rudiments of Aerodynamic Force

the position shown, and that via the supporting cords or rods other forces would be exerted on it. We are only interested in investigating the answer to the specific question of how *aerodynamic* force is created. Our answer will of course tell us nothing about the total set of forces on the object or of its effect.

We have chosen to impose a uniform free stream airflow. This means that if the object were not there, the velocity vector at every point in the flow would be identical in both magnitude and direction to that at every other point. The presence of the object obviously disrupts this uniform free flow in the region surrounding it, but far enough away (in any direction) for the object's effect to be unnoticed, the undisturbed flow will still be uniform. There should really be much more space between the uniform airflow arrows and the object in the figure, but space does not permit. We have deliberately not drawn its direction horizontal, as that would be imposing an unnecessary constraint which might lead us to incorrect conclusions.

Clearly the object in some way pushes the air around it out of the way, and exerts force on the air. Furthermore, the air (by Newton's Third Law) exerts force on the object, the focus of our attention. What is (or are) the fundamental physical mechanism(s) by which force is exerted by the air on the object?

Once again, this is one of those searching basic questions which scientists and engineers with experience and expertise sometimes have more difficulty in answering than the uninitiated enquirer, because they bring in train knowledge of a host of technical terminology and concepts, some of which may be useful at this point but much of which is not. Let us try to answer the question from a commonsense point of view, bringing in technical terms only when relevant and useful.

The air somehow splits itself and flows all over the surface of the object, in a presumably very complicated way. At every point on the object air is in contact with the surface and is sliding over the surface. It must be at these contact points that the force is exerted between air and object, but how?

NORMAL FORCE DISTRIBUTION

The answer is two-fold. Air, like all fluids, possesses a property called pressure, which is its propensity to try to escape from any container. In the next chapter we will look at the vital subject of pressure in more detail, but for now we will observe that any fluid always presses against any surface with which it comes into contact. Air pressure thus exerts a pushing force at every point on the surface of the object.

What is the direction of this force? If you imagine yourself pushing against an extremely slippery wall, it is clear that the only direction in which you could possibly push without slipping is at right angles. When examining pressure alone, we can assume that the wall is indeed very slippery to the air, and that there is no sideways resistance to the air sliding over it, and thus the force at every point is exactly perpendicular to the surface at that point. It is common to use the word *normal* rather than perpendicular (with which it is synonymous), as in the heading of this section. Normal will be used in this sense (rather than in the sense of 'usual') in this book.

In Figure 3.1 we have drawn a set of little force vector arrows all round the object pointing directly inwards at right angles to the surface at each point. We have drawn them all the same length (magnitude) as each other because on our randomly shaped object we don't have any better information to go on, but in practice there will be a complicated distribution of big ones and small ones. However, they will all point inwards as shown rather than outwards, since air can no more exert a pull on the surface than you can exert a push on your dog through his lead. (Suction is just a lower pressure in one place than in another.) Strictly nature does not give us an array of lots of little arrows as we have drawn, but a smoothly varying distribution of pressure over the surface. However, approximating this pressure distribution by many small discrete forces is a very convenient way of conceptualising, and also a very powerful tool for mathematical analysis of the system.

TANGENTIAL FORCE DISTRIBUTION

We have not yet arrived at the complete answer to our question about the force mechanism(s) involved, because we made a slightly false assumption in the above discussion about pressure. We assumed that the wall was so very slippery to the air that there was no sideways resistance to the air sliding over it. In fact there is a small amount of friction force present acting along the surface as the air flows over it, but it is very much smaller at each point than the normal force, and is often ignored at a first approximation. However, as we will see later, ignoring this frictional force completely can have extremely disruptive effects on the fundamental theory of aerodynamics, and can lead to results which are clearly absurd and outrageously wrong.

To convince yourself of the difference in order of magnitude between normal and tangential forces, think about the difference between a sail and a flag. A yacht's sail is designed to take advantage of the normal (pressure) force of the air, and large forces may thus be obtained. A flag on a mast, however, may be approximately the same size as a sail, but it is only attached down one side, so that it spreads itself out and streams out down-wind and only experiences a very much smaller force, the tangential force of the air flow. A large flag on a mast would scarcely be an effective substitute for a sail, for moving the boat along! Consider for yourself how the same principle is involved in the working of a weather-vane.

So at each point on the surface of our object there will not only be a normal force but also a tangential force, and these have been shown in Figure 3.1 by a second distribution of little arrows around the surface of the object. We do not expect that they will all be of equal magnitude, or all anti-clockwise, as shown, but they are drawn like that by default in the absence of more specific information. Once again, we have made discrete vectors out of what is really a smoothly varying force distribution, for convenience.

We called each normal force a pressure force, and we now give each tangential force its proper name, which is a viscous force, or a force due to viscosity. Actually, in physical reality, there are not two neat little separate forces at right angles to each other at each point on the surface, but one force at an angle to the surface which is the resultant of the two. It is merely convenient for us to split this resultant into its two perpendicular components, which we can give separate names (pressure and viscosity) and can conveniently treat separately on the whole. To visualise this, think back to the example of pushing against a very slippery wall, but this time it is not quite so slippery. You *can* now push at a bit of an angle. You *can't* split your physical push into a normal part and a tangential part, but that is a very convenient way of analysing what is going on.

WHAT AERODYNAMIC FORCE IS NOT

Often the most difficult part of learning is unlearning what is superfluous and contradictory. When I first acquired a car that had its direction indicator stalk switch on the left-hand side of the steering column instead of on the right, as on all previous cars I had driven, I was for ever operating the windscreen wipers or washers when I wanted to indicate to go round a corner! I had to work very hard at unlearning the old habit, and indeed this was far harder than learning how to use the indicators in the first instance. It was not until over three years later that I could say that I was completely cured of the old way of operating the indicators.

Some people who have learnt mechanics or aerodynamics from an analytical point of view are unable to distinguish clearly between the physical phenomena which produce aerodynamic force as discussed above and a sophisticated mathematical model which can be used to analyse forces. This principle, which is simply another form of Newton's Second Law, states that force is the rate of change of momentum. (Don't worry if you don't understand this – these comments are primarily aimed at those who *do*.) Not only is this a powerful analytical tool, but it also represents a true and sound physical principle. The problem arises when people believe that rate of change of momentum constitutes an *additional* mechanism for the transmission of force, as well as pressure and viscosity, which it does not.

When we introduced Newton's Second Law in the previous chapter, we discussed it in terms of cause and effect. The force was the cause, and the effect interesting us in the present context was the change of motion in the form of a change of velocity or an acceleration. Since the phrase rate of change of momentum is almost synonymous with acceleration, (especially for an object of constant mass), it is clear that we are here talking about the *effect* of the force, and not an additional *causative* agent through which the force is exerted. We repeat that pressure and viscosity are *the only* two agents by which aerodynamic force is generated.

Later in this chapter we shall consider the way in which a wing experiences a force by deflecting a flow of air, or accelerating that airflow or changing its momentum. This is a perfectly legitimate and powerful way of thinking, but bear in mind that the *mechanism* by which the air's deflection is caused is still just the pair of pressure and viscous force distributions around the aerofoil.

LIFT AND DRAG

Having identified the two mechanisms whereby aerodynamic force is produced, we are left with a rather unmanageable picture of the overall result, which could do with some tidying up. Acting on our object we have not one aerodynamic force but a very large number of very small forces. It would be more useful to replace these many small forces by their one single resultant force, and this we do by the method of adding or combining vectors explained in Chapter 2. Starting with any one of the vectors, we draw all the vectors one by one in a long chain, each one starting from the front of the previous one circus-elephant style. It does not matter what order they are combined in, and so perhaps we would arrange all the pressure arrows first and then all the viscosity arrows in front of them. The resultant is simply the vector arrow going from the tail of the back one of the chain to the head of the front one of the chain.

The force represented by this resultant vector is called the aerodynamic total reaction. The magnitude and direction of the total reaction will depend entirely on the two distributions of pressure and viscous forces on the object, which in turn will depend on the shape of the object and on the nature of the airflow. These dependencies form the bulk of our study from Chapter 5 to the end of the book, but for now we will take it that the distributions *can* be determined. For our random-shaped object reproduced in Figure 3.2 the total reaction will be a vector in some random direction as is shown by the dashed arrow.

We have now introduced a second random direction into the picture, that of the total reaction, and so it would be convenient if we could refer everything to *one* of these directions. The direction of the uniform airstream is clearly a fundamental reference datum, often (but not in this case) corresponding with the horizontal, and so we will use this as our reference direction. We will split up the total reaction

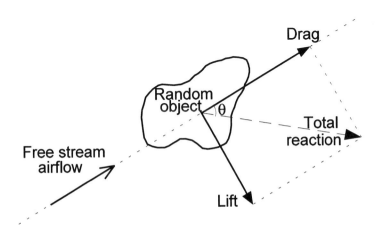

Figure 3.2   Defining Lift and Drag

into two perpendicular components (by the method explained in Chapter 2), one parallel to the free stream direction and the other perpendicular to it. These have been represented using solid arrows in Figure 3.2 to remind us that they are there instead of, not as well as, the dashed total reaction which they replace.

We are now in a position to introduce names for these two components, which we do as shown in Figure 3.2. The force component along the line of the free stream airflow we fairly naturally call *drag*, as it represents the resistance to the object's relative motion through the airflow. But the naming of the other component *lift* may cause you a little more surprise if you had thought that lift was always vertically upwards. Bear in mind that the shape of our object, and hence the direction of the total reaction, is random, and if we wanted lift to be the other way we could turn our object round. Furthermore, a reading of the sub-section 'Aircraft in Steady Climbing or Descending Flight' in Chapter 2 will help you to understand *why* lift has been defined as normal to the flight-path rather than vertical. Lift *could* have been defined in some other way – it is not a God-given law of nature – but it wasn't.

So quite naturally and with no effort whatsoever, complete and total definitions of the terms lift and drag have emerged from our discussion. Before reading these definitions which are printed in bold print immediately following the next paragraph, take a sheet of paper now and cover them up. On the basis solely of what has been presented in the last few paragraphs, try to write down in words complete definitions of the terms lift and drag, before checking your definitions with those given after the next paragraph.

One final point about these definitions: bear in mind that the direction of the free stream air flow is the direction of that airflow *a long way removed* from the object, in fact so far away that the object does not have any effect on the flow direction there. Close to the object, there is not likely to be any point at which the airflow truly represents the free stream airflow magnitude or direction, since the object causes the flow to be disturbed for a large region all round itself, especially both upstream and downstream. The airflow arrows in both Figures 3.1 and 3.2 are therefore not representative of the actual airflow at those points, but rather indicate the direction that the flow would be following *if the object were not there*. In Figure 3.2 a dotted line has been drawn right through the figure representing the direction of the free stream airflow. Sometimes as in Figure 3.1 the term relative airflow is used to mean free stream airflow, but it is not as good a term, as it doesn't emphasise the relationship with the undisturbed free stream. Finally, for you to check with, here are the definitions of lift and drag.

Drag is the component of the total reaction parallel to the free stream airflow.

Lift is the component of the total reaction perpendicular to the free stream airflow.

THE AEROFOIL

We have discussed a random-shaped object producing a rather futile randomly directed total reaction of arbitrary magnitude. A major task of an aircraft wing designer is to come up with the best shaped object in order to achieve a specific goal. This goal is to reduce the drag component of the total reaction to as small a magnitude as possible, whilst increasing the lift component to as large a magnitude as possible relative to the drag. This requirement may also be expressed as wanting as large a ratio of lift:drag as possible, and it is clear from Figure 3.2 that this corresponds to making the angle θ as near as possible to 90°.

Ideally we would like to make the angle θ become fully 90°, which would imply zero drag and a lift:drag ratio of infinity, but clearly nature will not allow this since there will always be some aerodynamic drag. We seem to be searching for a sort of aerodynamic bell-crank, which takes an input (airflow) in one direction, and produces an output (force) in a perpendicular direction, with no residual force at all in the original direction.

The name given to this aerodynamic bell-crank is an *aerofoil*. If the ultimate design goal is $\theta = 90°$, before reading on, try to hazard a guess at to how near to this goal it has been possible to get with aerofoils that have been developed.

There is actually another significant parameter in this quest which we have not yet mentioned. If we call our object with this aerofoil shape a wing, then we are also concerned with how long this wing is, in relation to the size of the aerofoil section that forms its cross-sectional shape. Aerofoil size is measured by the *chord length,* which is the distance from the front of the aerofoil to the back of it. The chord of a wing will often taper from a larger size near to the wing root to a smaller value near its tip, and so the concept of average or mean chord is often used instead. To measure the length of the wing in relation to its mean chord we introduce the term *aspect ratio*, which is defined as the ratio of the total span (wing-tip to wing-tip) to the mean chord of the wing, or more briefly span:chord.

The reason for our concern with the wing's aspect ratio is that air will spill over wing-tips, so making the wing less efficient in the wing-tip regions. An infinitely long wing would have no wing-tips; but all good things must come to an end, and so we require the wing to be as long as possible in relation to its average chord length. The limit is usually imposed by consideration of the structural strength of the wing. The subject of wing aspect ratio is dealt with at length in Chapter 11. If we are testing the performance of an aerofoil in a wind-tunnel, it is normal to span the entire tunnel width from wall to wall with a length of 'wing' having a constant chord length and cross-section of the aerofoil under test. There are consequently no wing-tips, and so we can assume that our test wing is infinitely long and that the results are not corrupted by any wing-tip effects.

In answer to the question posed in the previous but two paragraphs, you may be very surprised to learn that some aerofoils commonly used for aircraft wings can produce lift:drag ratios exceeding 100. This corresponds with an angle θ of 89.4°, only about half a degree away from the elusive right angle. But of course this is for a perfectly formed and tipless aerofoil under ideal wind-tunnel conditions, and lower lift:drag ratios are achieved in aircraft flight.

Figure 2.7 in Chapter 2 showed how the resultant of the lift and the [thrust minus drag] force must always be equal to the weight for non-accelerated flight, even if climbing. In the final paragraph of that section you were challenged to reverse the figure in your mind as appropriate to represent steady descending flight, simply by mentally switching aircraft nose and tail, and re-naming the forces as necessary. If you do this, and assume that the aircraft is descending along its natural glide-path, (i.e. the engine thrust is reduced to zero,) then the [thrust minus drag] force becomes just drag, and the weight is exactly balanced by the resultant of lift and drag, as shown in Figure 3.3.

It will be clear from this figure that the lift-drag vector rectangle is

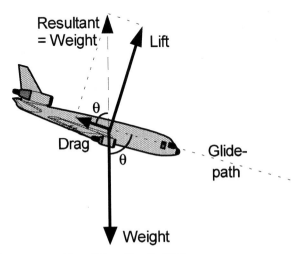

Figure 3.3   Forces on an Aircraft in a Steady Glide

identical with that of Figure 3.2, and that the angle θ of Figure 3.2 corresponds with the angle between the drag component and the vertical resultant of Figure 3.3, and is consequently equal to the angle between the glide-path and the vertical (represented by the weight arrow). Furthermore, if you are familiar with trigonometry, you will observe that the ratio lift:drag is equal to $\tan\theta$.

We thus see that the shallowness or flatness of the glide-path slope of an aircraft is directly related to the lift-to-drag ratio, and that therefore the lift-to-drag ratio is a very important indicator of the aircraft's flying efficiency. Although airliners are not designed to be particularly good gliders, they will be seen to have very much higher aspect ratios (more slender wings) than, for example, combat aircraft or light training aircraft, in order to reduce drag. However, more extreme designs are to be found in the world of gliders. The designer of an unpowered glider is freer to optimise the gliding performance of his aircraft and consequently high-performance sailplanes will be seen to have extraordinarily high aspect ratios compared with any other class of aircraft. If the aerofoil of the wing section could be observed and interpreted as easily, it would be found to be that of a very low-drag section whose design is optimised for relatively low air speeds flowing over it. Furthermore, the wing surface is very smooth.

Together these characteristics result in extremely high real-life lift:drag ratios, and consequently very shallow glide-paths, which we will illustrate with two modern examples of high-performance sailplanes. First of all, the DG 300 by Glaser Dirk is a fairly high-performance single-seater glider with a 15 metre wing-span. At its best gliding speed of 66 knots[1], the DG 300 has a declared lift-to-drag ratio of $41\frac{1}{2}$:1. This means also that it descends by one metre in every $41\frac{1}{2}$ metres of forward flight, an angle of descent of 1.4° from the horizontal. The DG 300 costs around £28,000, but if you are willing to spend around £70,000 (or £110,000 including all the trimmings) you can purchase the really high performance of the Schleicher Ash 25, a two-seater 25-metre span sailplane with an astonishing lift:drag ratio of 59:1, a descent rate of only one metre in 59 metres of forward flight, or a descent angle of less than one degree from horizontal!

AERODYNAMIC COEFFICIENTS

When it comes to stating performance figures of aircraft as we have done in the previous paragraph, it quickly becomes apparent that just

---

[1]A knot is a speed of one nautical mile-per-hour, and is usually used for measuring aircraft speed. A nautical mile is the circular arc length along the Equator which subtends an angle of one minute at the centre of the Earth, and is thus $1/(360 \times 60)$ of the circumference of the Earth. This works out to be about 1.15 statutory miles. Thus 66 knots equals 76 miles per hour.

to give a naked figure with units is not enough. We find that it is necessary to give a substantial number of supporting figures which specify the exact circumstances under which the quoted figure is correct. Change just one of these supporting values and the quoted figure becomes changed. And so, of course, to specify all possible values of the quoted figure under all possible circumstances, it is necessary to present not a single result but a table of results, or even a set or a book of tables if the number of different supporting values is more than two.

Rather than being completely overwhelmed by masses of meaningless figures in this way, a very powerful and simple alternative approach has been devised, which is to use dimensionless *aerodynamic coefficients* for the quantities being specified, and this method is used very extensively in aircraft aerodynamics where it is found to be particularly effective and useful. True, taking the ideas on board at first does make a bit of an intellectual demand, but with a little effort it is not too difficult to come to terms with, and a few minutes spent thinking about it now will pay rich dividends in the future, when we will of necessity use the language of coefficients very extensively. The use of coefficients, rather than making our life more complicated, in fact allows us to do some very clever thinking that without them would require Herculean or computer-like feats of mental reasoning and data handling.

As we saw very early on, our main interest throughout our study of flight is force, and so we will derive the dimensionless coefficients for the forces that we have met, namely lift and drag. The treatment given to dimensionless coefficients at this juncture is introductory and will be relatively superficial as is appropriate at this point. In Chapter 9 on Scale Effect and Modelling, we will return to the subject of the derivation of dimensionless coefficients and treat it somewhat more rigorously. To be fully flightwise (as with gaining competence and understanding in any subject) it is highly beneficial to approach the same topic from more than one angle, as this undoubtedly gives greater depth of understanding.

Coefficient of Lift

Let us start by trying to state intuitively (guided by the wisdom of experienced fore-runners) what items or factors are likely to have an effect on the lift force produced by an aircraft wing, and so will have to be taken into account when designing our aircraft. We are not now asking what force is *required*, the subject of our earlier pursuit, but rather what factors must be taken into account when attempting to satisfy this requirement.

We have already surmised that the *shape* of the wing has a very major effect on the lift produced by it. This is the most important feature over which the designer (and the pilot, as we will see later) has specific control, and so it is of course crucial. However, there is no direct way of quantifying shape with a simple number that we could measure and use in a formula, and so we are faced at the outset with a problem. Let us leave this problem for now, and we will see how, being the *only* such problem, we will be able to supply an answer to it after considering the other factors.

Apart from shape, what else does the lift force of the wing depend on? We suspect from experience (riding a bicycle, standing in a high wind on a mountain top), that aerodynamic force depends in some (as yet unknown) way on the *speed* of the wind, higher windspeeds producing greater forces. We are also very well aware of the almost too obvious connection between the size of the object in the airflow and the force produced. Large aircraft have large wing areas commensurate with their weight, and *vice versa.* You could not provide enough propulsive force for a full-size yacht with the sail from a small model sailing boat, however efficiently designed and accurately made that sail was.

One final less obvious thing affecting the force produced is a property of the air itself. The properties of the air which are of interest to the aerodynamicist are the pressure, the temperature, the density and the viscosity of the air, and these properties are all inter-dependent on each other. The viscosity, as we have already seen, is responsible for a tangential force on the surface of the wing and a corresponding shear force on the air, which although extremely important we can and will safely ignore for our present introductory approach. Of the other three properties, it is found that the air density directly affects aerodynamic forces on objects, and so must be included in our deliberations[2].

Density is defined as the mass of one unit of volume of a substance, or the mass per-unit-volume, and is therefore calculated by dividing the total mass of the substance in a given volume by that volume. Density is the quantity which substitutes for mass (or 'quantity of matter') in situations where we are not talking about a single discrete object (such as an apple or an aeroplane) but of an indefinite amount of a substance. We would refer to the *density* of steel, but to the *mass* of, say, a steel hammer head. Density is particularly useful when dealing with fluids such as air, since we are almost always referring to an unbounded amount of the air, so that it would be meaningless to try to identify its total mass.

---

[2]Pressure and temperature both affect density, but using density rather than pressure and temperature allows us to introduce just one new parameter rather than two.

We are now handling rather a lot of numbers or parameters, and are reaching the point at which written English becomes too clumsy to cope effectively, and so we will introduce algebraic symbols for the quantities of interest. For those quantities which are vectors, it is only the magnitudes that concern us here, and so we need not use bold print symbols.

We will use L to represent the magnitude of the lift force. For the air speed we will use V, and for the air density the Greek letter ρ ('rho'), as is customary. The other quantity we have introduced is the 'size' of the object, which we have not defined very carefully yet, but being size it will be something that we can measure using length units (presumably either length, area or volume). We will plump for a length ℓ, and if it should have been an area, then we will expect to discover later that we should have chosen length squared; if volume, then length cubed. Since we have not yet specified the shape of our object, it is not yet possible to specify any particular length, and so we will simply say that the letter ℓ represents some 'characteristic length', say the aerofoil chord length for example, to be decided when the shape has been determined. This sounds a rather convoluted approach, but it will serve our purposes well, and we will in fact discover that our requirement for definition changes somewhat in the course of the discussion.

In the section of Chapter 2 entitled 'Returning to Newton's First and Second Laws', we introduced and explained the concept of proportionality. We will meet this again in the present context, and so we will introduce the symbol $\propto$ to stand for the phrase 'is proportional to'. We also recall that 'is proportional to' means exactly the same thing as 'equals a constant times', so that '$.\,.\propto.\,.$' can be replaced by '$.\,.=K.\,.$'

Having now prepared the ground, we want to try to find a relationship between the lift L and the other quantities ρ, V and ℓ on which we expect it to depend, if one exists. This presents us with a new and interesting challenge. How can we investigate a behavioural relationship between a number of different measured quantities without actually trying it out in practice? The standard 'scientific method' would require us to guess on a likely relationship and declare this as a 'hypothesis', and then to do practical experiments and take careful measurements in order to try to demonstrate that the hypothesis holds true. It can never be proved, but it can be given more and more credence, taking on eventually the mantle of truth, so long as no experimental results emerge which *disprove* the hypothesis.

Certainly we could approach the problem in this way. But this being a book rather than a laboratory, it would have to present you the reader with an account of other people's experimental work and with the resulting relationship which they had experimentally 'proved'.

However, we can actually do better than that, since engineering scientists (particularly those in the field of fluid mechanics which includes aerodynamics) have actually developed a method of finding out almost[3] everything about such physical relationships, without going near a laboratory, but just by using their powers of reason and logical deduction, together with a little bit of inspired guess-work! This very powerful and well developed method is called *Dimensional Analysis*.

The basis of the method of dimensional analysis is that any relationship is an equation, and the quantities of each term on both sides of an equation must be of the same kind as each other. If you add five apples and two apples, you get seven *apples*, and not seven of something else such as daffodils. The equation $5 + 2 = 7$ in this case actually means 5 apples + 2 apples = 7 apples. We say that an equation must be *homogeneous*. If we tried to add five apples to two oranges, although the *numerical* answer is again seven yet the equation is non-homogeneous and meaningless, since there is no answer to the question 'seven what?' except perhaps seven fruits, which is a new and different concept from both apples and oranges.

This principle can be applied to equations about physical quantities. All the physical quantities that we will be involved with are measured in units that are combinations of only three basic and unrelated types of measurement units; those of mass, length and time. For example, mass, length and time can themselves be measured in kilogrammes, metres and seconds (as in the SI), or in slugs, feet and seconds (in the British Engineering system, as described at the end of the section on Units in Chapter 2), or any other preferred system. Although not so obvious, all other units are derived from these by some process of multiplication[4] and/or division[5] (remember that 'per' simply means 'divided by'): for example, in the SI acceleration is measured in metres-per-second-per-second or metres-per-second-squared as we have already seen. Density (discussed above) is mass-per-volume and so will have units (in SI) of kilogrammes-per-cubic-metre (kg/m^3). Less obviously, pressure is defined as force-per-area; force (by

---

[3]At the end of the day, a small amount of experimental work is required to produce the final form of the relationship, but this is minuscule in comparison with the experimentation required by the traditional scientific method. Furthermore, frequently everything but a single dimensionless number can be established by this method, and so the complete *form* of the relationship can be known without any experimental work at all.

[4]including repeated multiplication, which is represented by raising a number to a power representing the number of repeats.

[5]including repeated division, which can (through the rules of indices) be represented as repeated multiplication by the same quantity raised to the *negative* power representing the number of repeats.

Newton's Second Law) is mass times acceleration, and acceleration is distance-per-time-squared, giving the following development:

$$\text{Pressure} = \frac{\text{Force}}{\text{Area}} = \frac{\text{Mass} \times \text{Acceleration}}{\text{Length}^2} = \text{Mass} \times \frac{\text{Length}}{\text{Time}^2}/\text{Length}^2$$

$$= \frac{\text{Mass}}{\text{Length}^2} \times \frac{\text{Length}}{\text{Time}^2} = \frac{\text{Mass}}{\text{Length} \times \text{Time}^2}$$

once again resulting in a relationship containing only some combination of the basic elements of mass, length and time.

You may have noticed that during the last paragraph we slid gently away from using specific units of measurement (such as the SI) to referring instead simply to the quantities to be measured: mass, length and time. These quantities are referred to as *dimensions*, and by using them all the time instead of a particular system of units, we are able to keep the work entirely general. For example, looking at the final expression for pressure above, the expression Mass/(Length × Time^2) could represent kg/m.s^2 or slugs/ft.sec^2 or any other set of units, but by keeping it in terms of dimensions rather than units its total generality is maintained. We therefore work throughout in terms of dimensions rather than units; hence the term dimensional analysis.

Let us attempt to form the relationship, or equation, for the lift *L*. It is likely (though this must be purely a guess inspired by experience) that the quantities that we have identified will occur in the relationship in terms of some power, which is likely to be a small simple number. For example, we may find that we have to talk about [density]^2 rather than just density. We do not yet know *what* power to associate with each of the quantities, and so we will introduce the letters a, b and c (as yet unknown values) for the powers of ρ, V and ℓ respectively.

It is, from experience, much more likely that we should have this sort of power relationship than one involving other mathematical functions such as, say, sine or cosine or logarithm[6]. Furthermore, experience shows that it is very likely that the expression will be one of direct or inverse proportionality (or a combination of both) in terms of some power of each of the quantities. Based on these inspired hunches, we can write:

$$L \propto (\rho^a, V^b, \ell^c)$$
$$L = K\rho^a V^b \ell^c$$

---

[6]In fact, *any* mathematical function can be expressed in terms of a series of power terms, and so we have not lost generality by assuming some power law.

where K is the dimensionless constant of proportionality[7]. We now write down a *dimensional equation* based on this equation, replacing each quantity by its dimensional equivalent as explained above. We will use the bold upright capital letters **M**, **L** and **T** to represent the dimensions of mass, length and time respectively. Lift is a force, and so (from three paragraphs back) the dimensions of L are $\mathbf{ML/T^2}$; those of the density ρ are mass-per-volume, or $\mathbf{M/L^3}$; those of the velocity V are $\mathbf{L/T}$; and that of the characteristic length ℓ is simply $\mathbf{L}$. Thus we have, by replacing each component of the previous equation by its dimensional equivalent,

$$\frac{\mathbf{ML}}{\mathbf{T^2}} = \left(\frac{\mathbf{M}}{\mathbf{L^3}}\right)^a \left(\frac{\mathbf{L}}{\mathbf{T}}\right)^b (\mathbf{L})^c \quad \text{or, if you prefer,} \quad \mathbf{MLT^{-2}} = (\mathbf{M^a L^{-3a}})(\mathbf{L^b T^{-b}})(\mathbf{L^c})$$

We are now getting a little bit into mathematics based on the theory of indices and powers, but the aim is simply to extract from the above equation the actual (unique) values of the numbers a, b and c which make the equation hold true. Nothing will be lost if you cannot follow the next paragraph. Just pick up again when we have evaluated a, b and c.

From our dimensional equation we are able to extract three separate equations, one for each of the dimensions mass, length and time. This is fortuitous since we wish to find the values of three unknown quantities a, b and c, and you need three simultaneous equations to solve for three unknowns. Each of the three equations is obtained by considering the powers of one of the dimensions (**M** for example) on each side of the above equation, and forcing them to be equal to each other because the equation must be homogeneous as discussed earlier. Thus for **M** the power is 1 on the left and a on the right, giving $1 = a$. For the other quantities we need to use the rule (invoked in the right-hand equation above) that a quantity raised to a power on the bottom of a fraction can be replaced by the same quantity raised to the numerically equal but negative power on top of the fraction. Thus we can get rid of all the confusing fractions by writing all the terms from the bottoms on the tops instead, and changing their powers to minus what they were before. The powers of each dimension then follow the rule that, if you multiply the same quantity with different powers, then you add the powers (or subtract if negative) to obtain the quantity's final power. Thus for **L** the power on the left is 1; on the right it is

---

[7]It is possible that any of a, b and c could turn out to be negative, in which case it means that we are *dividing* by that quantity to that power rather than multiplying.

$-3a+b+c$. After using the same rules for the **T** equation, the following three equations result:

$$1 = a$$
$$1 = -3a + b + c$$
$$-2 = -b$$

From these we can immediately see that $a = 1$ and $b = 2$, and by substituting these values into the second equation and manipulating it we find that $c = 2$. We now re-write our original equation for lift (which we repeat here for reference) and substitute into it the numerical values $a = 1$, $b = 2$ and $c = 2$:

$$L = K\rho^a V^b \ell^c$$
$$L = K\rho V^2 \ell^2$$

We are now nearly at our mission's end. By considering only the dimensions of the various quantities occurring, and without even raising the subject of what physical principles were involved, we have succeeded in establishing a complete equation which expresses the lift in terms of the quantities density, speed and size that we assumed it depended upon. We would only need to substitute one set of corresponding measured values of lift, density, speed and characteristic length, to establish the value of the constant K, and then we would have a full working equation. Certainly it will require some verification in view of the assumptions and guesses that we made, but you may take it on trust that the equation is very sound.

This equation is so useful and important that it is worth looking at it in some detail, and making a couple of adjustments to it so that its value to us may be further enhanced. Let us examine the component parts of the equation from right to left.

The last factor on the right, ℓ^2, has the dimensions of length squared, which is the same as the dimensions of an area. (We thought it might.) Since we have not yet defined the characteristic length ℓ, we will not after all bother to do so, but instead we will define a reference *area* for our wing. You may have noticed from the beginning of this discussion on the lift coefficient of a wing that we have tended to refer to the wing (singular) of an aircraft rather than its wings (plural). Although the wing usually consists of a pair of symmetrical halves (or wings), yet it is quite convenient and commonplace to think of the entire span, including the part through the aircraft fuselage itself, as the 'wing' of the aircraft. That being the case, what would be a sensible area to define as the wing's reference area? Since we are considering the lift force produced by the wing, and since that is fairly obviously closely related to the planform area of the wing, it is the planform area of the wing (i.e. the area of the shadow of the wing cast on the ground by the sun when it is directly overhead) that we will take as reference area. Furthermore, since we are regarding the entire span of the wing including the part through the fuselage as the aircraft's wing, we will likewise define the plan area to include the (maybe imaginary) part of the wing where it crosses or passes through the fuselage. To define this part geometrically we simply continue the lines of the leading and trailing edges of the wing until they meet on the fuselage centre-line.

Having decided on an area rather than a characteristic length, the terminology ℓ^2 of the formula is not very suitable, and so we replace it with S, a symbol representing the plan area of the wing as defined. Why S? you may well ask. The answer is that I don't know; all I do know is that it is an unfortunate choice in that it suggests 'surface area', and the surface area of a wing is somewhat more than twice the plan area. (Can you see why?)[8]

You may be puzzled by our very arbitrary way of defining a reference area. Surely one cannot just choose any arbitrary value for one of the variables in the equation and still hope that the equation will hold true? For example, if we had defined the planform area to *exclude* the part through the fuselage, the value of S would have been smaller, and so without changing any of the other quantities on the right-hand side of the equation the value of lift would have worked out smaller – despite the fact that we had done nothing at all to alter the actual lift produced by the wing. The answer to this puzzler lies in the 'constant' K. We have said nothing at all about this constant yet, except that we could find its value by measuring one set of values of all of the other quantities and substituting them into the equation. If we did this twice with two different values of S, one including the centre-span region and the other excluding it, we would use the same value of lift L in each case, and so would come out with two different values of K. The point is that there must be one quantity in the equation whose value is determined finally by all of the others. Whilst we have two such unfixed quantities (S and K) we may choose to define either one of them arbitrarily, but the other one will then be rigidly constrained. Thus, having decided on a definition of the reference area S, K will come out as some value over which we have no control. We will discuss K further in a few minutes.

The lift formula now appears as follows, where the brackets have been inserted to focus our minds on the next step in the discussion:

$$L = K (\rho V^2)S$$

[8]'Twice' because the surface area includes both top and bottom surfaces, whereas the plan area only takes the wing into account once. 'Somewhat more than' since the surface area is curved, whereas the plan is a flattened projection with a consequently reduced area.

The factor (ρV^2) will probably not mean very much to you at this stage, since we have not met anything like it in the book thus far. However, by the time you are thoroughly flightwise you will without doubt have become excessively familiar with a very similar expression, $\frac{1}{2}\rho V^2$. This quantity, called *dynamic pressure*, is the all-important property of the airflow which tells us all we normally need to know about it. It encompasses the two properties of the air (speed and density) which are the only ones which vary substantially and have a significant effect on the aerodynamic forces produced. It is such an important concept that it is discussed at length under the topic of pressure in the next chapter. Suffice it to say at the moment that it has the dimensions of a pressure, or a force-per-unit area.

Since $\frac{1}{2}\rho V^2$ appears so very often in aerodynamics, it would be tidy and consistent if it were to appear in our formula (with the $\frac{1}{2}$) rather than the very similar ρV^2. This can be very easily arranged, since we have not yet said anything about the value of K. If we simply replace K by a new constant which we will call K' whose value is twice that of K, and insert a compensating $\frac{1}{2}$ into the equation, the value of the right-hand side remains unaltered. So we now have

$$L = K' \left(\tfrac{1}{2}\rho V^2\right)S$$

Continuing to move leftwards, we will now examine the mysterious constant of proportionality K'. What does it mean? What does it tell us? To answer this question, we must take our minds right back to the beginning of this section, and recall what we identified as the first feature affecting the size of the lift force. It was, of course, the shape of the object in the airflow, which we temporarily dismissed as being too difficult to quantify. Now, however, we have a formula which gives the lift force as the simple product of three quantities: a reference area encapsulating the size of the object, the dynamic pressure encapsulating the relevant properties of the airflow producing the force, and an as yet unidentified number representing something else. Let us suppose that we have a model aircraft of known wing area S, with an airflow of dynamic pressure $\frac{1}{2}\rho V^2$ flowing over it in a wind tunnel, and we measure the lift force. Without changing S or $\frac{1}{2}\rho V^2$, what could we alter in order to get a different measured value of lift? The answer can only be the shape – although there is more to that word than meets the eye, as will be explained in the next but one paragraph. But if the shape is the only thing that can be altered and the value of K' is the only undesignated quantity on the right-hand side of the formula, it follows that the value of K' *must* represent the shape that we earlier decided we could not easily quantify. It has now quantified itself for us!

The value of K' is consequently a very important parameter which tells us about and provides us with a numerical value for the *lifting effectiveness* of the aircraft's wing. Being so important, we remove from it the amorphous temporary symbol K' and give it the special name Coefficient of Lift, and the symbol C_L. The formula now finally reads

$$L = C_L \cdot \tfrac{1}{2}\rho V^2 S$$

Let us look more closely at this word 'shape' which we have bandied around rather loosely, and let us do so with reference to Figures 3.1 and 3.2 which both referred to the same random object in a uniform airflow. If we were to alter the shape of the random object, we would expect this alteration to have some direct effect on the *shape of the airflow* around the object. This accords with Newton's Third Law about action and reaction, in that any force which is produced on the object (represented at each point by the little arrows) is matched with an equal and opposite force acting on the air, which causes the air to deviate from the straight free stream direction. So the force distributions depend not only on the shape of the object but equally importantly *on the shape of the airflow around the object.* Thus, to see the entire and effective 'shape' of the system, we really need to be able to see the airflow around the object as well as the object itself. Often, as we shall see in Chapter 6 on the Boundary Layer, very small changes in shape of the object or in the nature of the airflow can have a very substantial effect on the shape of the airflow around an object, and hence a very significant effect on the aerodynamic forces produced. It must therefore be remembered that any change in the coefficient of lift C_L may be accompanied by a change in shape of either the object or, even more significantly, the shape of the invisible airflow around it. Only if both remain unchanged will the C_L value remain unchanged.

There is one very important way in which the shape of the airflow around the object can change substantially even though object shape and size and airflow properties all remain unaltered. This occurs if the relative direction of the airflow changes with respect to the object. Now, if the airflow is fixed, this can be achieved by rotating the object so that the airflow meets it at a different angle. Thus when referring to shape, not only must we include the shape of the airflow around the object, but we must also include the orientation of the object to the airflow. Any change in orientation will be accompanied by a change in coefficient of lift value.

Let us briefly take this discussion to its logical end and apply the thoughts to the specific form of an aerofoil, the object designed to achieve high lift-to-drag ratios and hence used in the design of aircraft wings. In Chapters 5 and 6 we will look very much more closely at the principles upon which the shape of the aerofoil is founded, but for now suffice it to say that an aerofoil section is long and thin to give it low drag, with a rounded front end and a highly tapered and pointed rear end. The pointed rear end is in fact the crucial part, and it works rather like a nozzle of a hose pipe, 'squirting' the air leaving the aerofoil in the direction in which it is pointing. If you have ever held the nozzle of a water hose delivering a large flow of water, such as a fireman's hose, you will know that it exerts a very substantial backwards force on you, the holder. You will notice that a fireman standing on the ground holding a hosepipe discharging forwards, will have one leg placed well behind himself to act as a prop to resist the rearward force acting on him. The aerofoil works in a similar way, in that by directing the airflow with a downward component (and we may safely use the word 'downward' if we consider an aircraft flying straight and level), there is an upward reaction force exerted on the aircraft. This is yet another prime example of Newton's Third Law.

Let us suppose that a pilot wishes to increase the lifting effect of his aircraft's wing quickly in order to get the extra lift needed to perform a turn, or to round out before hitting the runway too hard. He is not going to change his speed or altitude, and thus the dynamic pressure of the airflow will remain constant. Even if he has the facilities to do so (which he usually does have, as we shall see at the end of Chapter 9,) he does not want to change the area or the aerofoil shape of the wings, since the mechanisms for doing so are too slow and cumbersome and are unnecessary for a quick change in lift. How else can the pilot quickly get more lift? The answer is that he pitches the nose of the aircraft up (by using the tail control surfaces) so that the wing meets the airflow at a different orientation; its finely tapered trailing edge deflects the airflow more strongly 'downwards' (relative to the aircraft's flight path), and so the wing produces more lift. The pilot has increased the wing's coefficient of lift simply by altering its orientation to the on-coming airflow, without in any way changing the basic shape of the aerofoil.

What are the dimensions of the coefficient of lift? The answer to this is easy to ascertain simply from a look at the formula. The left-hand side, lift, is a force, which has the dimensions of force. The right-hand side must therefore also have the dimensions of force for the equation to be homogeneous. The last two factors on the right-hand side, $\frac{1}{2}\rho V^2$ and S, are a pressure and an area, and the product of a pressure and an area is a force. Therefore C_L must be dimensionless if it is not to disturb the balance of force dimensions on both sides of the equation. C_L is a pure number, whose typical values range from 0 up to about 2 or 3 or 4.

To summarise, the coefficient of lift of a wing (or of its aircraft) is a dimensionless numerical measure of the *lifting effectiveness* of the wing. The chief way its value can be altered in flight is by tilting the wing nose-up, and thereby changing the wing's orientation to the air-flow, or in other words its *angle of attack* (which is more precisely defined in Chapter 9 under the heading 'Aerofoil Terminology'), but on many wings it can also be varied by altering the shape or plan area of the wing itself by various mechanical devices such as flaps.

Coefficient of Drag

Since drag is of equal importance with lift and is often considered alongside lift, it is useful also to derive a coefficient of drag for an air-craft. The method by which this may be achieved is identical to that dis-cussed at length above for the coefficient of lift, and the final formula is

$$D = C_D \left(\tfrac{1}{2}\rho V^2\right) S$$

where D is the drag and C_D is the coefficient of drag. The only surpris-ing feature of this formula, which matches the lift formula very close-ly, is the use of the *same* reference area S, whereas one might reasonably expect to use another area which more closely relates to the dragginess of the aircraft. The frontal area would seem to be a more sensible and appropriate value.

Whilst such a suggestion is certainly very valid, there is a stronger reason why the same reference area is chosen as for lift. As we have seen, a very important value in aircraft design and performance is the ratio of lift to drag. Very often we do not have values of lift and drag (which are flight-condition dependent), but we do have the values of C_L and C_D. Having the same reference area S for both formulae means that if we divide the right-hand side of the lift formula by the right-hand side of the drag formula, the dynamic pressures and the reference areas all conveniently cancel out, with the very convenient result that

$$\frac{L}{D} = \frac{C_L}{C_D}$$

Clearly there is no *error* in defining the reference area exactly as we choose – it is purely arbitrary. But as we have seen, once we have cho-sen it, we have pinned down our value range of C_D. But herein lies another advantage of choosing the same area for both formulae. Because of this choice, values of C_D are directly comparable with val-ues of C_L, and are therefore easier to interpret than they would be if different reference areas had been used. Typical C_D values for aero-foils are of the order of 0.01. For aircraft they will be considerably higher than this, but still normally considerably smaller than the C_L values.

CHAPTER 4
Pressure and Energy

INTRODUCTION

In the previous chapter we introduced the word pressure into our discussion, thus starting to add a little flesh to the skeletal concept of force. Since the ideas of pressure are so important in their own right, we will briefly depart from our 'just-in-time' principle of introducing theoretical ideas as and when they are required, and will spend a little while investigating the concept of pressure. Furthermore, because it will prove useful in explaining these ideas, we will also introduce the idea of energy.

Conventional textbooks will at this point (or earlier) give a chapter over to the 'Properties of the Atmosphere', and although a little dry such a chapter will be essential reading for anyone whose aims go beyond those of this book. But keeping to the 'Flightwise' approach we will devote a little more attention to understanding the essential background ideas relating to pressure, rather than analysing all aspects more sparsely.

ENERGY

The word energy has in recent years come to be a catch-all word encompassing a number of apparently almost unrelated technological and natural concepts, such as the Sun, electricity, food, tidal power, nuclear energy and fossil fuels such as coal and oil. The word has even taken on somewhat emotive overtones in its connection with such ecological topics as rain forests and the ozone layer. When each of my daughters at about eleven-years-old was taken through a very thorough school project on energy, I was impressed by the far-reaching nature of their investigation, but was somewhat bemused (although not unduly surprised) to discover that, when I asked them what energy actually *was*, they were not able to give anything approaching a precise or satisfactory answer. Certainly no-one had attempted to give them a *definition* – because we all *know* what energy is, don't we?

I would not wish in any way to denigrate this general ecological and sociological approach to the subject of energy, which is very valuable in its place. However, the scientific concept of energy, with its meaning precisely defined, can be extremely useful to us in clarifying issues which arise when investigating the nature and effect of force and discussing pressure, the main agent of aerodynamic force.

So, we open the batting by giving the scientific definition of energy:

Energy is capacity for doing work

But I would take my hat off to anyone who is any the wiser for that! We have just heaped confusion on confusion. The trouble is that we need to define another scientific term, *work*, first. As with so many terms, a large number of different meanings of the word 'work' will be found in any good dictionary, each of which is appropriate in its context. We are in the field of science, and so it is the scientific meaning that interests us. And this is where the link-up with force (and our theme) begins to emerge.

We have seen that a force is a push or a pull, a *cause* of some *effect*, and that the effect with which we are mainly concerned is movement. Whenever an object to which some force is being applied experiences some movement as a direct result of that force, the force is said to be *doing work* on the object. No movement, no work done; so that even if you burst a blood vessel pushing with all your strength against an immovable object such as a building or a car with the hand-brake firmly on, you will have done no work at all! Only if a force causes movement is it said to do work. For example, if an object is allowed to fall under the effect of gravity, then the weight (a force) does work on the object.

It is very useful to give a precise quantitative meaning to the word work, which we do as follows:

The work done by a force is the product of the force and the distance that its application point moves in the direction of the force.

We will take it for now that the force is acting and the motion is occurring in the same direction, although the above definition is in fact general enough to allow for other situations. We see from the definition that work is the product of a force and a distance, and this is not the sort of quantity (in terms of dimensions or units) that most lay people are used to. We are familiar with composite quantities formed by division, such as speed (in metres-per-second or miles-per-hour, say), or cost (such as petrol costing so many pence-per-litre), and these quantities we can evaluate by taking the 'per' to mean 'divided by'. We are less familiar in everyday life with composite quantities involving multiplication, such as 'man hours', although we do use area (length times length) and volume (length cubed) without much difficulty. In 'man hours', confusingly we do not use any operator word (such as 'times') between the two primary quantity names in the way that we use 'per' for division. Work, the product of force and distance, is quantified in a similar way to this, and so the SI unit of work is the 'newton metre' (Nm), with nothing between the words, and an 's' only on the second word for the plural form. A newton metre is also given the name of a joule, abbreviated J. The British Engineering unit of work is the foot pound force.

Let us consider a parachutist 'jumping' (i.e. falling) from a stationary hot-air balloon 2,000m above the ground, and let us assume that the parachutist's mass (including all equipment and parachute) is 120kg. Taking g to be 10m/s^2 for simplicity[1], the total weight, or force of gravity acting downwards on him, is 1,200N, and remains at this value throughout the descent. So when he has fallen to the ground, gravity has done 1,200 × 2,000 or 2,400,000 joules of work on him. Notice that we have needed to ask no questions at all about what accelerations and speeds he actually experiences or moves with at various phases of the descent, what other forces such as air resistance are acting on him, or even whether he has opened the parachute at some point during the descent and what difference that has made. None of these very significant factors in any way affects the amount of work *done by gravity*, which is simply the weight force (which doesn't vary)[2] times the distance (which doesn't vary). Even if the parachutist had jumped from a fast-flying aeroplane and some of the other quantities had been very different, it would have made absolutely no difference to the answer, since the direction of the weight force is vertically downwards, and height is also measured vertically.

If an aircraft is flying straight and level at a steady speed, then we already know, from Newton's First Law, that thrust equals drag and there is no *resultant* force in the direction of motion. But this does not mean that no work is done in moving the aircraft along – if it did, we would have a perpetual motion machine and would need no engines at all in the cruise. When thinking about the amount of work needed to produce motion, we must no longer consider the *resultant* force, which certainly is zero and unhelpful, but instead the relevant contributory force(s), in this case thrust. Since thrust and drag are equal and opposite, an equal amount of work is actually done *against*, or *to*, or *on* the opposing air, since the movement is in the *opposite* direction to that of the drag force.

We can now go back and look at our definition of energy, which was capacity to do work. The capacity for doing work in the first case, (the parachutist,) results from the parachutist initially being at a height above the ground, and so he is said to possess *potential energy*. Its

---

[1]g is the acceleration due to gravity, and so from Newton's Second Law an object's weight is its mass multiplied by g.
[2]Actually, weight varies a little with height, since the gravity effect of the Earth diminishes as one gets further away from her, but we are ignoring this small effect here.

quantity is easy – it is exactly the same as the work that would be done by gravity in bringing him down to Earth, in other words 2,400,000 joules. The capacity for doing work in the case of the aircraft flying continuously at a steady speed in level flight is in the form of chemical energy stored in the fuel. A certain amount of fuel will take the aircraft a certain distance before it has all been burned up. Once again, the amount of energy needed is the thrust (which is constant) times the distance to be flown. More energy than this must actually be stored in the fuel in the form of *chemical energy*, as the conversion process (carried out by the engines) can never be more than partially efficient at converting the energy, and so energy losses will always occur.

There is a large number of different forms of energy. In other words, there is a large number of ways of storing (or temporarily transmitting) the ability to do work, and any thing or system which could (through some ingenious process) be a source of doing work is an energy source, even if applying a force through a distance is never what is actually required of that energy source. It is at this point that we could happily get carried away into a broad discussion of 'energy in society', but we will resist the temptation.

PRINCIPLE OF CONSERVATION OF ENERGY

There is one important principle relating to energy, however, which must not be overlooked, and that is the principle of conservation of energy. This principle is derived purely from scientific observation and is presumed true since it has never been disproved or found wanting. It states that:

> **Energy can never be created or destroyed, but only converted from one form into another.**

So what happens to all the energy of the parachutist, when he has reached the ground and all the potential energy has been used up? Most of it will have very slightly warmed up a substantial volume of air on the way down, and some (depending on the speed of impact with the ground) will finish up heating up the earth and parachutist a little, and perhaps creating some sound, which also finishes up as heat when it has finished being sound. In the case of the aircraft flying at a steady speed, the work done produces a disturbed motion in the air, and when the air eventually settles down again it has been slightly warmed up. Once again the energy finishes up as heat.

In the case of an engine, fuel is burned, releasing its chemical energy and thus deliberately converting it into heat, which is itself a form of energy, and then the heat is converted into work through the action of pistons or turbines. This work output may drive our aircraft, in which case it finishes up warming lots of air a little bit and is of no further use. The engine may operate a crane or a lift, in which case the energy would be converted into potential energy stored in the raised load, but when the object eventually descends under the action of gravity its energy will again be converted into heat as we have seen.

In fact, to cut a long story short, all energy eventually finishes up as heat energy. To do any further work, it would have to give up some more of its energy, now in the form of heat, thus finishing up at an even lower temperature. However, once this temperature becomes close to that of its surroundings no effective further temperature drop will be possible, and the residual energy becomes incapable of doing any more useful work.

KINETIC ENERGY

Let us move back now from the rather general discussion and consider the more specific forms of energy which are referred to as mechanical, of which potential energy due to height is one. An interesting situation arises if an object falls from rest under gravity down the inside of an evacuated tube, so that there is no air resistance, nor any air for the energy to be given over to during descent. When the object hits the bottom of the tube, it stops, and in the short duration of the collision all of the energy is dissipated in the form of heat and sound which finishes as heat. The question is, what has happened to all the potential energy *at the instant just before* the object hits the bottom? The object has virtually fallen the entire distance, and so it has no potential energy left. Yet the collision has not yet happened, and so no transfer of energy to heat has yet occurred.

The answer is that all the energy is still stored within the falling object, but no longer in the form of potential energy due to height. It is in the *speed* of the object's motion that the energy is temporarily stored, and this gives rise to a new form of energy called *kinetic energy*, from the Greek verb *kinetikos* meaning 'movement'. Let us see how this relates to the potential energy that the object possessed before it started to fall. This potential energy is the same as the work done by gravity in pulling the object from the top position to the present position. If the object's mass is m and it has fallen through a distance h, then the weight is mg (where g is the acceleration due to gravity), and the energy converted into kinetic energy is the work done by gravity or mgh. Now let us use v to signify the speed of the body just before hitting the bottom. There is a useful formula[3] (which we will take on trust here) based purely on the relationships between

---

[3]This is from the constant acceleration formula $v^2 = u^2 + 2as$, putting the initial speed u equal to zero.

distance, speed and acceleration, which states that if an object acceler-
ates from rest with an acceleration a for a distance s, then $v^2 = 2as$. In
our case we will write g in place of a since it is the acceleration due to
gravity, and h for s since this is our distance, giving $v^2 = 2gh$, or
$\frac{1}{2}v^2 = gh$. If we now multiply both sides of this equation by m we obtain
$\frac{1}{2}mv^2 = mgh$, and you will observe that the right-hand side has become
our expression a few lines back for the work done by gravity, or the
potential energy before the fall. Thus, since the two sides of an equation are equal, the left-hand side of this equation, $\frac{1}{2}mv^2$, must represent
the kinetic energy that has replaced all of the potential energy.
Because they are so important, let us summarise these energy results
now:

Kinetic Energy $= \frac{1}{2}mv^2$
Potential Energy $= mgh$

We will now leave the topic of energy for a few minutes, although
this is a very inconclusive point, and turn to look at pressure. But we
are now ready and prepared to pick up our energy ideas from here, at
the point where they will help us in understanding certain aspects of
pressure.

ATMOSPHERIC PRESSURE

Any object near the earth (unless specially protected in some way) is
immersed in the invisible air of the atmosphere, and experiences a
pressure force, called *atmospheric pressure*, on every point of its surface due to this atmospheric air. What is happening is quite simply
that the object is being bombarded from all directions by millions of
fast-moving air molecules, which simply get bounced away. Clearly a
force is needed to bounce away an approaching projectile, and by
Newton's Third Law it follows that there will be an equal force in the
opposite direction on the surface against which it is bouncing. Since in
still air any non-perpendicular bits of all of these little forces cancel
with each other out, it is found that the resultant pressure force at any
point on the surface is always normal to the surface at that point.

You will probably have met (perhaps at school) some experiment
which demonstrates the extremely large pressure forces that actually
exist in the atmosphere. One of the most simple yet dramatic is the
collapsing can. Into an empty metal 1-gallon (or 5-litre) oil can is
poured an egg-cupful or so of water, and this is then heated with a
Bunsen burner so that it boils well and water vapour billows plentiful-
ly from the open neck. (Make sure it *is* open, or the can will explode
very dangerously.) The Bunsen burner is then withdrawn or turned
off, and *immediately* the can's screw top is replaced tightly (protecting
your hand from scalding). As the can cools down, the water vapour

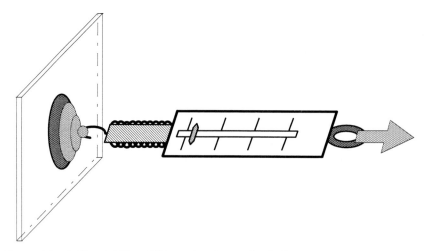

Figure 4.1   A Simple Way of Measuring Atmospheric Pressure

inside condenses to its original state of liquid water, which occupies only a tiny amount of space compared with water vapour, and there is nothing left (i.e. a vacuum) in the large space which the water vapour had previously been occupying. Consequently the can quickly collapses in on itself under the immense pressure of atmospheric air pressing inwards all over the outside of it.

How great is this pressure? The simplest way of obtaining an approximate idea of its size is to measure it directly by means of a small domestic rubber suction cup on a pane of glass and a spring balance, as shown in Figure 4.1. After making sure that the sucker and glass surfaces are smooth and clean and moistened to create a good seal, press the sucker very firmly onto the glass, flattening it so that all air is expelled. The sucker is then being held against the glass surface purely by atmospheric pressure. Now pull the sucker steadily at right angles to the glass surface using a suitable spring balance until the sucker is suddenly released. Clearly the reading of the spring balance must have been under constant observation up to this moment, since the reading will immediately be lost. If this rather crude measurement is repeated a number of times, it will be found that most successful pulls release the cup at fairly consistent forces, and the average of these values should be worked out.

It is not only the force that is of interest, but also the area over which the air is acting to press the cup onto the glass. In fact, if the sucker has an area of more than one or two square-inches, it is likely that you will have great difficulty in pulling it off at all. The pressure, as we have seen earlier, is defined as the force acting per unit area, and in our case this is calculated by dividing the force to release the sucker by the area of the sucker's face, which is the area over which the force is distributed. To find the area, measure the diameter d of the sucker face with a ruler, and use the formula $\pi d^2/4$ to calculate the area. Then to find the pressure, divide the average force by the area.

The results that this experiment gives for atmospheric pressure are likely to err on the low side, since any imperfection of the seal or the rubber will cause a premature release. But if all goes well and if you measure the force in newtons and the area using a metric ruler, you should get an answer in the region of 0.1 newton per square millimetre, 10 newtons per square centimetre, or 100,000 newtons per square metre. 100,000 newtons or 100kN is the weight of 200 sacks of builder's cement, which is a pretty colossal force to be acting on every surface (vertical, horizontal or inclined) that is immersed in atmospheric air! You may well ask why most things don't simply collapse under such enormous pressure, and the answer is that the pressure is balanced out by acting from all sides and directions at once.

If you worked out your answer in British Engineering units, you should have got around 14 pounds-force per square-inch, which is not far short of a ton = force per square-foot. It is therefore not surprising that the oil can collapsed. If its opposite faces have areas in the region of a square foot each, then they are being squeezed with a compressive force of about a ton.

Atmospheric pressure is so great because we are at the bottom of a very deep ocean of air, the atmosphere, and there is a lot of air above us. This 'bottom-of-the-atmosphere' air is in fact surprisingly heavy, a cubic metre of it having a mass of about $1\frac{1}{2}$ kilograms, or a weight of about 12 newtons. But we are not usually aware of the mass or the weight of the air, since it is supported in its surrounding ocean of air, just as any given volume of sea-water, weighed *in situ*, would be weightless because of the buoyancy of the surrounding sea-water on it. However, if an isolated cubic metre of this air (in an imaginary very lightweight box whose weight we could ignore) were placed on the ground in a place without any surrounding atmosphere, it would load its square metre foot-print with a distributed load of its weight of 12 newtons, and this would constitute a pressure force of 12 newtons per square-metre acting downwards on the ground, and an equal and opposite pressure force of 12 newtons per square-metre acting *upwards* on the bottom of the box, by Newton's Third Law. But we have said that atmospheric pressure is about 100,000 newtons per square-metre, not 12, and to get this much load on the foot-print we would need to have a stack of 100,000/12 or over 8000 cubic metres of air on top of one another, or a tower of air 8 kilometres high!

This is in fact almost the situation that exists, with the height of the tower corresponding to the depth of the atmosphere around the Earth. The entire surface of the Earth is covered in identical towers all packed close together, forming the atmosphere. Note, though, that it is only the weight of the tower *directly above* any spot that has any effect on the pressure at that spot, and so the pressure in a fluid is due only to the depth, and not in any way to the horizontal extent. It doesn't even matter if the path is not straight. Thus the pressure at 6 metres below the header tank in the water pipes of a house is just as great as the pressure 6 metres beneath the surface of an ocean.

We said that the air tower explanation *almost* explains atmospheric pressure. For completeness and accuracy, although it won't affect us very much at first in our Flightwise work, we should notice that actually the atmosphere is much deeper than eight kilometres. The reason is simply that air is very compressible, as you know if you pull out a bicycle pump's handle, put your thumb over the open end, and then push the handle in with the other hand. You *can* do it, because the air inside is compressible, but you couldn't do it if the pump were filled with water. Since air is compressible, the more weight of air there is above it, the more compressed any one cubic metre will be, and so the cubic metres of air near the bottom of the tower of air (where we are) will have much more mass (many more molecules) of air squeezed, or compressed, into them, than the cubic metres near the top, which have far less weight above them. (Imagine building a large model of a skyscraper out of foam rubber. Near the bottom the foam will be much more compressed than at the top.) In other words the density of air is greater lower down, and smaller higher up. There is therefore a clear connection between density of air and air pressure, but they must never be confused with each other, as they are totally different kinds of quantity.

Returning for the moment to the simplified model of the air being incompressible, we have seen that the magnitude of the atmospheric pressure at the bottom of the 1 metre-square 8 kilometres-high air tower is the weight of the tower, or its mass times g. Now its mass is its density times its volume, and the volume is simply equal to the height (in metres) since the cross-section is one metre square. Therefore if we use ρ for the density and h for the height of the air tower, the pressure p at the bottom is given by the equation

$$p = \rho g h$$

This is in fact the correct formula for working out the pressure due to depth in an incompressible liquid, so that we can use it for example to work out the pressure in the domestic water system which we mentioned a few paragraphs back. The depth is 6m, the density of water is

1000kg/m^3, and we will take g to be 10m/s^2, and so the pressure p is given by

$$p = \rho gh = 1000 \times 10 \times 6 = 60 \text{kN/m}^2$$

On the face of it this appears to be less than the atmospheric pressure of 100kN/m^2, but we must remember that this is only the pressure due to the depth of *water*, and it exists in addition to the ubiquitous atmospheric pressure. To find the total (or *absolute*) pressure, we must *add* to this the pressure of the atmosphere, giving in this case 160kN/m^2. But of course we often aren't concerned about the pressure of the atmosphere, since we are immersed in it all the time and we regard it as the norm. Atmospheric pressure is therefore often regarded as the starting value from which pressure is measured. Using this system, the pressure of 60kN/m^2 as given above is called the *gauge* pressure, and is the value *relative* to atmospheric pressure.

We can't actually use the formula $p = \rho gh$ directly for working out atmospheric pressure, since the density of the air varies with height as we have seen and the atmosphere peters out at the top rather than stopping at some specific depth h. Instead we have to work it out by adding together the results of lots of thin slices all the way up through our air tower of varying density, but this is the province of the Calculus, with which we will not involve ourselves. Suffice it to say that each of these bits to be added together will be of the same form as ρgh, having the same dimensions, and therefore the final answer will also be of the same form and dimensions. Pressure therefore is always of the *form* ρgh, where ρ is a density and h is a height.

Remembering that density is mass per volume, ($\rho = m/v$), we could write this pressure formula in terms of m and v as follows:

$$p = \rho gh = \left(\frac{m}{v} \right) gh = (mgh)/v = (mgh) \text{ per unit volume}$$

Glancing back to the previous section, we spot the interesting fact that we have now come across the potential energy formula mgh in a completely different context, that of pressure. This should prompt us to enquire whether there is any connection between pressure and energy. To tackle this question, we can see quite unequivocally from the form of the above formula that

Pressure is energy per unit volume.

This is a simple and very useful concept to take on board, as we shall see shortly. But in order to investigate the question a little more thoroughly, we might ask the question, what *energy* calculation, if any, would give us the pressure in a fluid?

Let us take again our simplified model of the atmosphere being 8km deep and of uniform density. Our expression '(*mgh*) per unit volume' from the above expression refers to the unit volume (the one metre cube) at the bottom of our 8km high air tower, and *m* is the mass of air in that cube. *mg* is the weight of the cube, or the force that would be required to lift it (assuming there were no air surrounding it to support it), and *h* is the height to the top of the tower. Thus the expression '(*mgh*) per unit volume' means the work that would have to be done to lift this cube of air from where it is in the atmosphere to the top of the atmosphere, or the potential energy that it would possess when it is up there.

There were rather a lot of 'ifs' and assumptions in arriving at that last conclusion, and in practice it turns out not to be a very useful concept. However, it is valuable to have seen the close connection between potential energy and pressure due to depth in a fluid, and especially to have taken on board the very important fact that pressure can *always* be thought of as energy per unit volume. Since the pressure of the air is not after all to be found directly from such a simple formula as ρgh, let us from now on simply use p to stand for pressure, always remembering that p can be thought of either as the pressure of the air or as energy per unit volume of the air.

BUOYANCY

Aircraft lift is produced *aerodynamically*, which means that it is a direct result of the relative *motion* of air and aircraft. Shortly we will introduce the concept of dynamic pressure which explains changes in pressure due to motion, but before that it will be instructive just to deviate briefly to look at another method of producing upthrust, that of buoyancy.

Buoyancy is very much more important to marine creatures and vehicles than to those which are airborne, simply because the density of water is very much greater than that of air, and is of a similar order of magnitude to the creatures and vehicles themselves. However, air does provide substantial buoyancy, which is witnessed by the fact that airships and lighter-than-air balloons, which depend for their lift on it, actually work. What causes it?

We have seen that all *aerodynamic* force depends on the agencies of pressure and viscosity, but we are now in the realms not of aerodynamic but of *aerostatic* force. Consequently there are no viscous forces because we will assume that the balloon is absolutely motionless in the air. (If the air moves in a wind current, the balloon will move over the ground with it – there is no *relative* velocity between balloon and air.)

We must conclude that the weight of the balloon is supported purely by the pressure distribution around it. This is rather odd, since it would seem logical that the resultant of the static pressure distribution over the surface of any immersed object *ought* to be zero, so that things would not start shooting off in all directions. What is amiss with our logic?

To answer this, let us consider a conveniently-shaped hypothetical 'balloon' having the form of our familiar one-metre cube box, being itself weightless but containing air, immersed in the atmosphere. We will raise the cube slightly above the ground so that the lower surface is not prevented from being acted upon by air pressure. The box is orientated with two opposite faces horizontal and the rest vertical. The forces due to atmospheric pressure on all of the vertical faces will be equal, and those on opposite faces will cancel out with each other in opposite pairs. Thus we have only to consider the forces on the top and bottom faces, and these forces will both be vertical in direction (i.e. normal to the faces), that on the top face being downwards and that on the bottom face upwards. Since each face has an area of one square metre, the force on each face is numerically equal to the pressure acting on that face. The column of air responsible for the pressure on the lower face is *one metre taller than* the column of air producing the upper face pressure, and so there will be a pressure *difference* between the top and bottom faces of ρg times [difference in heights]. The difference in heights for the one metre cube is one metre, and so the force acting upwards on the lower surface is ρg greater than the force acting downwards on the upper surface. There is therefore a buoyancy force acting on the cube of ρg. But of course, the weight of the cube's contents (being a volume of one cubic metre) is also ρg, and so it is neutrally buoyant. Remember that we assumed the box itself to be weightless.

This same principle applies to any shape and size of weightless container (or imaginary closed surface) containing a fluid and immersed in the same fluid. The principle states that the pressure distribution has a resultant which is upwards in direction, i.e. an upthrust or buoyancy force, which is exactly the same in magnitude as the weight of the fluid in the container (or the closed surface). Put another way, any weightless container full of the same fluid as it is immersed in will be neutrally buoyant, and furthermore, if the container walls are then removed, the situation pertaining between the 'contained' and the 'outside' fluid will remain unchanged and there will be no movement, even though there is no longer any physical boundary. This is the principle which is attributed to the Greek mathematician Archimedes, usually stated briefly as 'the upthrust equals the weight of fluid displaced', on his discovery of which, whilst in his bath one day, he leapt excitedly from the tub and ran down the street stark naked shouting *'eureka!', 'I've found it!'*

Archimedes' Principle might appear to be rather a disappointing 'nothing' principle, but its usefulness arises when the exact conditions specified are departed from. Consider an ordinary party balloon blown up with air. Contents and environment are both air, but in this case the container is not weightless. The balloon fabric density is substantially greater than that of air, and so, although the fabric volume is far less than the contained volume, it makes the weight of the overall 'balloon' (container plus contents) greater than the weight of an equal volume of air, and so the balloon is negatively buoyant and will fall to the ground. If we want the balloon to float, its overall weight must be reduced to less than the weight of the same volume of air. Reducing the density of the containing fabric to less than that of air would achieve this, but is clearly not a practical possibility and would in any case produce very little buoyancy. The only way to obtain positive buoyancy is to replace the contained air with something less dense than air, such as helium or hydrogen (or air of a lower density, which is how the hot-air balloon works).

A common misapprehension is that somehow a gas such as helium or hydrogen, being lighter than air, defies gravity and exerts some upward force on the balloon or an airship. But both helium and hydrogen have positive (if small) densities and hence weight, and if not buoyed up by the surrounding atmosphere both would sink to the ground. It is important to realise that the upthrust arises *only* from the pressure distribution on the outside of the balloon or airship, and that its magnitude depends purely on the *volume* of the balloon or airship, which is the same as its *displacement*, or the volume of atmospheric air that it displaces or pushes out of its usual place. The size of the upthrust force has got nothing at all to do with how heavy the balloon or airship or its contents are.

This leads us to a rather surprising revelation about modern large aircraft such as the Boeing 747 Jumbo Jets, whose enormous fuselages (ignoring their wings and tails) have volumes comparable with some of the early and smaller airships. With a fuselage volume of around 120,000 cubic feet (or 3,240 cubic metres), the 747's fuselage is of a similar volume to the lifting envelope of the Goodyear Blimps that were built between the two World Wars and carried six passengers. Since the buoyancy depends solely on the volume and not on the weight, we can conclude that the fuselage of today's Boeing 747 produces as much lift due to buoyancy as did those six-seater Goodyear Blimps. By Archimedes' Principle, the upthrust equals ρg times (volume), or about $1.2 \times 10 \times 3240$ newtons, which equals about 40kN, or about eighty bags of cement!

But this buoyancy is not very useful to us. Whenever we weigh any-thing, including an aircraft, we weigh it immersed in the atmosphere, and so the ever-present buoyancy is already allowed for in the figure we give for the weight. What this means is that if we were to weigh any object in a vacuum, be it aeroplane or shopping bag, then the weight measured would be a little greater than normal, since the buoyancy is no longer present. It also means that, whereas we had presumed the mass of an object to be proportional to its weight (under identical gravitational conditions), yet if weight is measured with the object immersed in atmospheric air (which it usually is), there will be an error in this assumption, since the measured weight is less than the true weight.

Of course the buoyancy effect of the atmosphere is not very great, which is why airships had to be so enormous. The largest, the *Hindenberg*, had a volume of 7,000,000 cubic feet, (about 58 times that of the Boeing 747 and of the Goodyear Blimps), and was over 800 feet long, (more than three times the length of the Boeing), but yet it only carried fifty passengers. On more conventionally sized objects, buoy-ancy is not usually a sufficiently large force to need to take into account, and certainly in aircraft design normally no account need be taken of it at all. But the underlying cause of buoyancy, which is the increase in atmospheric pressure which occurs over the small height difference between the top and the bottom of an object, gives us an interesting additional insight into the workings of pressure and of the atmosphere.

STATIC PRESSURE AND DYNAMIC PRESSURE

Around an object that is at rest relative to the air, we have seen that we can usually ignore the small atmospheric pressure difference between top and bottom of the object and the resulting buoyancy force, and so we can assume that the pressure at all points on the surface is the same. But that is not yet the whole picture, and we must now examine how this situation is altered if the object is *moving*

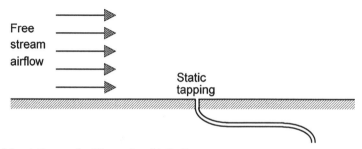

Figure 4.2   A Sensor for Measuring Static Pressure

relative to the air, creating aerodynamic rather than just aerostatic forces.

First of all, consider just a simple uniform airstream flowing without any obstruction, as is shown flowing from left to right in Figure 4.2. If we want to think about the pressure of this airstream, then there must be some contact with a surface for the pressure to act upon, and so at the bottom of the figure we have introduced a flat surface running parallel to the free stream direction. If we think of this surface as being ultra-smooth (so that it does not create any viscous force) and stretching infinitely far in every direction, then it will have no effect on the shape or form or pressure of the airflow above it. We can therefore regard the surface as a convenient platform for measuring the pressure of the air.

To measure this pressure, first of all we will need a pipe for transmitting the pressure to the measuring instrument. The sensing end of the pipe must be very close to the flat surface, and the pipe can then conveniently be led away from the airflow through the flat surface. But if the sensing end protrudes *at all* into the flow, it will actually disturb the flow around it, and so will affect in some way the pressure that it is measuring. Even if it does not protrude, but if the hole is of any significant size, then it will act like a pot-hole on the road to the airflow over it, again causing a disturbance and probably a local change in the pressure that we are trying to measure. It is thus absolutely essential that this pressure-sensing hole in the surface is very small and absolutely flush with the surface. Such holes in practice are often so small that they are difficult to see, and so naturally they are liable to get blocked with dirt, or perhaps with polish by a well-intentioned person cleaning the surface. On aircraft this can be a very serious hazard, since the flight instruments which depend on pressure measurement won't work properly.

A pressure-sensing hole of this sort in a surface over which air is flowing is called a 'static tapping', and the pressure that it measures is called the *static pressure*. You may be thinking (quite correctly at the moment) that this is no different from the atmospheric pressure at this point, and so why should we confuse the issue by inventing a new name for it? The reason is that, as we will very soon see, this surface pressure can vary (up or down) away from the local atmospheric pressure, as a result of the air's motion, and so it needs a name of its own. The name static pressure is appropriate in that it is the pressure due only to aerostatic conditions, or in other words to the atmospheric conditions that we have already considered, and is not influenced in any way at all by the fact that the air is now flowing past the sensor with a velocity. We have deliberately and carefully made the sensor so small and smooth that it will not disturb the airflow, or hence the static pressure, at all.

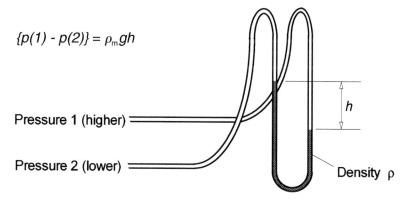

$\{p(1) - p(2)\} = \rho_m gh$

Pressure 1 (higher)

Pressure 2 (lower)

h

Density ρ

Figure 4.3   A U-tube Manometer

We now have our pressure sensor and a pipe to transmit the pressure away from the scene, and so we need some pressure-measuring device at the other end of it. The simplest pressure-measuring device is a U-tube manometer, which consists of a U-shaped glass tube with some liquid (often water) in the bottom of the U, as shown in Figure 4.3. A U-tube manometer always measures the *difference* between two pressures and not an absolute pressure. The difference between the two pressures in the two limbs causes the liquid to be pressed down in the limb with the higher pressure, so that it rises in the other limb. The difference between the two pressures is the pressure that would be produced by a column of liquid whose height is the difference between the two levels. The pressure difference can be worked out by exactly the same formula as we had before; namely $p = \rho_m gh$, where p is now the pressure difference, ρ_m is the density of the manometer liquid, g the acceleration due to gravity and h the difference in levels, which can be measured with a ruler.

But we are getting ahead of ourselves. At present in Figure 4.2 we only have one pipe coming from the static tapping, which we can connect to one of the U-tube limbs, but the manometer must measure a pressure *difference*. What are we going to connect to the other limb? This gives us our opportunity to investigate a new type of pressure that arises from the air's motion. We have seen that pressure p (previously atmospheric, but in our new terminology static) can be regarded as energy closely associated with potential energy. Let us call this form of energy *pressure energy*. But since the air is moving with a velocity, it must also possess some *kinetic* energy due to its motion. We saw earlier that a mass m has kintic energy $\frac{1}{2}mv^2$, and so the air's kinetic energy is $\frac{1}{2}\rho v^2$ per unit volume of air.

Every unit of volume of the airflow therefore possesses two types of energy, p (pressure energy, which is related to potential energy) due to atmospheric pressure and $\frac{1}{2}\rho v^2$ (which *is* kinetic energy) due to motion. But we notice something else of very great significance about these two quantities: since the first one is also a pressure, and since the two quantities are alike to each other in kind, then the second expression $\frac{1}{2}\rho v^2$ must *also be a pressure.*

Thus not only does our air flow possess two kinds of energy (pressure energy and kinetic energy), but it also possesses two kinds of pressure which correspond exactly to these two kinds of energy. The first kind we have called static pressure, and the second, since it is directly related to the motion of the air, we call *dynamic* pressure.

We can't actually measure dynamic pressure as it is, because strictly it is not yet a pressure – the only real pressure in the flowing air is the static pressure which presses sideways against surfaces. Remembering the Principle of Conservation of Energy, we can convert the dynamic pressure to real (static) pressure if we convert all the kinetic energy into pressure energy. Taking away all the kinetic energy will involve bringing the airflow completely to rest, but since it will be converted into pressure energy, we will find that there is an accompanying pressure increase. So the pressure that we now have consists of the static pressure that we had before, *plus* the pressure due to the motion that the air had before coming to rest, the dynamic pressure. We logically define this new pressure as the *total pressure*, so that we have the important relationship:

Total pressure = Static pressure + Dynamic pressure.

We said in the last paragraph that we cannot directly measure dynamic pressure. But we can measure total pressure simply by bringing the airflow to rest locally at a pressure sensor, and from the above relationship we see that dynamic pressure equals total pressure *minus* static pressure – a pressure *difference*, just what a manometer is good at measuring. So now we can set up our complete pressure-sensing and measuring system as shown in Figure 4.4.

The sensor required for measuring the total pressure is called a *pitot tube*, and is simply a thin tube (thin enough to produce no more than a negligible disturbance in the flow) pointing straight into the approaching airflow. Since the other end of this tube is connected to a limb of the manometer, it is closed-off by the manometer liquid, and so none of the freestream airflow can flow into the tube at the open end. Instead, just inside the mouth of the pitot tube, the velocity of the freestream airflow is brought totally to rest, and so all of the kinetic energy is converted into additional pressure energy. We can now connect the two pipes to the manometer limbs as shown, and, referring back to Figure 4.3, obtain the difference between total pressure and

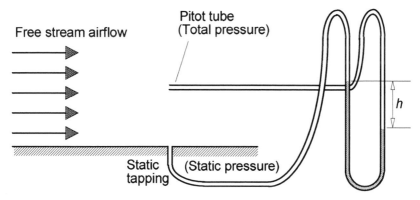

Figure 4.4   Measuring Dynamic Pressure

static pressure, which will be $\rho_m g h$. This gives us the dynamic pressure.

One practical outcome of the previous ideas is that we now have a very direct means of measuring the speed of our airflow, and this method is also used for making air-speed indicators for aircraft. We have seen that dynamic pressure can be obtained by measuring the difference between total pressure (measured with a pitot tube) and static pressure (measured at a static tapping) and that this pressure (calculated from $\rho_m g h$) equals $\frac{1}{2}\rho v^2$. If when the dynamic pressure has been determined it is doubled, divided by the density ρ, and then square rooted, the answer is v, the speed of the airflow, or of the aeroplane. Of course, if the pitot tube and the static tapping are in different places where the airflow is at different speeds, the answer will be nonsense, and to overcome this a device called a *pitot-static probe* (Figure 4.5) can be used, which enables the total pressure and the

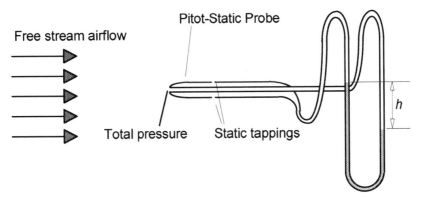

Figure 4.5   Measuring Dynamic Pressure with a Pitot-static Probe

static pressure to be sensed at almost exactly the same point in the air-flow. The pitot-static probe consists of two concentric tubes, the inner one of which is open at the front (the pitot tube), and the outer one of which is faired and sealed to the inner at the front so that no direct airflow enters it. The whole thing should not disturb the airflow more than minimally. One or more small static tappings are pierced through the cylindrical face of the outer tube. The inner and outer tubes divide at the rear as shown, and are connected by pipes to a manometer or to the two sides of the pressure-measuring diaphragm of an air-speed indicator.

But there is one hidden snag, and that is what value to use for the air density. We have already seen that it changes with height in the atmosphere, but without measuring it separately the air-speed indica-tor cannot use the right value for the air density ρ. Instead it always uses the same value, which is the sea-level density of the air, and so the air-speed indicator is always reading a false (low) value of speed (which is called the 'indicated air-speed') unless the aircraft is actually flying at sea-level, a rather hazardous procedure. So if he wants to know his true air-speed the pilot always has to make a correction to the air-speed indicator reading.

In fact this is not really a problem. The chief reason that a pilot needs to know his speed is to help him to fly the aeroplane accurately and efficiently, and this depends on the aerodynamic forces on wings and tail. Now, it is the *dynamic pressure*, $\frac{1}{2}\rho v^2$, which dictates the aero-dynamic forces, and so this value is far more use to him than his true air-speed would be, for actually flying the aeroplane. Although the numbers on the dial have been converted into speed units, (for his-toric, though not entirely sound, reasons,) yet the air-speed indicator is really measuring dynamic pressure, and is one of the most impor-tant flight instruments to the pilot. This is discussed at more length in the section headed 'So what?' in Chapter 11.

FLOW AROUND OBJECTS AND BERNOULLI'S PRINCIPLE

We will now turn to consider an object of some sort in our airflow. If we watch the object moving through the still air past our observation point, it is extremely difficult to make useful observations of what is going on. Firstly, as the object moves past it temporarily moves the air out of its way, and then the air has to close up again after it has passed, so that the air displays an unsteady motion which changes with time. If we want to examine this airflow, we must examine an errati-cally moving target. Secondly, we have two separate movements to consider, that of the object as well as that of the air. Thirdly, we only have a very short time to make our observations, since no sooner has the object come into view than it has gone again. Fourthly, it is virtually an impossibility to measure the forces (e.g. lift and drag) on the object while it is moving past us.

We have to thank another great benefactor of modern science and aeronautics for first solving this problem for us, no less a man than Leonardo Da Vinci, who pointed out that the features under investigation will be completely unchanged if we bring the object to rest and instead make the air move past it. All the forces and velocities of interest are properties of the *relative* motion of one to the other and so will be unchanged. This is the principle on which the use of a wind-tunnel is based, and it immediately solves all of the problems of the previous paragraph. For our present discussion, it will be convenient for us to imagine that we jump on board the moving object so that we travel along with it, or at least alongside it so that we can look at it continuously. It is now the air that is moving past, whilst we and the object effectively remain stationary.

We saw in Chapter 3 that the aerodynamic force on a randomly shaped object depends on the pressure distribution and also on the viscous force distribution around that object, and that the pressure forces are substantially greater, although the viscous forces cannot safely be ignored as they have very far-reaching effects. Now that we have met the concepts static pressure and dynamic pressure, and the principle of the conservation of energy, let us take a further brief look at the airflow around the object.

From our human experience it is beyond doubt that aerodynamic force is achievable, and that it is more attributable to the pressure (normal) forces than to the viscous (tangential) forces. We have seen that, if there is no airflow and we ignore the relatively insignificant buoyancy force of the air, the resultant of the pressure forces on an object is zero. It follows that in a moving airflow the pressure of the air must vary in some way from place to place as it flows around the object.

There will be situations in which an element of air will be flowing from a point where the pressure is high to another point where it is lower. In such a situation there is a greater pressure behind the element of air than in front of it, and so the progress of the air is aided by the pressure difference – it is pushed. By Newton's Second Law, the element of air will accelerate in the direction of its motion, and so will increase in speed. Conversely, when the element of air has to flow from a lower pressure region to a higher pressure region, the opposing force on it will cause it to slow down. There would appear to be a direct link between the pressure in the air and the speed of flow of the air. In fact, the air behaves rather like a roller-coaster.

Imagine a fun-fair roller-coaster, which is so expertly designed and built in every detail that it has absolutely no friction in the wheels or other moving parts at all, and so superbly streamlined that there is absolutely no air resistance to its motion. We will follow its progress from the moment when, having been winched up to the first very high point, it is free-wheeling very slowly as it approaches the first big plunge.

At this point all of the roller-coaster's energy is in the form of potential energy. (It has a negligibly small amount of kinetic energy since we assume that the speed is only just enough to get it to the top of the first descent and no more.) As the roller-coaster plunges down the first descent, the potential energy is progressively but very rapidly given over to kinetic energy as the speed increases. At the bottom, there immediately follows a free-wheeling climb which the roller-coaster tackles by making use of the speed that it had gained on the descent. As it goes up the slope, its kinetic energy is transferred back into potential energy. Being of impeccable design, there is no loss of energy through friction or any other cause, and so the track has been designed to go back up to exactly the same height as it started at. The roller-coaster just makes it, all the kinetic energy is converted back into potential energy, and all is ready for the next excitement, another plunge.

The progress of this roller-coaster can continue indefinitely, down vertical plunges or gentle slopes, round turns and vertical loops, and back up via steep or gradual climbs. All the time, there is a continual exchange going on between its kinetic energy (increasing during the descents) and its potential energy (increasing during the ascents). The total energy, which is the sum of the two parts, remains exactly constant throughout the ride, and the roller-coaster track can keep returning to its high starting level (but never any higher) as often as it likes. The process is never-ending.

If there were no viscosity, then the progress of airflow around an object would be very much like that of the roller-coaster. We have already seen the strong link between pressure energy and potential energy, and in the case of the air the energy interchange does not occur between potential and kinetic energy, but between pressure energy and kinetic energy. As the air 'descends' from high pressure to low pressure, it increases in speed. When it 'climbs' from low pressure to high pressure, it slows down. The sum of the pressure energy and the kinetic energy is constant.

Without doing any mathematics or hard physics, we have actually arrived at the most important principle of aerodynamics, which is called Bernoulli's Principle (or law or equation). Applying the words from the end of the last paragraph to one unit of volume of the air, it says that pressure energy per unit volume plus kinetic energy per unit volume is constant. As we have seen, this may be alternatively stated as static pressure plus dynamic pressure is constant, and in the last section we defined this as the total pressure. Bernoulli's Principle can therefore most usefully be written down as

$$p + \tfrac{1}{2}\rho v^2 = \text{constant}$$

or

$$p_1 + \tfrac{1}{2}\rho v_1{}^2 = p_2 + \tfrac{1}{2}\rho v_2{}^2$$

where the subscripts 1 and 2 in the second form refer to the conditions at two different points along the path of the same element of air. In the next chapter we will see how this helps us to work out the actual pressure distribution around an object, provided we can first of all find out how the velocity is behaving.

This formula is strictly called the Incompressible Bernoulli's Equation, and is only an approximation to the truth which is appropriate for relatively low air speeds, (say less than about half of the speed of sound). The reason for this is tied up with our assumptions about energy. We have assumed that kinetic and pressure energy are the *only* forms of energy that air possesses. Strictly we should have said that they are the only types of energy that get involved in the energy transfer process that we have been looking at as speed and pressure change. Actually the air does contain other forms of energy, in particular in the form of heat (or more technically, internal) energy, but conveniently for us it is not until we get to speeds closer to the speed of sound that heat energy becomes a significant player on the scene. Below such speeds we assume that it just remains constant, and it would be a waste of our time to add it to both sides of every equation we wrote down when it doesn't actually affect the answer.

CHAPTER 5
Working Out Aerodynamic Force

INTRODUCTION

Flightwise has arrived at a watershed. Having started with an overview of the very diverse demands that are made of the designer of a flying machine, we have examined the place that aerodynamic force fulfils in meeting these requirements and have built up an understanding of the physical principles involved in the development of aerodynamic force. From now on we want to seek out answers to the more intricate and subtle questions and problems which arise in designing an aircraft. To do this, we must be prepared to look at conceptual ideas which are analogous to the physical ideas under investigation, in which the most important features are given most weight, and other considerations are sometimes ignored for the time being. The conceptual ideas may then be simplified by using appropriate approximations in order to render them amenable to mathematical treatment. The use of mathematics is not conceived as an aid to better understanding of the principle being modelled, but in order to enable the designer to predict the magnitudes of actual quantities. But even though the models may not themselves have been devised for the purpose of assisting understanding, they can often focus the mind most effectively on the important features of the topic in question, and help in clarifying ones ideas and mental processes.

In the present chapter, we will introduce the fundamental building system of all aerodynamic analytical theory, a system which is called *potential flow*. We will show that, using this system, it is possible to develop a method for actually predicting the pressure force distribution, and hence the lift and drag forces, on an object in an airflow. But we will end the chapter on a rather perplexing note of apparent failure to achieve any useful or meaningful results.

In Chapter 6 we will immediately turn our attention to investigating the anomaly revealed at the end of Chapter 5, and this will give rise to an introductory discussion about viscosity and the boundary layer.

Then at last in Chapter 7 we will be properly placed to start to answer the key question in matters of aircraft flight: how is the lift force actually produced? This is going to involve our bringing together virtually all the concepts that we will by that stage have met, and will open the door to the work of the remainder of this volume. The remaining chapters will continue to develop the concepts introduced thus far, and show how they apply to the actual design of the shape of different types of aircraft.

So we will turn our attention now in this chapter to obtaining a thorough understanding of the principles of what is called Classical Aerodynamics, and in this and Chapters 6 and 7 we will trace the logical ideas and developments by which theory eventually became sufficiently sophisticated to be applied to what was hitherto the trial-and-error black art of aerofoil and wing design and development. As we have seen, the concepts baffled even the geniuses of history until relatively late in the history of scientific development, and some extremely sophisticated ideas and reasoning were demanded to make a break-through.

We will be paddling in the shore waters of some mathematics which is extremely advanced by any standards, and many people have been put off the subject of aerodynamics because of its apparent concentration on advanced mathematics. But I have promised to avoid any mathematical treatment beyond the use of simple algebraic formulae, maintaining that mathematics is not a tool of explanation or amplification, but of analysis for the designer who wishes to make precise predictions. Where mathematical ideas crop up, we will treat them as *systems*, or black boxes which perform some function. Our interest will be in the purpose of the black box, or in other words what outputs we want it to provide, in exchange for what inputs; and it will be useful to have an idea of the principles by which the black box achieves its purpose. An analogy might be the use of a motor car. Its purpose is to transport you and your passengers and goods to the places required; the necessary inputs are regular maintenance and petrol, and to achieve these ends we have a *process* going on under the bonnet, of which any driver will agree it is useful to have at least a partial understanding, in order to get the best out of it. But all that is essential is that we provide the inputs, 'turn the handle' of the black box (or press the pedals and operate the controls of the car), and get the required results or outputs. This will be our approach here.

THE TWO-DIMENSIONAL CIRCULAR CYLINDER

We must start by postulating some convenient shape for our object, the aerodynamic forces on which we are to examine. We want something simple, and it would be useful to use a shape which might later allow us to develop the idea of a wing. With this in mind, let us consider some long (and relatively thin) object whose long axis we will place perpendicular to the freestream airflow direction. Although most wings are in fact tapered towards the wing-tips, we will for simplicity in the first instance assume that our object is going to have a uniform cross-section throughout its length. (We will investigate alternatives later.)

It would be nice if we could also assume that the airflow would behave in a uniform way around all cross-sections right out to the ends, although in practice this cannot be the case, and allowance will later have to be made. The only way theoretically of obtaining this effect is to have an object that is infinitely long, so that wherever we cut it, or wherever the air flows over it, we have exactly the same situation and exactly the same shape of both cross-section and airflow, because we are never near to an end. We refer to this type of object as being *two-dimensional*, which is rather odd since it is actually infinitely long in the third dimension, and infinity is in no way negligible! Actually the term is really quite logical, since what it means is that we can consider just one two-dimensional slice through the object, at right angles to its long axis and thus parallel to the airflow. Knowing that wherever we take this cross-section the resulting shape of object and airflow and thus the resulting pressure distribution will be exactly the same as at any other cross-section (whether near-by or far away), we can conclude that there will be no flow at all in the direction of the length of the object. Consequently we can represent our random cross-section on a two-dimensional sheet of paper and rest in confidence that we can also draw the flow lines on that sheet of paper, without risk of them coming out in front of the plane of the paper or going behind it. We thus have a 'two-dimensional model', although its representation on paper is that of an object sticking out from the paper both in front of and behind the plane of the paper infinitely far in the third dimension.

In practice in aircraft wings of course this is not achievable, since all good things must come to an end, and all wings must have wing-tips. In a test set-up in a wind-tunnel, however, we can get very close to this two-dimensional situation, by making the wind-tunnel working section (the place where the wing model goes) rectangular in shape (viewed in the direction of flow), and by letting the model, of uniform cross-section, span completely from one side of the tunnel to the other, normally to the tunnel walls. There will be a little interference with the flow at the end walls, but this will be small compared with aircraft wing-tip effects, and by taking pressure observations at the centre of the span the wall effects will be negligible.

We have decided on a two-dimensional model stretching indefinitely normal to the airflow, but what cross-sectional shape shall we use? It will be best to start off with a shape that is simple, that we can define precisely with elementary mathematical ideas, and that (if possible) possesses some symmetry. Squares, triangles and polygons have sharp corners, which intuitively look as if they might be unhelpful and problematical when considering the airflow, so we will choose a smooth curve. It must be closed (like a circle or an ellipse, not like a parabola) in order to exist in isolation. For simplicity then, let us choose a circular cross-section, and thus our object under investigation is an infinitely long circular cylinder. Our aim now becomes to investigate in detail the aerodynamic force on a two-dimensional circular cylinder in an airflow.

UNIFORM, INVISCID AIRFLOW

Turning our attention to the airflow, let us choose, as an obvious simplest case, a uniform airflow. In our diagrams we will show the direction of the airflow as being horizontal, and will for consistency let air flow from left to right, or let aeroplanes or objects move through still air from right to left. This does not in any way imply that we are only referring to (or simulating) level flight conditions, since we are considering *only* aerodynamic forces, and not unless we were including the force of gravity would the horizontal direction of the airflow be significant. In the absence of considerations of gravity, we can take it that we have simply aligned our blank sheet of paper to the airflow, before drawing the figure.

Let us follow in the path instinctively followed by the mathematical pioneers of this investigation, and let us initially make our task as simple as possible by considering only the force agent that appears to be the dominant contributor to aerodynamic force, that is, pressure. So for now we will make a sweeping assumption, that no viscous forces occur at all in the air. It will not do merely to say that the surfaces in contact with the air are smooth and frictionless, since air will also slide over air within the flow, and we therefore postulate that the air itself is *inviscid*, or has zero viscosity, or 'stickiness', a word which we will define at the start of the next chapter. Such a fluid, with zero viscosity, is called an *ideal* fluid. No ideal fluids exist in practice, but it is a useful concept. As we have mentioned earlier, this assumption will in fact land us in serious difficulty later on, but it certainly appears to be a logical starting point. Our work based on this assumption will not be wasted, since it still forms the foundation of all aerodynamic theory, and the incorporation of viscosity later on will be achieved by building on the foundations laid, rather than by pulling everything down and starting again.

So we now have an infinitely long circular cylinder, immersed in air which is assumed to be inviscid flowing perpendicular to the axis of the cylinder, and the airflow (other than where disturbed by the cylinder's presence) is uniform. We can represent this by a two-dimensional cross-sectional view which we illustrate in Figure 5.1, in which we have temporarily omitted the airflow in the region surrounding the cylinder. The straight line segments are the actual paths of reference particles of air within the airflow, and are known as *streamlines*. You will observe that we have refrained from putting arrow-heads onto

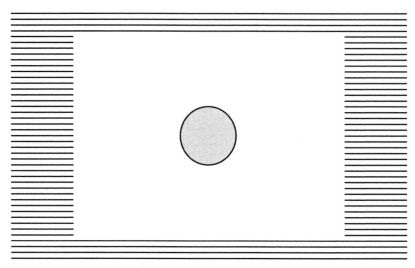

Figure 5.1   Streamlines 'At Infinity' Around a Circular Cylinder

any of these streamlines, because the flow would be exactly the same if we had drawn it from right to left as it is from left to right, by symmetry. This symmetry will demand our attention further in a few moments.

How would you define a distance of 'infinity'? Probably using some phrase invoking the idea of an extremely or impossibly large distance. The aerodynamicist uses the word infinity in a rather different way, to mean 'just far enough away from the object that we are considering for that object to have no effect'. Figure 5.1 has been drawn on the assumption that the streamlines, at some distance far enough upstream, downstream, above and below the cylinder, will be unaffected by the presence of the cylinder, although how far has not been established, and to represent it accurately we would probably need to draw the cylinder and the streamlines at a smaller scale. However far away from the cylinder this may be, the aerodynamicist refers to it as 'at infinity'. Infinity in some situations turns out to be a very small distance, perhaps a millimetre or two, as we will discover in the next chapter when considering boundary layers. But in the present situation it is probably somewhere in the tens of diameters of the cylinder in the stream direction, and about two diameters above and below the cylinder.

The question crying out to be tackled now is, how do we fill in the blank space in Figure 5.1? What does the airflow look like in the vicinity of the cylinder? Let us tackle this question by a number of logical steps. The first of these yields a conclusion that is the most important and yet the hardest to understand and accept. It is that the flow can go

either way along the streamlines, and thus that we were right and justified in leaving out the direction arrows. This conclusion arises directly from the following three tenets:

- The air in any *streampath* (a useful word that we will use to
  mean the region between any adjacent pair of streamlines)
  always remains within its streampath, and can never stray
  across either of its bounding streamlines into another streampath. This is a direct consequence of the fact that we regard
  air as a continuum. It is possible for cars on a three-lane road
  to pull across from lane to lane in the spaces between the
  other cars, but if all the cars were joined together like continuous trains in each lane, which represents the continuum
  model, then it would clearly be totally impossible for any car
  to change lanes, try as hard as the driver likes.
- The only forces acting from outside on the air in any streampath are the pressure forces acting at right angles to the
  streamlines, from adjacent streampaths. Being normal to the
  flow direction, these forces are not affected at all by the sense
  of the flow, since if the flow were to be reversed, the 'normal-
  ness' and magnitudes of these pressure forces would remain
  intact.
- Even where there is a relative speed and sliding motion
  occurring between two adjacent streampaths, there is no
  resulting force, since we have assumed that the air has zero
  viscosity. Had there been any such force, it would have been
  tangential to the streamlines, and so along the direction (forwards or backwards) of the flow. Viscous forces if present,
  then, would be flow-direction dependent, but with our zero
  viscosity assumption there are no such viscous forces.

Thus there are no forces acting on the streampaths *anywhere* in the
field of Figure 5.1 which are dependent on the direction of flow. Since
any curvature of the paths along which particles of air will flow must
be caused by a force, (the corollary of Newton's First Law), and since
the only such forces that exist are independent of flow direction along
the streamlines, it follows that

**In inviscid flow, the sense of direction of airflow along the
streamlines has absolutely no effect on the path shape of the
streamlines.**

Let us look now at Figure 5.2, which contains a series of one-step
developments of Figure 5.1. In the first, (a), consider that you are travelling piggy-back on an air particle along the streamline that is in
direct line with the centre of the cylinder, and assume for the moment

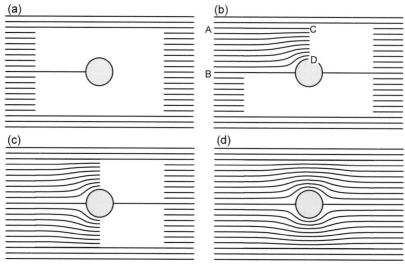

Figure 5.2 Development of Inviscid Flow Streamlines Around a Circular Cylinder

that the flow comes from the left of the figure. Then, as you look around you to your left (above, in the figure) and right (below, in the figure), you will observe that everything is absolutely symmetrical, as there is nothing to cause it to be otherwise. Thus as you approach the cylinder along the centre-line, there will be no difference in the pressure forces from your left or right, and so no sideways force to cause you to veer to left or right, and this will remain the case right up until you reach the surface of the sphere. At this point, there is a rather violent bump, as your particle can no longer go straight on, and it slows down and stops dead. But it cannot stay here, since there is a continuous stream of particles behind it still coming, and it cannot move into any other streamline for the reasons discussed in the first bulleted subparagraph above. Where can it go? It must stay absolutely close up to the surface, and it must go either left (upwards in the figure) or right (downwards). Which way the particle that you are riding will go is entirely arbitrary, since half of the particles will go each way. They will thereafter move around the surface of the cylinder, and not depart from it because of the ever-present next layer of particles just outside preventing escape. So our streamline (which is a geometrical line representing the air particle's path) actually merges with the surface of the cylinder and (in the drawing) becomes indistinguishable from it.

What happens to the particles of this divided streamline when they get round to the back? The easiest way to reason out the answer to this is to step back out of the picture for a moment, and reflect on two facts:

(i) streamlines do not have any associated direction of flow, and (ii) the figure (free stream flow and cylinder) is exactly symmetrical left and right. Therefore if the flow were from right to left the *dividing stream-line,* as it is called, would have to be drawn on the right as the exact mir-ror-image of the line on the left, and this has been drawn in Figure 5.2(b).

What about the rest of the flow? In Figure 5.2(b), the air which flows between points A and B must also flow between C and D. It is prevent-ed from going below this region by the dividing streamline BD, and from going above it by AC, the first streamline above the cylinder which is not disturbed. Furthermore, we have seen in Chapter 2 how a moving mass is deflected to follow a curved path by a normal force, and cannot turn sudden sharp corners. Consequently we simply need to draw, by inspection, the curved lines which match up with the individual streamlines between A and B, and which space out smoothly between C and D (closer near the cylinder at D, and tending towards the free stream spacing at C). Of course, this is not a rigorous mathematical approach, but it gives us a very good idea of what the flow looks like. We will come back and consider the mathematics (without actually *doing* it!) a little later.

The figure and the entire flow pattern is clearly symmetrical about the mid-cylinder line, and so without further ado we can invert and replicate the upper-half flow below the dividing streamline, which we do in Figure 5.2(c).

Now finally for the big surprise – but we are now ready and mental-ly prepared for it. Since a streamline does not carry with it any associ-ated flow direction, and there is no difference between left and right of the basic system, the entire figure must be symmetrical about a *ver-tical* line drawn through the centre of the circular cylinder. This means that we can immediately reverse and insert our streamline pattern that we have so far derived, and obtain the final complete flow pattern shown in Figure 5.2(d). You may be jumping up and down and protesting that air doesn't really behave like that at the *rear* of any obstruction; we know from many examples in our experience that *wakes* exist behind things in all fluid flows, and so the smooth symmet-rical flow pattern must be a figment of the imagination.

Yes, it has to be agreed, the system has been rumbled – but what has gone wrong? Is our carefully thought-out logic faulty? No, the fault doesn't lie anywhere in the logic, but merely in the *initial assumption,* that the flow is inviscid. As we will see shortly, even a little bit of vis-cosity makes the system go seriously wrong, and the airflow behaviour depart substantially from the above predictions. The inviscid assump-tion will still prove extremely powerful in establishing a good working model of aerodynamic flow, although it will later have to be modified.

Surprisingly, it is possible to achieve a *real*[1] fluid flow around a circular cylinder which almost exactly matches the predicted inviscid flow model that we finished up with in Figure 5.2(d), but not with air. To do so, we must use a liquid with very *high* viscosity (such as glycerine), and allow it to flow extremely slowly, a situation which is rarely of any practical use. The reason why high-viscosity fluid works whereas our theory says the viscosity has to be zero is complicated, and depends on the Reynolds Number of the flow, a concept which will be introduced in Chapter 8. But even if the inviscid flow pattern doesn't really occur in air flows, we ask you to take it on trust for now that it will be extremely useful to our study to assume that it does.

Reaching our conclusion about the flow pattern around the circular cylinder has involved some rather intense intellectual gymnastics, and I would suggest that a cup of coffee or tea might well be called for at this juncture. Although the outcome is central to the development of the classical approach to aerodynamics, I have never yet met any text book which considers it worthwhile to try to explain and justify the 'why'. They all just superficially present the result, implying 'it's obvious', but I know that when I was being taught the subject I greatly appreciated the lecturers who did give time to explaining the reasoning.

TAKING STOCK

Before moving on, let us take stock and remind ourselves of our aim, and where we have got to so far. We contrived the simple but rather artificial model of inviscid airflow around a two-dimensional circular cylinder in order to investigate the aerodynamic forces on an object in an airflow. We have got to the point now where we have a good idea of the shape of the fluid flow pattern around the cylinder, and so where should we go from here?

We would like to be able to evaluate the total reaction and hence the lift and drag forces on the circular cylinder. To do this, we require to determine the pressure distribution around the cylinder. (There will be no other forces present, since viscosity is being assumed to be zero.) What do we know about pressure distributions? We know Bernoulli's Equation, which tells us precisely the relationship between the pressure in the flow and the speed of flow, as the air moves along any path. So we require to determine the speed distribution along the appropriate path. The path that will interest us in particular is the path of the fluid right close up to the surface of the cylinder, the dividing streamline, since it is only the pressure of the air along this streamline that directly impinges on the cylinder and produces the aerodynamic

---

[1]A 'real' flow is a non-'ideal' flow, i.e.one with non-zero viscosity.

force. (Pressure at other points in the fluid merely acts on adjacent elements of fluid, producing the flow pattern that we have established.)

So, to determine the pressure distribution around the cylinder, we need to determine the velocity distribution around it, especially very close to it. It was for this purpose that we have come on our journey so far, to the point at which we can look at the flow pattern and make deductions from it. In order to establish the relationship between the flow pattern and the flow speeds, it will now be necessary for us to introduce one more very fundamental and crucial idea, and that is the principle of *continuity*.

THE CONTINUITY PRINCIPLE

The term Continuity Principle is really an incomplete phrase, since it means some unspecified law of conservation, a statement that something is not changing from one point under consideration to another: such as, for example, energy in the principle of conservation of energy. However, it often does get used in isolation when being applied to perhaps the most basic conservation principle possible, that of the conservation of matter, and that is the context in which we use it here. Strictly we should talk about the Principle of Continuity of Mass, but for brevity we will usually use the short form.

Let us consider the mass flow of air flowing past the two positions (or *stations*) numbered 1 and 2 in a length of streampath as illustrated in Figure 5.3. By mass flow we mean the flow *rate*[2], measured usually

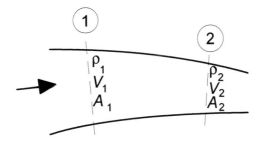

Figure 5.3 Diagram for Investigating the Continuity Principle

in kilogrammes-per-second or pounds-per-second. The streampath could have streamlines as boundaries, or it could be a length of pipe or ducting with solid walls. The principle of continuity simply states that, since matter cannot be created or destroyed, provided we have steady conditions of flow, what enters by passing station 1 in a certain

[2]The mass flow rate is also sometimes referred to as the *flux*.

amount of time must also leave by passing station 2 in the same amount of time.

Of course, if the flow rates are not steady, then there could be an accumulation in or an evacuation of the region between stations 1 and 2, but neither process could go on for ever. If the inflow rate through 1 were greater than the outflow rate through 2, then eventually either the system will burst under the strain or the rates will moderate themselves to reach an new equilibrium flow rate. If the outflow exceeds the inflow, the longest that such a situation could be maintained would be until the section is totally evacuated. However, all established aircraft aerodynamic theory is based on the steady flow assumption, so that this accumulation or depletion is not a problem. The quest to master the air by means of ornithopters (wing-flapping flying machines) was abandoned around a couple of centuries ago, and no man has ever flown by this means, as man learnt that he could not compete with the birds. The complication of unsteady flow aerodynamics probably had a lot to do with the demise of the search for flapping-wing flight, since this continuity principle is a fundamental and essential starting point for our study, but is not available if the steady flow assumption cannot be made.

Let us state the principle concisely in a usable form. Let us suppose that a mass m of air flows past station 1 in every second. Then the principle states that the same mass m also passes station 2 per second. We will use the 'dot notation', (an m with a dot over the top of it) to mean mass-flow per-second, and subscripts 1 and 2 for the two stations. Thus

$$\dot{m}_1 = \dot{m}_2$$

Now mass-per-second is the same as (density $\times$ volume) per-second, or grouping it differently, density $\times$ (volume-per-second), or density $\times$ (cross-sectional area $\times$ distance advanced per-second)[3], or density $\times$ c/s/area $\times$ speed. Thus:

$$\rho_1 A_1 V_1 = \rho_2 A_2 V_2$$

where the As are the cross-sectional areas and the Vs are the speeds.

In order to draw this discussion and derivation temporarily to a useful conclusion, we will now make the very bold and extraordinary assumption without comment, that the air is *incompressible*, which means that its density ρ is constant. This is such an important and significant assump-

---

[3]If this step makes you wince, imagine a cylindrical lump of air the length of which is such that it all just passes a fixed point in a second. Its speed is its length-per-second. The volume of this cylindrical lump is its cross-sectional area times its length, and this is the volume passing the point per-second.

tion that it deserves immediate thorough investigation, but first of all let us see where it will lead us. If ρ_1 equals ρ_2 (call it ρ) in the above equation, the ρs cancel out by dividing both sides by ρ, leaving finally a result which is full of deep significance, and to which we will return as soon as we have dealt with the assumption of incompressibility:

$$A_1 V_1 = A_2 V_2$$

THE INCOMPRESSIBLE ASSUMPTION

Leonardo Da Vinci presented a very plausible explanation of birds obtaining lift by compressing the air under their wings, but he turned out to be wide of the mark. The word 'compressing' suggests quite strongly the idea of pressure, and indeed it comes from the same Latin root word *pressare* (to press) as does the word pressure. It is primarily variation in pressure which is essential to the production of aerodynamic force, and so it would seem on the face of it that compressibility was the very feature of the air responsible for aerodynamic force. But yet in the previous paragraph we have apparently asserted that compressibility relates to changes in *density* rather than to changes in pressure, and we are making the assumption that air is incompressible. Many people understandably find this a very puzzling business.

Actually, we are certainly not asserting that air is incompressible. Such a suggestion would clearly be preposterous in view of our earlier discussion about atmospheric pressure and the conclusion that air at the bottom of the atmosphere is highly compressed compared with that higher up, because of the weight of the air above it. We saw that *both* the density *and* the pressure of the low-altitude compressed air are much greater than the density and pressure of the less compressed air at high altitude, and that air is highly compressible compared with liquids (such as water).

What *is* being asserted is that, when considering the aerodynamic forces on an object in an airflow such as an aeroplane, provided the speed of the airflow is not too great, (say no more than about a third or half of the speed of sound which is approximately 760 miles-per-hour at sea-level,) we can get reasonably good results by making the simplifying assumption that the *density* of the air (not the pressure) remains constant. The word 'incompressible' is used to mean just this.

It must be remembered that the incompressible assumption is an *approximation* and that Bernoulli's incompressible equation (which is what we derived in the last chapter) is never exactly correct except at zero speed, which is not very useful! In the following table are shown[4]

[4]Obtained by using the Prandtl Glauert correction factor $1/\sqrt{1-M^2}$ where M is the Mach number.

the percentage errors that will arise in aerodynamic force calculations if the incompressible assumption is made and no allowance is made for variation in density. The Mach number M is simply the speed expressed as a fraction of the speed of sound.

Mach number M	0.2	0.3	1/3	0.4	0.5	0.6	0.7	0.8
Incompressible assumption error		2%	5%	6%	9%	13%	20%	29%	40%

From this table it is clear that the speed up to which one may accept the incompressible assumption as being valid must depend very much on the accuracy that is required of the answers produced. For answers accurate to better than six per cent one must not assume incompressible flow at more than one-third of the speed of sound.

In any gas (including air), there are *three* most fundamental and important properties: pressure, density and *temperature*, and these three properties are all inter-dependent on each other. This means that, if any two properties (say the pressure and density) are known, then the third (in this case the temperature) can be directly inferred. A change in any one implies a corresponding change in each of the other two.

A change in temperature of our air would be inconvenient for our calculations, because temperature embodies one part of the air's total energy, its *internal* energy. When we considered Bernoulli's Principle earlier, we assumed (for simplicity) that the only forms of energy that took part in the energy interchange were pressure energy and kinetic energy. If the airflow's temperature and thus its internal energy had also varied, then we would somehow have had to incorporate the internal energy into our Bernoulli Equation,[5] and we would have lost the simplicity of the incompressible form of the equation. It is on this basis that so-called 'compressible flow' theory is built, and by means of which the percentage errors in the above table are calculated.

Strictly speaking, because of the relationship between temperature, pressure and density of air, if the density and thus the temperature are assumed constant it follows that the pressure also remains constant, and so we would not be able to predict *any* forces. The reason that we can in fact use a theory based on the incompressible assumption is

---

[5] Actually this can very easily be done. If we convert our Bernoulli Equation to '... per unit mass' instead of '... per unit volume' by dividing each side by the density, and then add the internal energy per-unit-mass to each side, we have the complete 'high speed' (variable density, or compressible) form of the equation. In this case, the new quantity incorporating total pressure plus internal energy is called *total enthalpy*.

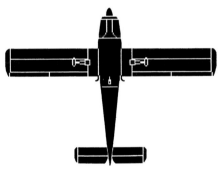

Figure 5.4 Piper Tomahawk

that all three of the quantities vary by a small amount. The small changes in density and temperature account for the percentage errors which we listed above, and which at low speeds may be small enough to ignore. The correspondingly small variations in pressure, however, *do* have a significant effect, because we depend on small pressure differences acting over the large area of the wing to produce lift.

To illustrate this, let us look for example at a Piper Tomahawk primary trainer, as illustrated in planform in Figure 5.4. The plan area of the lifting part of the wing is 11.61 square-metres, and the maximum take-off weight[6] is 757kg, which equals 757 × 9.81 or 7426 newtons. This works out at a lift force of 7426/11.61 or 640 newtons of lift being supplied by each square-metre of wing[7], for straight and level flight at maximum take-off weight. If we make a silly assumption just for the sake of illustration, that the lift were produced just by an increase in pressure on the bottom of the wing, then an average excess air pressure of $640N/m^2$ would be needed. Remembering that atmospheric pressure at sea-level is about $100,000N/m^2$, this pressure is only 0.64% (less than one per cent) above atmospheric pressure. Even if we allow for three or four times this lift in tight turns, and regardless of how the pressure (above or below atmospheric) is distributed around the wing's surface, it is clear that only small changes in pressure are required to achieve the sort of aerodynamic forces that we are looking for. Thus we see that, when we adopt the incompressibility assumption, the small density and temperature changes that occur have a trivial enough effect to be ignored, but yet the similarly small pressure variations occurring are very significant because of the large areas over which they act, and certainly cannot be ignored.

---

[6]Strictly mass, but we must be tolerant of normal usage.
[7]This quantity is known as the *wing loading*.

REFLECTIONS ON THE CONTINUITY EQUATION

Let us now return to the formula $A_1V_1 = A_2V_2$ which we derived earlier but left hanging there without comment. This is in fact by far the most important equation in the building up of classical aerodynamic theory, even more crucial than Bernoulli's Equation with which it is used hand-in-hand. So it is worth making sure that we have a good feel for what it is saying and what it implies.

If we extend the concept beyond two stations to any number of stations along our stream tube taken in pairs, then we can re-state the equation by saying that

The product of speed and cross-sectional area is constant,

which means that, if we put a constriction into a flow path that reduces the cross-sectional area to, say, half of its previous size, then the flow speed is not reduced, as we might naturally expect, but is actually doubled!

If you find this surprising, consider a few everyday examples which illustrate the point. An old-fashioned sand-in-glass hourglass (Figure 5.5) works by sand trickling down through a narrow neck from a large upper chamber into a large lower chamber. Compare the sand in the upper chamber with that at the narrow constriction. Where is the sand moving faster downwards? Clearly at the neck. It has to go faster in order to make way for the much wider passage of sand coming behind it. Notice that we are talking about the speed of flow (e.g. in metres-per-second) and not the mass flow (in, say, kilogrammes-per-second).

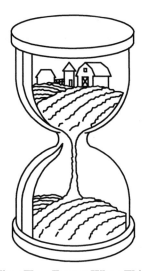

Figure 5.5   The Sands of Time Flow Fastest When Things Get Tight!

The mass flow is certainly the same at each place since we are not adding or extracting sand, but the speed increases as the cross-section decreases.

How often have you been cruising along a motorway, suddenly to be confronted with a solid jam of three virtually stationary lanes of traffic? You join one of the lanes and settle down patiently (you have no choice!) to crawling along at almost literally a snail's pace. You reflect, during perhaps an hour or more of this inflicted torment, that such a major hold-up *must* be due to some major catastrophe a little way ahead. But then you come to a place where one of the three lanes is coned-off, and everybody from that lane is filtering into the adjacent lane. Shortly afterwards the two remaining lanes merge into one lane as you enter a road works zone, and you discover that there was no major accident or incident causing the hold-up at all; it was just the road-works! A sign tells you that the roadworks will continue for a further five miles, which makes your spirits drop!

But then, to your surprise, you find that, rather than going slower than ever, the traffic actually begins to speed up quite substantially, and you are soon driving at an at-least reasonable speed, for the remaining miles of the single-lane restriction. The reason for this is another manifestation of the continuity equation 'speed times cross-sectional area is constant'. The cross-sectional area (number of lanes) has been divided by three, and so the speed is multiplied by three. If your average speed in the three-lane bit was a walking speed of 4 miles-per-hour, then your average speed in the single lane would be expected to be 12 miles-per-hour.

In this case a convenient equivalent quantity for mass flow would be the number of vehicles passing a check-point per minute. If we place check-points one just before the vehicles converge down from three lanes and one just after they have converged into a single lane, we know (and observation will prove) that the flow rate will be exactly the same. It is the speed, not the flow rate, that changes in inverse proportion to the width of carriageway.

If you, as a driver in the 4mph traffic jam, are conversant with this theory and have worked out (as above) that once you get into the single-lane section you should move with an average speed of 12mph, you will be in for a pleasant surprise. because you actually find that, in the single lane section, it is not long before you get up to a speed considerably greater than 12mph, perhaps 30 or 40 mph, depending on conditions ahead. Has the theory gone wrong? Yes it has, because our formula was the *incompressible* case. In the case of road vehicles, the incompressible assumption means that the vehicles are all moving with a fixed spacing distance between them, like carriages of a train, but in fact clearly this is not the case. Instead, as we drive towards the end of the restriction, the spacing between vehicles will increase, and the 'density' of cars will alter quite markedly, making it necessary to extend our theory to include 'compressible' flow if we want to investigate further. But notice that the mass flow (i.e. number of vehicles per minute) at *any* point, even after spacing out, will still be the same, provided the flow is steady.

This steady flow stipulation is important. A few miles back up the motorway the flow rate is greater than it is at the area where there is a restriction. But the drivers many miles 'upstream' are not aware of the restriction ahead, and so they keep coming at a flow rate which will not be sustainable at the restriction. The result of this is that the flow coming into the restricted area is greater than the flow leaving it, and this is not a steady flow situation. The only possible consequence is that the space between a pair of check-points before and after the restriction fills up with vehicles, which means that the length of the three-lane crawling queue steadily increases. This would continue indefinitely unless something else breaks the trend, such as the tail-back reaching the previous access point allowing branching off, the hold-up being announced on the radio, or the coned restriction being lifted.

The natural confusion in people's minds between speed of movement and mass flow rate is used to very good psychological effect by the designers of pleasure grounds and theme parks. Where all-inclusive tickets are issued and rides are free at the point of use, rides are rationed only by queuing time, and on a busy day it may be impossible to get on more than half-a-dozen rides all day because of the queuing time necessary. The only real way to solve this problem would be to provide more rides or restrict the number of customers allowed through the gates, both of which are not ideal economic solutions.

Given this state of affairs, designers have had to face the challenge of how to prevent people being dissuaded from queuing for a ride because of the boredom factor, when queuing times may be between one and two hours. One way that they achieve this is simply by making sure that queues always move pretty fast! This is achieved by making the queuing passage very narrow, usually only wide enough for two people to stand side-by-side. Of course, this means that queues become very long, and to prevent the psychologically bad image that long straggly queues would create, the queuing lines are simply concertinaed into a very small space by the use of strong fencing laid out as illustrated in Figure 5.6. In these queuing pens you will observe parents frantically dragging their young children to keep up with the fast-moving queue, thinking that they must be nearly at the front of the queue, and quite oblivious that the total length of the queuing path may be about half a mile! The psychology is further enhanced by

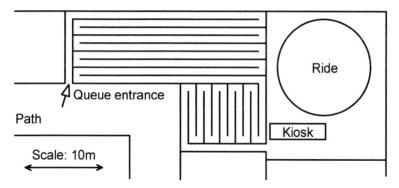

Total queue length is 435m

Figure 5.6   Queuing Arrangements for a Theme-park Ride

varying the direction of the zig-zags occasionally, and by routing the queue within viewing distance of the ride.

The psychology of queuing has now evolved further, since there was some resistance to the notion of being 'penned-in' rather like animals. Today the queue fences often take the queuing folk for long, straggling walks around the gardens, up and down hills, and over and under the tracks of roller-coaster rides, with the aim of overcoming boredom. But still the paths are very narrow, in order to make sure that the queuers move relentlessly forward at a respectable pace.

Back to aerodynamics. Looking again at the equation AV = constant, we notice that the terms in it include only the dimensions of length and time. Area is length squared, and speed is length divided by time. Having cancelled out the density term (and hence the dimensions of mass) when we imposed the incompressible assumption, there is nothing left in the equation which has anything to do with mechanics at all. The equation can be described as a purely *kinematic* equation. Kinematics is the subject which considers distance and positions and how they change with time – in other words, kinematics is simply time-dependent geometry, or the study of how geometry changes with time. It involves only the dimensions of length and time, and nothing else.

Now we have said that we are considering only steady flow conditions, and so it follows that nothing in our theory can vary with time. The fact that AV at station 1 is equal to AV at station 2 is not dependent on *when* we make the observation – it is true continuously. Therefore, although our equation includes the dimension of time, yet in fact, dimensionally speaking, this is irrelevant. The values of V are *properties* of the flow at stations 1 and 2, and the existence of the time dimension does not detract from the fact that the relationship is in fact completely independent of time. We therefore have in effect, not merely a kinematic equation, but a purely geometric equation.

This is very significant. It means that the equation AV = constant is the equation of a streamline, a geometrical line, since it is true at every point of the line. It is actually a relationship that is true of the flow *at every point* along a streampath, which in our two-dimensional model means the flow in the path between any adjacent pair of streamlines, but since we can draw any pair of streamlines as close together as we like until they effectively merge into one, we can see that something very like this equation will be true along a single streamline. *Any* relationship that is true at all points along a line is called the equation of the line, and provides us with a mathematical handle for that line; if you like, the line's signature. But it is much more than simply a means of identifying the line. When mathematically modelling what is going on, the equation of a line effectively *is* the line, allowing all sorts of manipulations to be done to that line that we could not do just by looking at it and discussing its physical geometry.

There is one more little step which we can take to make the equation even simpler to understand and to apply in our two-dimensional model. An alternative way of thinking of a two-dimensional model, rather than conceiving of it as being infinitely thick or deep in the dimension perpendicular to the paper, is to consider just a piece with a depth of one unit of length perpendicular to the paper, as in Figure 5.7. It doesn't have tips at the ends of this unit length, as it is regarded as simply one unit out of the still continuous infinite span. But we can now apply three-dimensional formulae and ideas to the model more simply. For the cross-sectional area A of our streampath, which is now a thin rectangular slice curling over the cylinder like pasta through a roller, we have $A = 1 \times w$, where w is the width of the stream tube at

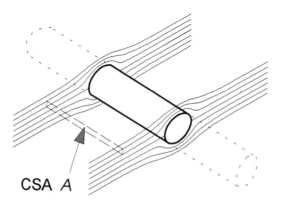

CSA A

Figure 5.7 Viewing a 2-dimensional Object as One Unit Span

the station under consideration, or the distance separating the bounding streamlines. Thus the two-dimensional incompressible continuity equation tells us that the product of w and V is constant, or in other words that

> **The speed is inversely proportional to the distance between the streamlines.**

Thus from this very simple and fundamental concept of continuity of mass flow, together with the simplifying assumption of incompressibility[8], we have arrived at an equation for each of the streamlines that we earlier sketched by logical deduction in Figure 5.2. True, our equation does not yet give a relationship between the co-ordinate positions (the x and y values) of points along the lines, but it is in a state now where it can be handed over to the mathematicians, and after some tricks involving the calculus of partial differentials and a method known as *Potential Flow Analysis* they can return it to us in the form of a set of actual x-y co-ordinate equations representing the set of curved streamlines around the cylinder in Figure 5.2(d).

CONTINUITY AND BERNOULLI COMBINED

We have developed two powerful but distinctly different ideas in the continuity equation and the Bernoulli equation, and it is when we merge them together that we get really useful results. Let us introduce the idea with a look at the *Venturi,* a device for which we are indebted to the Italian physicist G. B. Venturi, and without a mention of which no work on aerodynamics would be complete. A venturi is simply a duct through which a fluid (e.g. air or water) flows, which is waisted down to a narrow section before broadening out again. In the case of a liquid, and also in the case of air so long as the speed of flow is low enough for the incompressible assumption to be valid, as the fluid goes from large to small cross-section, so the speed of flow speeds up by the continuity principle. As the flow speeds up, the kinetic energy per unit volume or the dynamic pressure $\frac{1}{2}\rho v^2$ increases, and since the total pressure remains constant (by Bernoulli's principle) the static pressure decreases producing a depression or a suction.

There are a number of uses for such a device. One use, illustrated in Figure 5.8, is as a flow-rate meter, called a *Venturi meter.* By

---

[8]Note that the incompressible assumption is only a *simplifying* one to make the working easier. It is possible, but much harder, to develop a corresponding theory which takes compressibility into account. The incompressible assumption is different in kind from the earlier inviscid assumption, which is not an approximation but an absolute statement that viscosity is zero. The latter is a *sine qua non* for the theory being investigated here.

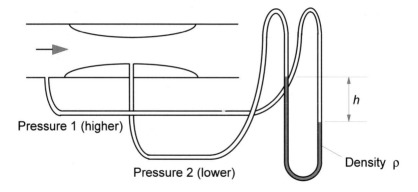

Figure 5.8   Venturi as flow-meter

measuring with a manometer the pressure difference between static tappings upstream of and at the throat (the narrowest part), and relating this to the cross-sectional areas of the upstream and throat sections, it is an easy task to express the speed as an equation involving the cross-sectional areas and the pressure difference, and then the pressure difference in terms of the manometer fluid density and height difference. When the three equations have been brought together and manipulated, the resulting equation (for a flow of air) is

$$V_1 = \sqrt{\frac{2\rho_m\, gh}{\rho_{air}((A_1/A_2)^2 - 1)}}$$

Don't worry if this looks a little complicated. The point to note is simply that on the right-hand side all of the mathematical symbols are recognisable and all of the quantities are quantities which we know or can be measured from the Venturi or manometer. Therefore the Venturi, in conjunction with this formula, can be used as a device for measuring V_1, the speed of the flow in the duct at station 1. If we wanted the speed somewhere else, we could then find it using the continuity equation, and if we wanted the mass flow, we would multiply the speed V_1 by the cross-sectional area at station 1 and by the fluid density.

A venturi (a slight narrowing in the air intake passage) is used in a carburettor on a petrol engine. The reduction in air pressure is sufficient to suck the petrol up from a lower chamber through a fine jet, into the air flow, where it is atomised and mixed with the airflow before entering the engine. In the case of a Bunsen burner, the low pressure of the gas emerging from a fine nozzle at high speed sucks air in to mix with it to provide an oxygen-rich mixture for combustion at the top of the burner tube. A similar principle used to be used for

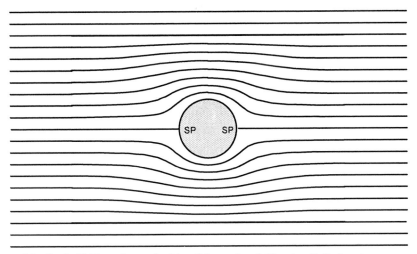

Figure 5.9   Inviscid Flow Around a Two-Dimensional Circular Cylinder

emptying domestic washing machines and containers in school laboratories. This device, called a Bunsen pump, consisted of a pipe attached to a water tap, through which the water from the tap would flow downwards into the sink. On the way, it would pass through a venturi where its pressure would drop, and another pipe was tee-ed into the first at this point. The other end of this pipe could be put into the washing machine tub or another liquid container to suck out all the water or liquid, which would mix with the water from the tap and go down the sink.

APPLICATION TO THE CIRCULAR CYLINDER
We are now in a position to return to thinking about the forces on our circular cylinder, and so it will be useful to reproduce the figure here from Figure 5.2(d). Can you now, by looking intelligently at Figure 5.9, work out roughly in your mind's eye how the pressure will be distributed around the cylinder, and from that can you make any observations about the total reaction acting on the cylinder?

Starting with the flow coming in on the left of the figure, let us consider just the air flowing between the centre-line streamline (the one going straight to the cylinder) and the closest one above it. As this flow moves towards the cylinder, its bounding streamlines are seen to get further apart from each other, until close to the front stagnation point, where the lines have reached their greatest separation. Greater separation means increased cross-sectional area, and by the continuity principle this means lower speed. Lower speed means less dynamic pressure, but, since the total pressure is constant by Bernoulli's principle the static pressure (that which actually presses on surfaces) is increased.

Now following the progress of the same streampath around the cylinder, it is seen to get narrower, and so its speed will increase and consequently its static pressure will reduce. The narrowest part, by symmetry, is at the very top of the cylinder, and so this is where the lowest static pressure is to be found.

We have already observed that the streamline picture, like the cylinder itself, possesses symmetry about both the horizontal centre-line and the vertical centreline. It follows directly that the pressure must also be symmetrically distributed about both of these lines. So we have high pressure at the front and rear of the cylinder, which gradually moderates around the sides of the cylinder to a minimum pressure at the top and the bottom.

There are two common ways in which this pressure distribution is represented in a diagram, and both are illustrated in Figure 5.10. In both cases a curved line is drawn all around the cylinder. If points of this line are each joined to the corresponding point immediately 'below' or 'above' on the cylinder surface by a straight line, then these straight lines represent the pressure force vectors acting on the surface in magnitude and direction. Arrow-heads show the sense of these pressure forces, and the positive pressures are shown in two different ways on the two diagrams. The right-hand system is probably more common, but that on the left is more realistic, since if the cylinder sur-face line were cut and unwrapped into a straight line, then it would

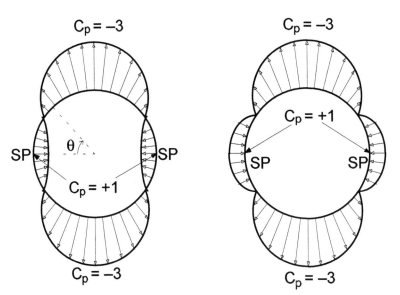

Figure 5.10   Two Representations of the Pressure Distribution Around the Circular Cylinder

directly represent the horizontal axis of the graph formed by the curve.

We have actually prepared all the mathematical groundwork on which we can go beyond this qualitative statement, to calculate the actual pressures at the front and back, those at the top and bottom, and in fact the entire distribution in between. But because it will make our life easier, we will not talk in terms of actual pressures (which involves all the tiresomeness of real units and sometimes messy numbers), but instead in relative terms, which is a very common simplifying procedure in many everyday situations, not only in aerodynamics. We frequently use expressions such as 'three times as big as', or '70% of', or even 'not 'alf!', and that is effectively what we are enabled to do by the use of dimensionless coefficients.

SIMPLIFYING AERODYNAMIC COEFFICIENTS

Earlier we introduced force coefficients by a relationship of the form

$$F = C_F(\tfrac{1}{2}\rho V^2)S$$

where F is any force such as Lift or Drag or any other. We may write the same equation in another form which effectively *defines* the force coefficient, and for many purposes this proves to be a much more useful way of thinking about it:

$$C_F = \frac{F}{(\tfrac{1}{2}\rho V^2)S}$$

Many people feel that they want to give up and close their minds at the mention of aerodynamic coefficients such as this, because they wrongly think that to use them involves learning parrot-fashion a whole lot of heavy and meaningless equations. In fact, it is very easy to *generate* (rather than remember) any aerodynamic coefficient that you require, or even to invent new ones, simply by properly understanding what they are, and by applying very simple principles. Notice first of all that the coefficients are always *dimensionless*. This means that they must be built out of a fraction in which the dimensions (the types of quantity) on top exactly correspond with the dimensions on the bottom, so that they cancel out and the answer does not have any dimensions left. So the first rule, since the answer has got to be a fraction, is:

1. **Draw a line.**

On top of the line we simply write the quantity that we wish to have the coefficient of. If we want the coefficient of drag, we put the drag force D on top:

2. Put the quantity in question on top.

We next decide what type of quantity this is, dimensionally speaking. In this case it is a force, and so the bottom of the equation has got to consist of some factors which, when multiplied together, give a force, so that the dimensions will exactly cancel out with those of the top of the fraction. For all aerodynamic coefficients, whatever quantity is on top, we *always* have the free stream dynamic pressure $\frac{1}{2}\rho V_\infty^2$ as the first factor on the bottom of the fraction, (where V with the 'infinity' subscript refers to the velocity of the free stream far enough away from the object to be unaffected by it,) since pressure is of fundamental importance as we have seen, and since this dynamic pressure contains the crucial information about the fluid flow itself. So the next rule is:

3. Write $(\frac{1}{2}\rho V_\infty^2)$ as the first factor of the bottom of the fraction.

Now we must decide what else we need on the bottom to make the dimensions match those of the top. In our case, the top is a force, and at present the bottom is a pressure. What must a pressure be multiplied by in order to give a force? The answer is an *area*. So we must now multiply the dynamic pressure on the bottom by some area. What area? Any agreed representative area; once agreed, it must be adhered to. As discussed earlier, for aircraft we always use the wing planform area including the bit (sometimes imaginary) going over or through the fuselage, and call this area S. For the coefficient of drag of road vehicles we use the frontal area, (sometimes including the space underneath, and sometimes excluding it). So the next rule is:

4. Write any other factors on the bottom as necessary to produce the same dimensions on the bottom as those on the top, using standard quantities.

This completes the derivation of an aerodynamic coefficient. As a more complex example, will be met in *Flightwise: Aircraft Stability and Control* another type of aerodynamic coefficient called the pitching moment coefficient, but provided we know what the dimensions of moment are (which are force × distance – we will have covered this when we need it), we know that, in addition to what we had on the bottom of the force coefficient above ($\frac{1}{2}\rho V_\infty^2$ and S) we will also require a length factor, and in fact we use the mean chord length of the wing, which again we will discuss when we require it.

CIRCULAR CYLINDER PRESSURE COEFFICIENT

So no memory feats at all are required to write down aerodynamic coefficients. Coming back to the requirement of the case in point, we would like to express our pressure distribution around the cylinder in coefficient form, and so we wish to define a *coefficient of pressure* C_p Following our rules above, we (1) draw a line: ———; (2) put the pressure p in on top: $\dfrac{p}{}$ (actually this is not quite right; we'll come back to it in a moment); (3) write $\frac{1}{2}\rho V_\infty^2$ on the bottom: $\dfrac{p}{\frac{1}{2}\rho V^2}$; (4) check dimensions of top and bottom – they are both pressure, so there is no need to do anything more. Thus we have the Coefficient of Pressure defined (but requiring the refinement discussed in the next paragraph)

as $C_p = \dfrac{p}{\frac{1}{2}\rho V_\infty^2}$.

We said that p on top was not quite right, and this is because we do not usually like looking at absolute pressures but at pressures relative to the local atmospheric pressure, which we call *gauge pressure*, as discussed earlier. So on top of the fraction we do not write p on its own, but instead we write $p-p_\infty$ where p_∞ is the pressure *at infinity*, or just far enough away from the obstacle in question (e.g. upstream) for the obstacle not to have any effect upon the airflow there. Using this form has the particular advantage that, whereas all absolute pressures are positive (and usually large) numbers, gauge pressures may be either positive or negative depending on whether the local pressure p is greater or less than p_∞. Thus we can immediately spot if a pressure is in fact a suction, because the gauge pressure and hence the coefficient of pressure will both be negative. If the pressure p is equal to p_∞, then the coefficient of pressure is 0 and there is no pushing or sucking force at that point.

We can now look back at Figure 5.10 and investigate where the C_P values shown in that Figure come from. Let us look first of all at the stagnation points. At the front stagnation point (and thus also at the rear stagnation point, which is identical by symmetry as we have already established), the flow comes momentarily to rest, before turning through a right angle and moving off again along the surface of the cylinder. So the velocity at this point, and hence the dynamic pressure, is zero, and thus the static pressure (that which acts on the cylinder) is the same as the total pressure, since total pressure equals static pressure plus dynamic pressure. Now by Bernoulli's Principle this total pressure at the stagnation point is the same value as the total pressure (i.e. static plus dynamic) at all points along the streamline from the point upstream at infinity, so that

$$p_{SP} = p_T = p_\infty + \tfrac{1}{2}\rho V_\infty^{\,2} \quad \text{or} \quad p_T - p_\infty = \tfrac{1}{2}\rho V_\infty^{\,2}$$

Thus at a stagnation point the coefficient of pressure is

$$C_p = \frac{p_T - p_\infty}{\tfrac{1}{2}\rho V_\infty^{\,2}} = \frac{\tfrac{1}{2}\rho V_\infty^{\,2}}{\tfrac{1}{2}\rho V_\infty^{\,2}} = 1$$

Now p can never be more than p_T since dynamic pressure can never be less than zero, and so the top of this fraction can never be greater than $\tfrac{1}{2}\rho V_\infty^{\,2}$, and C_p therefore has a maximum value (the stagnation value) of 1.

The value of the coefficient of pressure at all the other points on the surface of the cylinder, including the minimum suction points at the top and bottom, cannot be worked out quite so easily, but requires some mathematical manipulation of the continuity and Bernoulli equations, and also a method of representing the cylinder itself mathematically (which we will look at in Chapter 7). The result that the mathematician achieves is a simple and elegant formula which we may view in passing, before handing it back to the mathematician for further use. It is:

$$C_p = 1 - 4(\sin\theta)^2$$

where θ is the angle from the front stagnation point clockwise around the cylinder[9], as shown in Figure 5.10. If the value of $\theta = 90°$ is substituted in this formula, it gives us the value of the coefficient of pressure at the top (and hence also bottom) points of the cylinder, and this is found to be $C_p = -3$, as shown in Figure 5.10. Thus the negative pressure at the fastest points of the flow is three times as strong as the greatest positive pressure at the stagnation points.

We are nearly at our quest's end in determining the lift and drag forces on the cylinder. We could (as in Chapter 3) vectorially add all the pressure forces of the distribution in a long 'circus elephants' chain to determine the total reaction, and then resolve it into its two components of lift and drag. However, it is actually more convenient to do the process the other way round, and take the components of each little element of the pressure distribution first. Then if we add all the drag-direction vectors they are all parallel to each other, so that the vector addition becomes purely an ordinary algebraic addition (as

---

[9]This is not the normal definition of θ nor the most suitable for mathematical work, but is the simplest and most direct for the present purposes. If you are not familiar with the trigonometrical function 'sin θ', (short for and pronounced 'sine',) it is simply a tool that gives a value of 0 at the beginning of a circle, smoothly increasing to a maximum value of 1 at a quarter of the way round, and thereafter smoothly decreasing to 0 again at the back, which is half-way round. That is all you need to know about sin θ for the present purpose.

long as we take account of the direction, or the sign, of each one). This process of integration (as it is called) we will again leave to the mathematician, but in this case we do not need to wait for him to come back to us with his answer, since we can spot what the answer will be directly, simply by looking at the picture. Once again appealing to our notions of symmetry, let us think firstly about the lift. There is no reason to expect a symmetrical object like our cylinder to produce any lift, and indeed the pressure distribution bears this out. Although there is a strong suction force upwards on the top surface, there is an exactly equal and opposite suction force downwards on the lower surface. Thus if the cylinder were hollow and had atmospheric pressure inside it, there would be a considerable force trying to pull the top half of the shell away from the bottom half.

There was no great surprise there. But if we consider now the drag force, we are looking at the overall horizontal resultant force (since the airflow is drawn horizontally), which we get by adding horizontal force contributions of the pressure vector arrows, once again taking account of their directions. All right-to-left contributions are positive, and all left-to-right contributions negative. Once again because of the symmetry, we may immediately conclude, without needing to do any sums, that the resultant force will be zero, so that there is *no drag at all*, but just an overall squeeze on the cylinder.

CONCLUSION AND D'ALEMBERT'S PARADOX

We started this chapter by devising a simple model with which we were to examine the forces caused by pressure only, assuming the flow to be inviscid. By introducing the important new concept of the continuity principle and invoking Bernoulli's Principle which we had already met, we were able to determine the actual pressure distribution around our cylinder, and thus by resolving and adding (which is called integrating) we could determine the lift and drag forces on it.

Although not surprised by the resulting fact that the lift is zero, the conclusion that the drag is zero appears to be patently absurd, completely flying in the face of our physical experience. We know that any object in an airflow actually does have some resistance to the flow, and so what good is a mathematical model which simply tells us that the drag is zero?

The rigorous mathematical treatment of this subject can actually be taken further than this, and can in fact be extended to literally *any* cross-sectional shape of the 'cylinder'; it is not even necessary for the shape to possess the symmetry which we have referred to so often in our simple model. Whatever two-dimensional shape of object the air flows around, smooth or jagged, symmetrical or asymmetrical, according to the inviscid potential flow model, the result of adding all the pressure forces to find the lift force and the drag force *always* yields the same absurd result – that the aerodynamic total reaction, and hence the lift and the drag, are all zero.

The French mathematician Jean Le Rond d'Alembert was the originator of the mathematical development which we have been outlining in this chapter. Born illegitimately in Paris in 1717, he first studied law and then medicine before resolving to give his whole time to mathematics, in which he made a number of very important contributions including this study of fluid flow forces that we have discussed. But when he reached, through faultlessly argued mathematical rigour, the same paradoxical conclusion that we have reached above, that the method predicted no drag force on any object, he was unable to find the cause of the paradox, and went to his grave a puzzled and dissatisfied man. In 1768 d'Alembert wrote:

> 'I do not see then, I admit, how one can explain the resistance of fluids by the theory in a satisfactory manner. It seems to me on the contrary that this theory, dealt with and studied with profound attention gives, at least in most cases, resistance absolutely zero: a singular paradox which I leave to geometricians to explain.'

So where has this journey of investigation brought us? We set out to try to establish a method for working out the aerodynamic forces on an object in an airflow; but, after considerable effort, we feel frustrated because, for all its elegance, it just doesn't seem to work. Instead we come up against this enigma which is today known as d'Alembert's Paradox. What has gone wrong? The answer to that question is the subject of the next chapter.

CHAPTER 6
The Boundary Layer and Drag

INTRODUCTION

The failure of d'Alembert's potential flow model to predict lift or drag was due to the initial fundamental assuption that one could ignore the viscosity of the fluid. Although it is quite true that the tangential forces due to viscosity are relatively small compared with the pressure forces, yet they are not generally negligible. Furthermore, the existence of viscosity gives rise to a phenomenon known as the *boundary layer*, the behaviour of which can drastically alter the entire flow pattern around an object from that predicted by the inviscid potential flow theory, and thus the pressure distribution.

The boundary layer is a region of slow-moving air near to the surface of a body in an airflow, in which the air has been slowed down by viscosity. As with all of aerodynamics, the study of boundary layers can be complex and highly mathematical, but we can learn sufficient for our purposes from a descriptive treatment.

In a real[1] two-dimensional incompressible system such as our circular cylinder model with the inclusion of viscosity, it is the boundary layer that is solely responsible for drag[2]. Not only does this arise on account of the direct tangential force on the surface (called *skin friction*), but under some conditions the boundary layer completely disrupts and breaks down the flow pattern around the object. The main flow then separates from the surface causing large scale turbulence and a big increase in the drag due to the *pressure* forces, this part of the drag being called *form drag*. When this flow breakdown occurs on an aircraft wing, the phenomenon is known as *stalling*, accompanied with which there will also be a serious loss of lift, and sometimes a violent buffeting of the airframe.

A large amount of Chapter 1 was given to illustrating how very important, for almost all types of aircraft, is the minimising of drag, and so the search for reductions in aircraft drag is very much alive. On airliners and cargo aircraft, substantial financial savings are available from relatively small reductions in cruise drag, and many avenues of

---

[1]A real flow is the proper term for a flow of a viscous fluid, and is the opposite of an ideal flow, that of an inviscid fluid.

[2]There also exist additional causes of drag in circumstances other than those specified here, which are not boundary layer dependent, and these will be considered in Chapters 10 and 12.

exploration suggest themselves. During the course of this chapter we will examine carefully the nature of both skin friction and of form drag, and the trade-offs that occur between them. But first we must get down to basics.

VISCOSITY

The time has now arrived to get to grips with another term describing a physical property of fluid, one more of those words that have been taken over by scientists and given a quantitative and very specific meaning. And it is not as easy to grasp as were some of the concepts we have met so far.

I recall first meeting viscosity with some distaste whilst at school preparing to sit the GCE advanced level physics examination. We were spending a few weeks studying fluid mechanics, and one week we were introduced to the concept of surface tension (which never concerns us in aerodynamics, since air being a gas never has a free surface). Being a lazy school-boy, I was delighted to discover that nothing could be easier than surface tension – it was simply a force divided by a length! This put me in good spirits for the work of the following week, which was to be on viscosity, but I was very soon to be disillusioned when I discovered that the defininition of viscosity was a really grotesque concoction involving a combination of force, area, speed and distance! There was nothing appealingly simple about viscosity, and so I mentally switched off. However, when in much later life I was confronted once again with viscosity whilst studying aerodynamics, I realised that I would have to get to grips with it, and by thinking it through carefully I discovered that really it was quite a simple concept after all. Let me share with you that process of discovery.

A primary aim of science is to discover and establish principles which exemplify the order that exists in the natural universe. One important approach often used to achieve this is to investigate the relationship between a *cause* (i.e. a phenomenon which has some effect on the world round about it) and the *effect* which this cause produces. If both cause and effect can be represented numerically in some suitable units, then the most convenient way of investigating their relationship is to plot the graph of one against the other. One very special relationship that often happens to emerge from this exercise is that of direct proportion. If one quantity is directly proportional to another, then the graph will be a straight line passing through the origin (the point where both values are equal to zero). For the purposes of technological application, science is very often content not to probe further into the reason *why* the cause is proportional to the effect – in many instances, even pure science does not have a complete explanation of the why. Many such relationships are named after the scientists who first discovered them, and may be regarded (provided any special restrictions or limitations are borne in mind) as the fundamentals of science on which we may safely build. The constant of proportionality of such relationships (which is also the slope of the graph) gives us a system property or 'signature' which is the 'cause per unit effect' of the relationship.[3] Overleaf is a list of some such relationships, and shown alongside are the cause, the effect, and the property thus defined.

The first of these relationships we have discussed copiously, but this provides us with a useful new light in which to view Newton's Second Law, as a relationship between a cause and an effect. The British Engineering unit of mass, the slug, is essentially defined by making use of this definition; in other words, the mass of an object (in slugs) is the number of pounds force (cause) required to produce one unit (foot-per-second-squared) of acceleration (effect) on that object; or, more briefly, mass equals force per unit acceleration. The words '... per unit ...' are recurrent in this context, and are synonymous with the words '... divided by ...'

The next two examples in the table, taken deliberately from the diverse subjects of electricity and heat transfer in order to illustrate the generality of the concept, follow exactly the same principles. In each case the property being defined is a property of an object or a body, and in each case, as before, the property may be defined as 'cause per unit effect'.

Let us now look a little more closely at Hooke's Law, since the ideas arising in the formulation of Hooke's Law actually carry over fairly directly into the definition and concept of viscosity, which we are leading up to. Furthermore, the two new terms stress and strain in the table leap out at us as demanding definition and explanation.

The simplest demonstration of Hooke's Law is to suspend a spring from a fixed support, and attach an assortment of weights to the lower end. For each weight attached (which equals the tension force in the spring) the extension from the original position of the bottom of the spring is measured, and extensions (i.e. effects) are tabulated against

---

[3]The slope of a straight-line graph is simply the amount the line goes up during a certain interval divided by the amount it goes across in the same interval. Putting this in terms of the measured quantities which are being plotted, the slope is the change in the vertically plotted quantity between two points on the line divided by the change in the horizontally plotted quantity. In graphs of direct proportion, one of the two points can be the origin, and so the slope, and hence the constant of proportionality, is simply the 'vertical' quantity of any point on the line divided by the 'horizontal' quantity of the same point. Reading 'divided by' as 'per', and plotting cause on the vertical axis and effect on the horizontal axis, the constant of proportionality thus gives the 'cause per unit effect' for the system being considered.

Relationship	Cause	Effect	Property defined and Definition
Newton's Second Law	Force	Acceleration	Mass = Force/Acceleration
Ohm's Law	Potential difference (volts)	Electric current (amps)	Electrical Resistance = Volts/Amps
Effect of heating an object	Heat energy supplied	Temperature rise	Thermal capacity = Heat input/Temperature rise
Hooke's Law (applied to a stretched spring)	Tension (force)	Extension (distance)	Spring stiffness = Tension/Extension
Hooke's Law (applied to an elastic object)	Stress	Strain	Young's Modulus = Stress/Strain
Elastic shearing deformation	Shear stress	Shear strain	Modulus of rigidity = Shear stress/Shear Strain
Property of a Newtonian Fluid	Shear stress	Rate of shear strain	Viscosity = Shear Stress/Rate of Shear Strain

tensions (i.e. causes). If a graph is plotted of tension (on the vertical axis) against extension (on the horizontal axis), provided that the spring has not been stretched beyond its normal operating range (its 'elastic limit'), it will be found that the points plotted will all lie on a straight line which passes through the real origin of the graph. Thus we find that the extension (the effect) is directly proportional to the tension (the cause), and this is the precise statement of Hooke's Law.

For a different spring, proportionality would again be observed, but the slope of the straight-line graph would be different, depending on the nature of the spring. Stiffer springs will require more tension force to achieve the same extension, and so their graphs will be steeper than those of more delicate springs. Since the graph passes through the origin, the slope of this graph gives the tension per unit extension, and this number is called the *stiffness* of the spring as defined in the table above.

Hooke's Law is in fact far more versatile than this, and can be applied to very many solid objects which become deformed as a result of the application of a force, either stretching or compressing. The only condition of the law's application is that the object under test behaves *elastically*, which means that when the load is removed it must return unaided to the shape that it was in before the loading started.

Let us for example consider a piece of steel wire hanging from a rigid support with a hook fixed to the bottom of it for hanging weights on. The extension of the wire will not depend only on the tension, but will also depend on two other factors which must be taken into account. First of all, it will depend on the original length. If the original length of the wire for a second experiment were double that of the first, it would be found (as one might expect) that, for the same load, the extension of the second would also be doubled, and so we really need some means of measuring extension which takes into account the original length. We do this by defining *strain*, which is simply the increase in length divided by the original length, or the increase in length per unit length. Strain (being a length divided by a length) is a dimensionless quantity, and it is sometimes given in terms of a percentage; e.g. if a one metre bar is extended by 2 centimetres, the strain is 2%. It is much more useful to regard the strain rather than the extension as the effect of applying a force, since this also takes account of the original length.

The other additional factor that must be taken into account is the cross-sectional area of the wire. If the wire consisted of a number of thinner identical wires in parallel with each other, its stiffness or resistance to stretching would clearly be directly related to the number of parallel strands making up the whole, and furthermore the same tension load would produce less extension (or strain) if the number of strands were increased. It is therefore more convenient to replace the actual tension with a quantity called *stress*, which refers the load to the cross-sectional area it is acting on, and is defined as the load per unit cross-sectional area. If the cross-sectional area of the wire were doubled, that would be the equivalent of doubling the number of strands; if the total load were also doubled, the load on each single strand, and thus the stress, and hence the extension, would be unchanged.

In passing, it is useful to note that the dimensions of stress are force/area, and that this happens to be the same as the dimensions of pressure. Although there doesn't appear to be much similarity between stress and pressure at the moment, the two concepts are in fact very closely linked with each other, since pressure is effectively a compressive stress applied through a fluid.

For the simple spring under Hooke's Law, the property that we defined was its stiffness, which is tension per unit extension, and this property is specific to the spring in question. For the more general case of the piece of elastic material (such as steel wire), a new and important property is defined, called Young's Modulus. Again it is defined as cause per unit effect, but this time the cause and effect quantities have been modified to give a more general relationship for the *material* rather than for the particular object under test: Young's Modulus is defined as stress per unit strain, or calculated from stress/strain.

Stretching and compressing is not the only way of distorting a solid with a force. An object may instead be subjected to a shearing force. Of course, as always, we should really be talking about a force pair. In the compression case it did not matter forgetting about the other half of the 'Newton's Third Law' force pair, the upward reaction holding the wire onto the support, but in the shearing case it is more easy to visualise what is going on if we do include this equal and opposite reaction in our drawings. Figure 6.1 shows, side-by-side, an object under direct force as just discussed, alongside a solid object under shear force, which we consider now. The notations in the two have been deliberately kept the same, as this will help to bring out the similarities between the two situations.

In Figure 6.1(a) a tensile load F acts on a cross-sectional area A, resulting in a direct stress of F/A. This stress produces an extension e on the rod whose original length is h, and thus a strain of e/h. By Hooke's Law, the stress is proportional to the strain, and the constant of proportionality is called the Young's Modulus of the material of the rod. Young's Modulus is denoted by the letter E, defined as stress over strain (or cause per unit effect) and the relationship may therefore be written

$$E = \frac{(F/A)}{(e/h)}$$

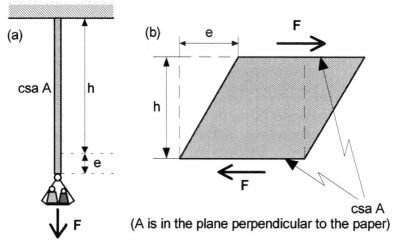

Figure 6.1 Derivation of Young's Modulus and Shear Modulus

Turning to Figure 6.1(b), a shear load F acts on a cross sectional area A, resulting in a shear stress of F/A. This stress distorts the block until the top surface of the block stops moving at a horizontal distance e from its initial position. The top and bottom surfaces are separated by a vertical distance h. We *define* shear strain as the ratio of the horizontal displacement to the vertical separation, which in this case is e/h. Experiment shows that, for an elastic substance, the shear stress (the cause) is proportional to the shear strain (the effect). The constant of proportionality is called the Shear Modulus or the Modulus of Rigidity of the material of the block, and is usually denoted by the letter G, and defined as shear stress divided by shear strain. The relationship may therefore be written

$$G = \frac{(F/A)}{(e/h)}$$

What has all this got to do with air, and particularly viscosity? We are actually very nearly there, since the last system we looked at involved shear forces, which is what we are interested in for viscosity of air. Let us postulate a small rectangular faced 3-D region of air within an airflow which is subject to some shearing, so that the air above the region is moving faster than the air below the region, in the same direction. We have avoided using the word 'block', as in the previous shear force example of an elastic block, because clearly such an isolated block of air cannot exist, but in every other respect the system is very similar to that of Figure 6.1(b). We can see a suitably modified diagram at Figure 6.2.

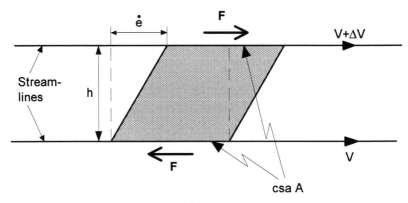

Figure 6.2   Shearing of an Element of Air

The forces F in Figure 6.2 are now being supplied directly by the sliding of the neighbouring layers of air past our layer, pulling it by friction (i.e. viscosity) as they go. Comparing carefully Figure 6.2 with Figure 6.1(b), you will observe that there is very little difference except for the introduction of the streamlines and velocity arrowheads labelled V and $V+\Delta V$. (ΔV, read 'delta V', just means 'a little bit of V', and so $V+\Delta V$ simply means 'a lifttle bit more than V'.) However, there is one very important but very small change: it is a symbol which has been introduced and exaggerated a bit in size so that it would not get overlooked, and that is the dot over the letter e. The dot means a *rate* of movement or a *rate* of change, just as we earlier used $\dot{m}$ to mean mass flow rate. The need for this crucial change arises out of the very feature which distinguishes a fluid from a solid, and that is that a fluid is not able to produce a static resistance to a shear force in the way that a solid can do. A fluid flows. If the solid block of Figure 6.1(b) were made of rubber, it is clear that if a moderate force F were applied (not big enough to break it), then the rubber would deform into the grey shape and would *stay there* so long as the force were being applied. However, if the block were a region of fluid (e.g.water or air), then on reaching the grey position it would have no tendency to stop and resist the force in the way that the solid does, but instead would simply keep going.

This means that it is not possible for us to define any meaningful term 'shear strain' following on from the way we defined shear strain for a solid, since the magnitude of e keeps growing all the time. However, what we *do* discover by experiment is that, for certain fluids, the *rate* at which the top of the region moves relative to the bottom and hence the rate at which e grows is proportional to the shear stress F/A. The constant of proportionality of this relationship depends on the fluid's perceived 'stickiness', and is called the *viscosity* (or *dynamic viscosity*) of the fluid.

Thus viscosity is another 'cause per unit effect' quantity, and it is usually represented by the Greek letter μ (pronounced 'mew'). Here is the defining relationship:

$$\text{Viscosity} = \mu = \frac{(F/A)}{(\dot{e}/h)} = \frac{\text{Shear stress}}{\text{Rate of shear strain}}$$

We mentioned above that only for certain fluids are shear stress and rate of shear strain proportional to each other, and such fluids are known as Newtonian fluids. We must not allow ourselves to get distracted into talking about the intriguing topic of non-Newtonian fluids, such as blood, thixotropic (i.e. non-drip) paint, and tomato ketchup, which seems to have a high viscosity and refuse to come out of the bottle until you have just given up shaking, and then to have a much lower viscosity and to come out in a gush and go all over the table and your clothes! Fortunately for our present study, air (like water) is a Newtonian fluid, and so we can use the above relationship with impunity.

As was said at the beginning of this section, the idea of viscosity *is* rather more complicated than that of most other concepts we have met and will meet. Provided that you don't try to think of it all in one lump, but rather break it down into the ratio of two other quantities (shear stress and rate of shear strain) which independently you remember and can understand, then you will find that you will soon gain respect for the term. As far as its units and dimensions are concerned, my advice to you quite honestly is, forget it! Provided you are working consistently in SI units and all your other units are based on the basic magnitudes of the system, then the easiest solution is simply to remember the definition and quote viscosity as being in 'SI units'. (Of course, you could easily work out the actual units, straight from the definition above, if you needed to, and that is exactly what I would do.)

Occasionally you will meet another term which is used as an alternative to the term dynamic viscosity introduced above, and it is obtained simply by dividing the dynamic viscosity μ by the density ρ. It is given the Greek letter ν (pronounced 'new'), and so we have

$$\nu = \frac{\mu}{\rho}$$

The effect of this operation on the dimensions of μ (to which we have turned a blind eye) is to remove all reference to mechanical quantities, i.e. anything containing mass or force, and thus the dimensions of v are simply those of length and time. Consequently v is a purely kinematic quantity, and is therefore called the *kinematic viscosity*. The usefulness of this kinematic quantity arises when handling the Reynolds number (which we will meet in Chapter 8), where it makes life a little easier by replacing two numbers by one. It also allows more direct comparison between the viscous effects of gases and liquids which have very different densities. Incidentally, its dimensions cancel down to area/time, and so it is sometimes facetiously quoted in such silly units as 'acres per year'!

Both dynamic and kinematic viscosity are sometimes referred to as the coefficients of dynamic and kinematic viscosity. Although this must be recognised as common parlance, yet it should be noted that they are not dimensionless coefficients in the same way as the other aerodynamic coefficients which we have met. Dimensionless aerodynamic coefficients use the notation C with an appropriate subscript letter, and always consist of a fraction with top and bottom deliberately having the same dimensions. This is not the case with μ or v.

THE BOUNDARY LAYER

In order to begin to investigate boundary layers, let us consider a uniform flow of air moving parallel to and in sliding contact with a large flat plate which lies parallel to the flow. If the air had no viscosity, the presence of the plate would have absolutely no effect at all on the flow, since it would just be like the next streamline down the page. But what effect does viscosity actually have at this interface between air and solid? Let's put our logical thinking caps on once again, and try to predict the effect.

Imagine yourself being shrunk to a microscopic size, and being implanted onto the 'smooth' surface of the plate. Regardless of how smooth it is, if you are small enough you would see the surface as a range of craggy hills and valleys, spikes and holes, ridges and grooves. Although you are now of a similar size to these surface irregularities, yet you are still very much larger than the molecules of air, so that the airflow past you at the surface still appears as the flow of a continuous medium (a continuum), and not as individual particles. If you have ever been in an open place when the wind is blowing, you will know that if you get very close to the ground so that you only stick up as far as the irregularities around you, (lying down in grass, or crouching behind rocks,) you can get into that bottom region of the airflow where the wind is actually not blowing at all and the air speed is zero. It is now exactly like that at the flat plate surface, since you have been shrunk to the size of the irregularities of the surface. It is not difficult to accept, then, that the airspeed right down at the surface will be zero, regardless of the free stream airspeed.

Thus the first firm assumption that is always made in analysing boundary layers is that the air speed at the surface itself is zero. This is called the *zero slip* or *no slip condition*. Although we cannot be said to have 'proved' this with our discussion of the imaginary situation depicted above, yet in fact this turns out to be one assumption about boundary layers which practical experiment has always upheld as being good and sound. It is one of the few assumptions about the nature of the flow in boundary layers that is simple, consistent and reliable, so let us be grateful for small mercies, in a subject where simplifying assumptions are few and far between!

Returning to the surface in our miniaturised state, let us now imagine climbing up a vertical mast into the airflow. If we go high enough, presumably we must eventually reach a point in the airflow where it is unaffected by the surface and is flowing with the undisturbed free stream velocity. (Remember that the surface is flat, so there is no funny shape to manoeuvre around which would alter the local flow speed as happened earlier with our cylinder flow.) But between the foot of the mast and this unaffected point the airspeed is found (as we would naturally expect) to increase smoothly from zero to the full stream velocity. In fact, it increases more gradually towards the top, so that the surface flow merges smoothly with the free stream flow, and it is difficult to discern exactly where the slowed down region finishes and the free stream region starts.

One might ask at this point how thick a boundary layer is, but frustratingly this is rather like asking how long is a piece of string. At the beginning of the surface causing the boundary layer, the thickness of the boundary layer starts from zero, and as one moves further and further downstream along the surface, the boundary layer is found to get progressively thicker and thicker, as more and more air becomes entrained in it. The boundary layer of the wind over the surface of the Earth may be hundreds of feet thick, but on an aircraft surface it will typically be measured in small numbers of millimetres or centimetres.

From this little investigation we can now draw a diagram (Figure 6.3) which will help us to visualise this *boundary layer*, the layer in which the air speed is gradually increasing from zero at the surface to the free stream velocity at some distance out. The diagram is essentially a graph, whose horizontal axis lies along the surface, and whose vertical axis represents the 'mast' of the above example. Distances from the surface (denoted y) are plotted very naturally up the vertical axis, and the speed at each height y is plotted horizontally. This is a slightly unusual way of drawing a graph, since it is more common to plot what is called the independent variable, the one which we can measure even while nothing is going on, on the horizontal axis, and the dependent variable, the one whose value depends on the process

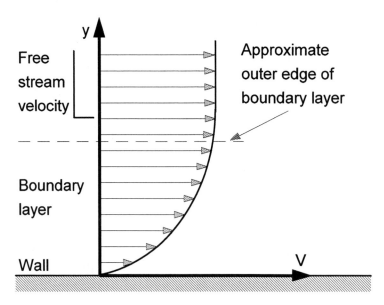

Figure 6.3   A Boundary Layer Velocity Profile

being measured, up the vertical axis. In the present case, the distance from the surface is the independent variable and the speed at each distance from the surface the dependent variable, but it would not look so natural to draw the graph with the vertical distances plotted horizontally. Furthermore, by using the convention that we have chosen and drawing vector arrows to the same scale as that of the horizontal graph axis, we can superimpose on the graph a range of the actual vector arrows representing the velocities of the flow with their points just touching the curve, since the velocities actually are horizontal. These vector arrows also coincide with the streamlines of the flow, since there is no flow in the vertical direction. However, this choice of axes will cause us a little difficulty in a few minutes, when we start to think about the slope, or gradient, of the curve.

If, as we saw above, the boundary layer just peters out at its outer edge as the speed becomes very close to the free stream velocity, some sort of arbitrary definition will be necessary for defining where the boundary layer stops. This is typically (but not necessarily) chosen as the y-value at which the velocity reaches 99% of its free stream value, and a dashed line has been inserted in Figure 6.3 to represent such an edge demarcation. The surface at the bottom of the boundary layer where the velocity is zero is referred to by aerodynamicists as the *wall*, as indicated in the figure.

LAMINAR AND TURBULENT BOUNDARY LAYERS

We have so far assumed that layers of air very tidily and smoothly slide over each other, rather like a pack of cards being manipulated in the hands of a conjurer. Unfortunately this is not usually the case. Only if a boundary layer is very new (i.e. it is still near the beginning of the wall that is causing it) and also the free stream velocity is quite slow will the layers slide nicely over each other, but at a certain inevitable combination of newness and speed (which we will consider in more detail in Chapter 8) the heretofore well-behaved air particles moving in their serried ranks within the boundary layer find that being on their best behaviour is just too much of a strain, and fairly suddenly pandemonium erupts amongst them. Although they all continue to move along parallel to the surface at much the same speed as they did before, yet within this overall motion there is superimposed a turmoil of motion, in which all of the particles start to move very eratically from layer to layer in a haphazard motion. Perhaps the best way of understanding this is to think of four or five close-together and parallel conveyor belts moving along in the same direction at different speeds, the speed gradually increasing from one side of the set of belts to the other. Standing and travelling on the conveyor belts are people, but their shoulders are as wide as the conveyor belts, so that they inevitably interfere with and jostle each other as conveyor slides past conveyor. Imagine that, at a certain moment, some additional little irritation which is the 'last straw' sets off an almighty fisticuffs battle amongst the exasperated travellers, which involves rapid to-ing and fro-ing from conveyor to conveyor and rushing about amongst each other. The conveyors are still moving as before, but superimposed onto the overall forward velocity of each person is now a random and rapidly changing velocity in two dimensions (forwards and sideways). Overall each person will not move far from his or her original point on the conveyor, so that each person's mean (or overall or resultant) velocity will still be that of the conveyor belt.

When a phenomenon analogous to this occurs in the aerodynamic boundary layer, the boundary layer flow is said to change from *laminar flow* to *turbulent flow*. The above analogy is of course two-dimensional, whereas the motion of the particles of air in the turbulent boundary layer is very definitely three-dimensional, with particles moving erratically from side to side as well as up and down in addition to forwards. A single particle's motion might be thought of as being like the flight of a fly in a moving bus.

Notice that there is no such problem of turbulence outside the boundary layer, since even if there are layers of air sliding past each other, it is found that the viscosity can with impunity be ignored where there is no solid surface involved. Such would be the case around our circular cylinder far enough away from the cylinder itself to be out of the boundary layer; but in the present case of the flow past a flat plate all the flow outside the boundary layer is uniform and so involves no relative sliding of layers.

For the sake of generality we did not actually specify whether the *boundary layer profile* of Figure 6.3 (as such a figure is called) was that of a laminar or a turbulent boundary layer, although the assumption of smooth sliding would have implied the former. In fact we can learn a tremendous amount about the behaviour of boundary layers by looking at a laminar boundary layer profile next to a turbulent boundary layer profile, and by carefully comparing the features of one with those of the other. This we will now proceed to do.

In Figure 6.4 we have shown a laminar and a turbulent boundary layer profile for a flow situation which is in all other respects identical: the free stream velocity is the same, and the distance from the start is the same. In practice, these conditions being fixed would normally be sufficient to determine whether the boundary layer was laminar or turbulent, and so the comparison is somewhat contrived, but it forces the issue in order to reveal some very important differences in the nature of the two types of boundary layer. Notice that the velocity vector arrows in the turbulent case can no longer refer to the velocity of the air at that position in the boundary layer, since the velocity at any point is now very unsteady, and may be of any magnitude and in any direction, even having a component out of the page. The velocity arrows *do*, however, still have important significance, and they show the average or mean velocity over a period of time at each level in the boundary layer. As long as we keep the difference in the back of our

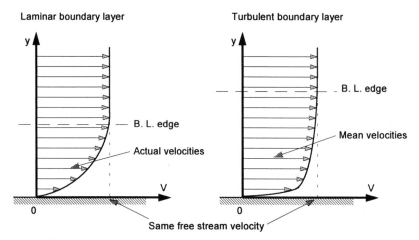

Figure 6.4   Comparison Between Laminar and Turbulent Boundary Layer Profiles

minds, we can treat the vector arrows in the two diagrams in the same way as each other. Let us look now at the important differences between the two types of boundary layers, as exhibited by their velocity profiles.

The first thing that we notice is that the turbulent boundary layer is *thicker* than the laminar. Some air layers that were above the boundary layer and thus moving at free stream velocity in the laminar case are now caught up into the boundary layer and so have been slowed down a bit. This is because the particles of air in the layers near the top of the laminar boundary layer have now adopted a turbulent motion and have started dancing around and moving back and forth out of their own layer into nearby layers both above and below their own. As they do so, there will inevitably be a jostling between particles and their neighbours, and such collisions will tend to bring the speeds of two colliding particles closer together, in much the same way as the dancers near the edge of a crowded dance floor may bump against the 'wallflowers' standing around the edge and goad them into activity, whilst being slowed down a bit themselves. Consequently layers which were previously above the boundary layer and oblivious to the slowing down going on within it are now forcibly entrained into the process and are slowed down, making the boundary layer thicker. By exactly the same mechanism, layers of air slightly lower down are themselves speeded up, so that the rate at which the velocity reduces as you go down into the boundary layer is less than it was in the laminar boundary layer, and thus the profile curve in this region is now steeper.

Exactly the same mixing and velocity-sharing effect[4] is apparent near to the bottom of the boundary layer. At a small distance from the wall, (say one streamline up in the diagrams) the velocity of the laminar boundary layer (the length of its vector) is very much smaller than the velocity at the same distance from the wall in the turbulent case. In the turbulent boundary layer, faster moving particles from the layers above the one being considered start moving turbulently from layer to layer, jostling with the particles in our layer and hence speeding them up. The shape of the velocity profile in the turbulent case is therefore much *fuller,* or more stretched out in the lower right-hand corner, than the laminar velocity profile.

Comparing the magnitudes of the velocities in the two curves in this way can take us so far, but it will be apparent from a glance at the

---

[4]Aerodynamicists usually refer to 'momentum transfer' rather than velocity sharing, and we recall that momentum is mass times velocity. If we consider elements of air that all have the same mass as each other, then it will serve our purposes just as well to talk of velocity sharing.

curves that there are distinct differences in the steepnesses of the two curves, which we need to investigate because they are in fact of utmost importance. We will therefore break off at this point, to introduce a little bit of the mathematical concept and language of rates of change. Although we could carry on without it, it will make any transition into further work in aerodynamics very much smoother and more straight-forward if we learn now to talk in the appropriate language.

RATES OF CHANGE

We have earlier established the concept of two quantities being direct-ly proportional to each other. We said that a graph of one against the other must be a straight line through the origin, and that the constant of proportionality is given by the slope of the graph. If the quantities plotted are known as x (horizontally) and y (vertically), then the con-stant of proportionality is also known as the rate of change of y as x varies. It is found by dividing a y value by an x value, and has units [y-unit] per [x-unit]. If the graph produces a straight line which does not go through the origin, the relationship is no longer one of direct pro-portion, but all of the above points (except for the term constant of proportionality) still apply. It is just a little more difficult to work out the slope of the graph since the origin can no longer be one of the two points of your chosen interval.

Although many quantities are related by straight line graphs, and many scientists have gone down in history by having their name attached to such relationships that they have discovered, of course many a real relationship will not render a straight-line graph but some sort of curve. We are still very interested in the rate of change of the vertically plotted quantity as the horizontally plotted quantity varies, but in this case the rate of change itself is seen to vary as we move along the curve. The easiest way to get around this problem is to approximate to the real curve by thinking of it (and even drawing it) as not a smooth curve but as a chain consisting of lots of little straight lines, like a child's 'join the dots' picture. The slope of the straight line between each pair of points can be calculated as before, and thus the approximate rate of change *in that small region of the curve* can be obtained. If we want to do this exercise more accurately, we simply have to take more points less spaced out on the curve, and work out the slope for each of the resulting shorter straight lines. Clearly the more accurate we want to be, the more work we have to do.

If we wanted precise mathematical accuracy, it would seem that our points would have to come so close together that the chain of straight lines would be indistinguishable from the curve itself, but each little straight line would be getting so small that it would be vanishing into a point. If before we reached that ultimate stage we drew a much longer line parallel to and coincident with the little line segment, sticking out beyond it at each end, and then we continued reducing the length of the little line, the new long line would finish up as being a *tangent* to the curve at the point in question. The slope of the tangent is exactly the same as the slope of the curve at this point. Since the tangent is itself a straight line we can easily work out its slope as before, and hence determine the rate of change of the relationship at this point.

We must now think rather carefully how we are going to specify or denote this rate of change. If the quantities are y (vertically) and x (horizontally) as before, then the rate of change is *not* given by y/x: this would give us the slope of the straight line from the *origin* to the point on the curve having values x and y, which is not what we want. What we want is a notation which tells us to divide a very little y-movement from the point in question by a very little x-movement from that point, such that the final point reached after the x and y movements is another point on the curve so close to the first that the distance between them has actually shrunk to 0. We will use the short-hand terminology dy to mean this 'very little y-movement', and correspondingly we will use the notation dx to mean 'a very little x-movement', and thus the slope, or rate of change, will be given by

$$\frac{dy}{dx}$$

Notice that we cannot cancel the ds – they are not numbers multiplied by x and y, but a special symbol meaning 'a little bit of . . , so tiny that it has actually shrunk to 0'. Actually, they don't even need to mean that! If we think of working out the slope of the tangent which we drew before shrinking the little line to no size, then we can get the slope of the tangent by taking the y and x differences between *any* two points on it, which may be well spaced out. In this case the dy and the dx both refer to quite big distances! The crucial thing to remember is that we must never let the dy and the dx become separated, since they are a pair, and only together as a fraction do they mean the slope or the rate of change, and only together like this do they make any real sense.

We have just ventured into the branch of mathematics called Calculus, where the ratio dy/dx is called the *differential coefficient* (being involved with differences). A large part of Calculus is devoted to developing methods for working out the value of the differential coefficient for different mathematical relationships. The original work in this area was done by both Newton and a contemporary of his called Leibeniz at about the same time, but the 'd' notation was that introduced by Leibeniz, and it is in universal use by mathematicians today. We met earlier the 'dot' notation which is what Newton introduced for the special case when the independent variable (in place of the *x* above) was time, the type of problem of primary interest to him. For comparison we can now write down mass flow rate (for which we earlier used the dot notation) in both conventions, using *t* for time, as follows:

$$\dot{m} = \frac{dm}{dt}$$

In this case the quantity should strictly always be called the 'time rate of change', since the term rate of change can equally well be used for other independent variables than just time. You should beware of a possible source of ambiguity here, since some people may use the term 'rate of change' to mean 'time rate of change'.

RETURNING TO BOUNDARY LAYERS

As an important example of the application of the ideas just introduced, let us go back to consider again the concept of rate of shear strain, which is an integral part of the definition of viscosity. Referring to Figure 6.2 we defined rate of shear strain as $\dot{e}/h$. The notation we used at that point was a temporary, simplified notation in order to introduce the new concepts arising at that point, but it is now appropriate to translate the definition of strain into notation which matches that which we have used in Figure 6.4, and which is far more conventional and convenient. Now $\dot{e}$ is the time rate of change of distance moved by the upper surface of the air element relative to the lower surface; in other words, since 'time rate of change of distance' is speed, $\dot{e}$ is the difference in speed between the upper and lower surface, which is ΔV in Figure 6.2. The bottom of the rate of strain fraction, *h*, refers to the vertical distance between the two streamlines in the diagram. If the streamlines belong to an airflow over a flat surface, above which we denote the height of a streamline as *y*, then *h* refers to the *difference* in *y* between the upper surface and the lower surface of the element. Using similar notation to that which we used for the velocity difference on the same element, we can now write Δy in place of *h*. Consequently the rate of shear strain may now be written as $\Delta V/\Delta y$ in place of the earlier $\dot{e}/h$.

The velocity profiles of Figures 6.3 and 6.4 are graphs of the two variables *V* and *y* plotted against each other in the boundary layers, but unfortunately as we have already noted we were persuaded to choose the axes for the graphs according to what would look more natural rather than what was best from a mathematical point of view. Mathematically, *y* is the independent variable which should be plotted horizontally, and *V* is the dependent variable which should be plotted

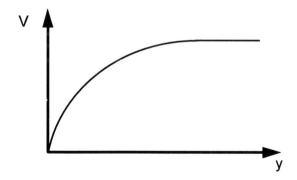

Figure 6.5   Boundary Layer Profile Plotted the Un-conventional Way-round

vertically. For the time being, we will use Figure 6.5, which is the same graph as Figure 6.3 simply re-plotted after swopping axes.

We have shown that the rate of shear strain is $\Delta V/\Delta y$, where ΔV and Δy are the differences in V and y values between two close layers of the air, or in other words between two close points on the graph of Figure 6.5. If we were to bring the two points closer together on the graph until the distance between them shrank to 0, then the fraction $\Delta V/\Delta y$ would become the slope of the graph at the point with values V and y; in other words $\Delta V/\Delta y$ would become dV/dy. Physically this corresponds with bringing the two streamlines so close together that they merge into one.

Thus we see that the rate of shear strain is synonymous with the slope of the velocity profile provided we plot it the 'wrong' way round. The slope dV/dy is also referred to as the *velocity gradient* of the flow at the point under consideration, and this is probably the term that will be used most often, since it relates the idea directly to the gradient, or slope, of the velocity profile. Thus the velocity gradient is an integral part of our definition of viscosity, and the other component of the viscosity definition is shear stress, which brings in the idea of force. We are now in a position to derive some useful ideas about the direct shear force acting on the surface of an object, which is called skin friction, by bringing together the various concepts that we have introduced.

SKIN FRICTION

So that we have a statement to work from which includes the shear force F which provides skin friction, let us first of all recall the definition of viscosity, and express it in the new notation introduced in the previous section:

$$\text{Viscosity} = \mu = \frac{(F/A)}{(dV/dy)}$$

We can re-write this so that the shear stress is represented in terms of the other quantities:

$$\left(\frac{F}{A}\right) = \mu\left(\frac{dV}{dy}\right)$$

Now F/A means force per unit area. To get the total force, we simply multiply this (later) by the area over which it is acting. The tangential force per unit area between two sliding layers of air is found from the above equation by multiplying the viscosity μ by the velocity gradient dV/dy. Let us look at these two factors separately.

The dynamic viscosity μ is a property of the air, and is a very small number. At sea-level it is about 1.8×10^{-5} SI units. The viscosity of air is dependent only on the temperature of the air and on nothing else (except insofar as other properties affect the temperature), and surprisingly it increases with temperature, whereas common experience with motor oil tells us that the viscosity of liquids decreases as the temperature rises – they become more runny. As viscosity is so small, from the above equation it is clear that the shear force will be very small unless the other factor dV/dy, the velocity gradient, is very large.

To examine the behaviour of the velocity gradient, we must refer back to the velocity profile figures. First we must transfer our thinking about velocity gradient back to the conventionally drawn profiles of Figures 6.3 and 6.4, so that we can dispense with the temporary inverted profile of Figure 6.5. We observe that a small dV/dy value, corresponding to a small slope (almost flat curve) in Figure 6.5, such as at the top right, corresponds to a very large slope (an almost vertical line) in the conventionally drawn velocity profile of Figure 6.3. Likewise, a large dV/dy value, corresponding to a steep slope (such as near the origin) in Figure 6.5, corresponds to a relatively small slope in the conventionally drawn velocity profile of Figure 6.3. To summarise, a large velocity gradient dV/dy implies a very flat velocity profile when drawn conventionally, and a small velocity gradient dV/dy means a very steep velocity profile.

Throughout the boundary layer, there will be viscous force pairs between layers of air, but each pair is mutually cancelling and does not produce any skin friction on the body. Skin friction only occurs at the point where the air comes into contact with the wall itself, i.e. where $y = 0$.

Referring to Figure 6.4, let us look at how the velocity gradients of the two types of boundary layer profile, laminar and turbulent, behave. Moving up through the laminar boundary layer profile, the velocity increases from zero at a relatively steady rate up to the free stream velocity, throughout the thickness of the boundary layer, and so the velocity gradient is of moderate magnitude and does not change very drastically anywhere in the boundary layer. By contrast, in the turbulent boundary layer, a large proportion of the free stream velocity is reached after we have gone up only a very small proportion of the boundary layer thickness from the wall, and there is very little increase across the rest of the boundary layer thickness. The velocity profile is very flat in this region close to the wall, and thus the value of dV/dy is very high. Putting this large value into the equation above for shear stress gives a much larger shear force per unit area than occurs in a laminar boundary layer. We thus conclude that

Skin friction drag is much greater in a turbulent boundary layer than in a laminar boundary layer.

This is not on the face of it a very remarkable conclusion to have reached, and it would suggest to us that, if we wish to pursue low drag on our aircraft, we should try if possible to ensure that the boundary layer is laminar. But this is by no means the whole of the story, and so we will return to re-consider this conclusion again towards the end of this chapter.

Close to the wall in this bottom region there is very little room for vertical motion, so that even in a turbulent boundary layer the air velocities here are forced to be predominantly parallel to the wall. The flow in this narrow bottom region of a turbulent boundary layer closely resembles that of a laminar boundary layer, and it is sometimes referred to (incorrectly) as the 'laminar sublayer'. A much more appropriate term which is also applied to this bottom layer is the *viscous sublayer* since the very large velocity gradient involved does give rise to large shearing forces, and the air behaves as if it were a very viscous fluid.

FORM DRAG

Form drag is otherwise known as *boundary layer normal pressure drag*, since it is a drag due to pressure, and not viscous, forces on the object, resulting from the existence of viscosity and hence the boundary layer. Since in inviscid flow d'Alembert's Paradox tells us that there are no resultant pressure forces, it follows that, if a pressure drag exists, it must be produced by the boundary layer in some way modifying the flow pattern, and hence the pressure distribution, over the object.

Outside the boundary layer on an object, potential flow methods can be accurately applied in just the same way as they are around the

Figure 6.6   Form Drag on a Streamlined Body Due to the Existence of the Boundary Layer

body itself in inviscid flow. The shape of a streamlined body[5] as shown in Figure 6.6 is effectively modified by the thickening boundary layer growing along its surface, and in particular a *wake* is created behind the body where the top and bottom boundary layers meet and merge. The effective body is thus no longer a closed body,[6] having a down-stream, infinitely long 'pan-handle'. Consequently the rear stagnation pressure predicted by the potential flow theory for closed bodies will fail to occur, and there will be a small pressure inbalance with the nose, resulting in *form drag*. Form drag from this cause is very small and may often be negligible. However, form drag can be very large indeed if the boundary layer *separates*, and so we must investigate the phenomenon of boundary layer separation. But before doing so let us take stock of the general situation, and step back to put the whole matter in context, lest we lose sight of the wood for the trees.

ONE EFFECT OF THE BOUNDARY LAYER – KINETIC HEATING.

When we earlier considered the inviscid flow around a circular cylin-der, we drew on the analogy of a roller-coaster that was totally friction-free and perfectly streamlined, so that there were no energy losses as it rolled freely down and up its track. We saw how there was total exchangeability between the roller-coaster's potential energy and its kinetic energy, so that however much descending and rising it did, it would eventually be able to return to its original height with no surplus speed. We then saw how the inviscid airflow around our cylinder behaved in a similar manner, exchanging pressure energy for kinetic energy, again with no losses since there was no viscosity, and ultimately reaching the rear stagnation point with the same amount of pressure energy (and no kinetic energy) as it started with at the front stagnation point. There was no boundary layer, and so the velocity profile graph at any point along the surface would have simply been a vertical line at the full stream velocity, coming right down to the surface.

But now we are considering real flow which does have viscosity, and viscosity means friction, and friction means energy loss. The air close to the cylinder wall is going to lose some of its kinetic energy in the

[5]This will be discussed later in this chapter.
[6]A closed body is one whose boundary can be drawn with a line which joins up with itself into a continuous loop – such as our cylinder in inviscid flow.

slowing up of the boundary layer. This energy is *not* converted into pressure energy in accordance with Bernoulli's Principle as one might at first glance expect, since Bernoulli's Principle is based on the conservation of mechanical energy, but now we have a loss of mechanical energy[7]. Remembering that 'energy cannot be created or destroyed, but only converted from one form into another', where does the energy that is apparently lost from the flow go to? In what form?

As nearly always with 'lost' or down-graded energy, it all finishes up as heat. So what gets hot, the air or the surface it is sliding over? A quick think will show that each little passing bit of air is only in contact with the surface for a very brief time, which is obviously not long enough to get heated up to any appreciable level. The surface, however, will be constantly being 'rubbed' by passing air, and so is continuously being heated. The process is called *kinetic heating*, and the object can get quite hot.

How hot is 'hot', we may ask? Is this kinetic heating a significant effect, or just something of academic interest that we can sweep under the carpet and forget about? We can easily and quickly work out the answer to this question by applying the following useful and simple approximate rule of thumb:

> **The temperature rise in degrees Celcius due to kinetic heating approximately equals the number of hundreds of miles per hour of the airflow, squared.**

Thus, if an aircraft or a car is travelling at 100 miles-per-hour, one squared is one, and so the temperature of the body will rise by one degree Celcius, which is not very significant. But what happens when we have rather faster aircraft? The following table shows some answers, although it is not easily possible to convert these into actual surface temperatures, since these speeds will often be achieved at high altitude where the temperature of the outside air may be anything down to about $-57°C$.

			M<1	M>1			
			Typical jetliner	Boiling water		Concorde cruise	Lockheed SR71A
Airspeed, MPH	100	300	630	920	1000	1400	2000
Temperature rise, °C	$1^2=1$	$3^2=9$	$6.3^2=40$	$9.2^2=85$	$10^2=100$	$14^2=196$	$20^2=400$

[7]If this were not the case and Bernoulli's Principle did apply, we would always have total pressure on every surface everywhere, since the velocity is zero by the no-slip condition. Therefore it would be impossible ever to measure static pressure – we would always get total pressure. Furthermore, pressure distributions which vary around objects would be unknown, and surface pressure coefficients would be 1 everywhere, making a nonsense of all the aerodynamics we have learned!

There is clearly not much of a kinetic heating problem with aircraft which are propeller-driven, but jet aircraft rapidly come into the realms of substantial heating, and when they go supersonic considerable engineering problems arise. For example, the Concorde supersonic airliner is said to become about a foot longer in the cruise, due to thermal expansion of its metal body, than it is when on the ground, and you can readily imagine the complications that this raises when control rods, cables, pipes, ducts, carpets and all manner of things have to be designed to allow for this regular variation in the aircraft's length.

Have you ever wondered why nearly all supersonic aircraft (including Concorde) have a maximum speed of around twice the speed of sound? The reason for this is to do with kinetic heating. Aluminium is an ideal material for use in manufacturing aircraft because of its combination of light weight, mechanical properties and relatively low cost. Unfortunately, though, these good mechanical properties are only maintained at temperatures up to that reached by an aircraft skin due to kinetic heating at around twice the speed of sound. Above this speed, aluminium is no longer a suitable material to use, and more expensive and less easily workable materials such as stainless-steel and tungsten have to be substituted. Thus, just as there is a sudden jump in the cost of air transportation at around the speed of sound, so there is another major jump in cost at around Mach 2, which is why, unless there are special tactical reasons for operating an aircraft faster than this, supersonic aircraft are invariably designed to fly up to about Mach 2 and no more.

One notable exception to this rule is the legendary Lockheed SR71 'Blackbird' supersonic reconnaissance aircraft, whose operating speed is known only to be 'above Mach 3'. The thermal expansion occurring due to kinetic heating in this case is very substantial, as shown in the last column of the table above, and calls for drastic design measures. The wings of this aircraft also form (rather than contain) the main fuel tanks, and exposed surfaces of these will be liable to very great thermal expansion at operational speed. Some surfaces are less exposed, and so there is considerable differential expansion of different parts of the tanks, which means that what would be the right sizes and proportions for the various components when the aircraft is standing on the ground will cease to be correct when it is flying at supersonic speed. The solution adopted to this problem has been to design the various panels of the wing fuel tanks to interlock with each other and to be the right sizes for the hot, supersonic condition. This means that they are wrong when on the ground, and so the wing tank panels do not fit properly together. The result of this is that, when the aircraft is not flying, its fuel tanks leak very profusely from all the joints between panels, and the joints only seal up properly when the aircraft has reached its cruising speed. Consequently, the aircraft is never fuelled up until the very latest possible moment in the protracted (about twenty-four hour) count-down that precedes every SR71 flight. From then on and during taxi-ing out and taking off, the aircraft is leaking fuel from all parts of its wings, all over the ground, at an alarming rate. Before losing all its fuel then, the aircraft must take-off and gain speed as rapidly as possible.

However, the problem is not yet over. A supersonic aircraft is a very inefficient flying machine at subsonic speeds, being optimised for its high speed rôle, and so it eats very heavily into its fuel resources for each mile flown when flying subsonically. Furthermore, the first task that the engines have to accomplish is to provide the aircraft with both kinetic energy (speed) and potential energy (height), before it can settle down into cruising flight. Adding to this the fact that the weight and hence fuel load of any aircraft must be designed to be as low as possible, compatible with other requirements, and also that the fuel tanks of the Blackbird are still leaking like sieves, the consequence is that the aircraft will almost have run out of fuel before it even starts its mission! The solution employed is to have an in-flight refuelling tanker aircraft already airborne and standing by aloft to refuel the SR71 before it departs on its supersonic mission. But the tanker is a sub-sonic aircraft, and the SR71 does not really take kindly to flying below the speed of sound – still leaking fuel at a high rate, and flying with a pronounced and inefficient nose-up attitude. So the tanker must now fly very fast, close to the speed of sound, whilst the Blackbird lumbers awkwardly along behind it, couples up to the umbilical cord and starts taking on fuel. As it does so, the weight of the Blackbird approaches its maximum all-up weight, so that the very ungainly attitude that it is already being forced to adopt becomes even worse as it struggles with its excessive load at an inefficient speed. Once this rather precarious and inelegant refueling operation is complete, the Blackbird can separate from its mother tanker and accelerate away up to its supersonic cruise speed of some three times the speed of sound, and the kinetic heating will seal up the leaking tanks in readiness for the long, secret mission ahead.

Before leaving this fascinating and unusual aircraft, it is interesting to observe one or two more features about the way its missions were conducted. Reference has already been made to the count-down, and, very much in the style and tradition of a space flight rather than an aircraft flight, both aircraft and pilot would be subject to an extensive count-down, which became more concentrated during the final twenty-four hours before flight, and during which every technical event was precisely scheduled and checked off. The physiological strain on the pilot of flying an SR71 mission was high, and so every pilot had to undergo a full medical examination before and after every flight. He had to be fed routinely on a high protein, low residue diet in view of the long duration of the flights. The cockpit was no comfortable office, being extremely compact and not fully conditioned for human comfort, and so the pilot would wear a full NASA space suit rather than a normal flying suit. The tiny glass panes of the cockpit canopy were very close to the face of the pilot, providing very little visibility, and as a continual reminder to the pilot of the kinetic heating and the inhospitable environment, these panes got so hot on the inside that, even wearing his space suit gloves, the pilot could only touch the glass briefly before being forced to withdraw his hand.

BOUNDARY LAYER SEPARATION

Coming back down to earth now, so far, apart from the brief allusion to the flow round a streamlined shape in Figure 6.6, we have only considered a boundary layer forming on a flat surface, which will cause no variation in pressure such as occurs around an object like our circular cylinder. If the cylinder is immersed in a steady uniform flow of a *real* fluid with viscosity, a boundary layer will form, and will interact in some way with the variation of pressure that occurs. Let us take a detailed look at the real flow and of the boundary layer behaviour over the top region of a two-dimensional circular cylinder, with flow as usual from left to right as shown in Figure 6.7. The vertical axes of the velocity profiles are drawn to a larger scale than the cylinder, for clarity.

As the flow comes from the left (front) stagnation point towards the top, our inviscid flow study predicted that the flow speed would grow, reaching a maximum at the top of the cylinder. Now that the flow is viscous, we can draw boundary layer profiles at any point around this leading quarter of the cylinder surface: we have drawn one (marked ❶) on the front region and one (❷) at the top. As we have already mentioned, a boundary layer grows in thickness as it develops downstream, which is illustrated by the 'B.L. edge' dotted line. (The boundary layer thickness is magnified, may be about ten or so times, in the figure.) Also, since the velocity outside the boundary layer is increasing towards the top, the top profile ❷ is wider than the one on the leading face, ❶. We also recall that the pressure at the top of the cylinder reaches a minimum (in inviscid flow), and so there is higher pressure behind (i.e. to the left of) the flow on the leading face than in front of it. We call this pressure difference a *favourable pressure gradient*, and it is this that pushes the flow along, speeding it up, up to the top. The flow can comfortably afford to sacrifice, through viscosity and wall friction, the velocity that it loses in the boundary layer,

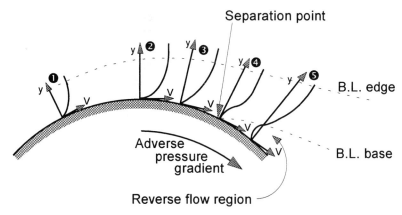

Figure 6.7   **The Process of Boundary Layer Separation**

because the favourable pressure gradient is making sure that it gets a helping hand to keep going.

We now turn our attention to the rear portion of the upper surface, where the flow velocity decreases towards what would in inviscid flow be zero speed at a rear stagnation point, and the pressure correspondingly increases. In inviscid flow, there was just enough kinetic energy at the top (like the roller-coaster at the bottom of a dip) to keep the flow going to the rear stagnation point and to overcome the steadily increasing pressure or *adverse pressure gradient*, by which time all the KE had been converted back into pressure. But now things are different, because within the boundary layer the flow has already forfeited a substantial part of its kinetic energy, and it has been lost to the cylinder surface through kinetic heating as we have already seen. It therefore does not have enough kinetic energy left to get back to the 'all-pressure' condition at the rear stagnation point, just as a roller-coaster *with* friction will not get quite as high as it came from after going down a dip. The result of this is a little complicated, and so we will look at what happens in some detail.

Looking at the sequence of boundary layer velocity profiles ❷ to ❺ in Figure 6.7, we first note that, since the free stream velocity is falling again, the tops of the profiles get narrower, but this of itself is not vitally important. It is the velocity vectors near to the *bottom* of the boundary layer which have the problem: since they have lost kinetic energy, they can no longer penetrate the adverse pressure gradient, rather like trying to cycle into a strong wind, but their magnitudes are reduced further as they attempt to do so. Thus the small velocities at the bottom of ❷ become even smaller in ❸ and the profile becomes steeper and narrower at the bottom. From ❸ to ❹ this process continues, with the lower layer velocities being forced right down to around zero – the flow being brought to rest, (the moment at which the cyclist falls off his bike!) Thus at ❹ there is no shearing of the flow at all down by the wall, the profile is vertical at the wall and dV/dy has shrunk to zero.

The process does not stop here, since the adverse pressure continues relentlessly to oppose the flow. Having brought the flow near the surface to rest, it now has the effect of actually reversing this flow just above the surface, so that in ❺ we see a little D-shaped loop to the left in the velocity profile. The no-slip condition still pertains, so that the profile still goes through the graph origin at the bottom of this loop, and also at the top of it there is a point where the profile crosses the vertical axis. The air at this level has now been brought exactly to rest by the adverse pressure gradient. Above this, there is still some positive, forward velocity, but the adverse pressure has been slowing this down as well, so that we get exactly the same sort of boundary layer velocity profile that we are familiar with, but it has moved bodily away from the surface which initially caused it. We say very naturally that the boundary layer has *separated* from the surface, and refer to the phenomenon as *boundary layer separation*.

In Figure 6.7 the base of the newly separated boundary layer has been inserted as a dotted line. It starts at the point where the velocity first becomes zero other than at the wall itself, and it follows the progress of the zero-velocity point as this point gets further away from the surface. As we have already mentioned, the region under this doted line is a region of reverse flow, but if it is no longer being supplied by the stream flow from the left, where does it get its supply of air from? There cannot be a vacuum, since the pressure was *increasing* to here and not decreasing. The answer is that the reverse flow region is supplied with its air from the left-to-right flow of air just above the boundary layer base dotted line, the flow curling down *across* this line. Although we said that the air had zero velocity at the depth of this dotted line, we will have to modify that statement now, and say that there is no *streamwise* direction component of velocity at the points on this line, but that there *is* a component downwards normal to the surface. Air swirls back in underneath itself, and so forms eddy currents which are typical of the region behind a boundary layer separation point.

So the boundary layer has now separated, and conditions are very different around the rear of the cylinder from those which we conceived of in the ideal flow case. If we want to know what effect this has on the drag of the cylinder, we need to know how the pressure distribution in the rear region has been modified from what we predicted for inviscid air. There is no good sound mathematical way of predicting this pressure distribution, since unfortunately viscous flow and flow separation is not amenable to neat, elegant mathematical treatment in the way that ideal flow is. We must therefore rely substantially on experience and experimental evidence, and by that means we know that the pressure beyond the separation point to the rear of the cylinder remains almost exactly unchanged from the value that it had reached by that separation point. Up to that point the pressure keeps very close to the potential flow predicted values, but thereafter it remains constant. Thus the swirling eddies have the effect of equalising the pressure. We therefore take Figure 5.10 in which we plotted the symmetrical pressure distribution around our circular cylinder, and modify it according to the above result from the top and bottom separation points rearwards, giving us the pressure distribution shown in Figure 6.8.

It is now quite clear that there is indeed a pressure drag, which results directly from the boundary layer behaviour and consequently from the viscosity of the air, even though (in this figure) there are no shear force arrows acting on the cylinder. The resultant of the pressure forces acts to the right and is called the *form drag*. It can only be measured, and cannot be calculated.

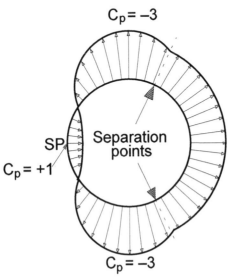

Figure 6.8   Pressure Distribution of Circular Cylinder in Real Flow

REDUCTION OF FORM DRAG BY PREVENTION OF SEPARATION

If on an object such as our earlier streamlined body (Figure 6.6) the boundary layer does not separate, form drag is usually negligible, and it is not likely to be amenable to further reduction. Thus to keep form drag low, separation must be prevented if at all possible.

We have seen that boundary layer separation is caused by the combined effect of viscosity (i.e. the boundary layer) and an adverse pressure gradient. We thus have two possible channels of attack on form drag: we can work on the adverse pressure gradient or we can tackle the kinetic energy deficiency in the boundary layer.

If possible, adverse pressure gradients should always be kept very small, by means of *streamlining*, which involves gently tapering the rear of the body, such as in Figure 6.6. However, this can only be done at the cost of increasing surface area and hence skin friction, and so should only be continued until an optimum net benefit is achieved.

Alternatively, if the kinetic energy loss from the boundary layer to kinetic heating of the surface can be made good in some way, separation can be delayed or totally prevented despite the adverse pressure gradient, rather like fixing a motor to our bicycle in the headwind. There are various ways in which this can be achieved, some of which we will consider a little later in Chapter 9, when we have established more of the ideas of aerofoil lift. But in the present context one particular approach to this problem will be considered here. We saw earlier that a turbulent boundary layer velocity profile is much 'fuller' than a laminar one. Consequently the turbulent boundary layer has much more kinetic energy near the wall than the laminar boundary layer has, and so it has much better penetration into an adverse pressure gradient. Thus, if separation is causing high form drag, a turbulent boundary layer is desirable for maintaining attached flow for as long as possible. By way of example, the coefficient of drag of a cylinder under certain free stream conditions with a laminar boundary layer is about 1.15. Under identical conditions but with a turbulent boundary layer the coefficient of drag is found to fall to about 0.35. Thus, although as we noted under an earlier section laminar boundary layers give lower skin friction, yet

> **Turbulent boundary layers give lower form drag where there is a serious adverse pressure gradient.**

The reason for this will be immediately apparent from a glance at Figure 6.9, which shows the pressure distribution on two identical cylinders, the first with a laminar boundary layer that separates early and leaves a wide wake, and the second having a turbulent boundary layer, which stays attached much further round the cylinder and consequently produces a much narrower wake.

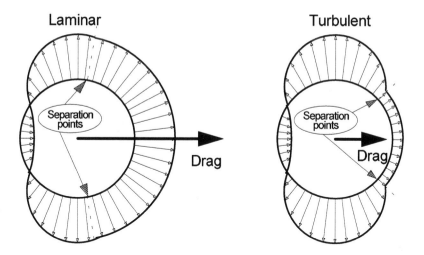

Figure 6.9   Cylinder Pressure Distributions, with Laminar and Turbulent Boundary Layers

A very good example of the effectiveness of this device is seen in the design of golf balls, which although spherical rather than cylindrical, follow the same principles. The dimples indented all over the golf ball surface are there to stir up the air near to the surface and thus make sure that it has a turbulent boundary layer. That being the case, the boundary layer stays attached much further round than it would if the boundary layer were laminar, with a very substantial reduction in drag. Table-tennis balls, on the other hand, have smooth surfaces and laminar boundary layers, so that the drag on them is much greater. Also, their mass is much less, and so for both reasons the table-tennis ball slows down much more quickly than the golf ball. The subject of the physics of balls used in different games is a fascinating one, and I would strongly recommend you to read C. B. Daish's book *The Physics of Ball Games*, published by Hodder and Stoughton.

We introduced the word 'wake' two paragraphs back, and its use gives rise to a little caution, not about what has been written here, but what appears in a large amount of 'popular' explanations of aerodynamic effects. Often in the present context wakes are treated rather as if they were draggy tails on objects, and so drag is explained as the force needed to pull this wake along, rather like walking with a long rope dragging along the ground behind you. But we know that there are only two ways in which aerodynamic force can be exerted – by normal (pressure) forces and by tangential (viscous) forces. Wakes are not ropes; they have been shed from the object once and for all, and can have no further effect on the object.

Sometimes a rather more subtle 'explanation' is offered, in that the very existence of a wake implies the imparting of energy to the fluid of the wake; this energy must have been provided by the object causing the wake, *and therefore* there is a drag force. The facts of this statement are perfectly correct, but it is not an *explanation* of drag – at least, if it is, the explanation of the link between the imparting of energy to the wake and the creation of the rearward drag force on the object lies hidden very deeply embedded in the word 'therefore'.

Wakes do exist. They can give useful information about what is going on, and can have physical effects on objects which cross their path. Their formation is associated with the aerodynamic forces on the objects causing them. But be very wary if ever you read or hear something that purports to *explain* a force by the formation of a wake. As likely as not, either the writer or speaker is taking you for a fool, or he or she does not know what he is talking about!

We have left out one vital part of the jig-saw in this chapter. We now know about the features and the relative pro's and con's of laminar and turbulent boundary layers, and have hinted that we might like some control over which type we get. But before that we will need to know how to detect which sort we have got (remembering that air is invisible) and to investigate what things affect the type of boundary layer that occurs, before we will be well placed to attempt to interfere with that process. This opens up a whole new chapter in the investigation of boundary layers, and will also introduce us to the important and fascinating subject of aerodynamic modelling – not mathematical models, but real scale models that we might use in wind-tunnels. But first we must leave space to catch up with the classical theory of lift in the next chapter, before returning to look at modelling in Chapter 8.

CHAPTER 7
Discovering the Aerofoil Shape

INTRODUCTION AND CAUTION

We are now ready and equipped to tackle the fundamental question that is usually the first thing asked by non-aviation people when the subject of aircraft flight is broached – how can an enormous weight like an airliner be supported up in the air by its wings? – or, more tersely, how is lift generated? We have already considered *why* lift is needed, have established that it is largely due to the pressure distribution on some object (the wing), and have considered the crucial feature of pressure, that pressure at a point on a surface is inversely related (by Bernoulli's Principle) to the local airspeed (outside the boundary layer) at that point. But the burning question of *what shape* our object (the wing) should actually be has not yet been broached.

Unfortunately it is necessary to start off with a negative note, and to refute and deprecate the obviously well-meaning attempts of certain popular books and articles to explain the lifting principle of the aerofoil. As illustrated by the friendly pair of air particles shown in Figure 7.1, it is maintained that, in order for the air particles, which are initially together, to reach the trailing edge (the back) of the aerofoil at the same time, the one travelling round the upper (the more curved, or cambered) surface must move faster than the one travelling in a straighter curve along the lower surface. By doing so, the pressure over the upper surface would be reduced in accordance with Bernoulli's Principle, and so the greater pressure on the lower surface would produce lift. This logic is faultless except in one detail. The fallacy lies in the assumption in the first place that the particles should *need* to arrive simultaneously at the trailing edge – why should they not in fact arrive at different times, and pair up with new partners? There is no reason why not at all. Furthermore, the idea also assumes that, if there really were such a requirement, the inanimate particles would be *mentally aware* of this requirement, and that they *have the ability* to make adjustment to their own speed at will. Clearly a number of absurdities are wrapped up in this pseudo-explanation, which with our growing insight we will now firmly discard.

The principle of lift used by aerofoils and wings is by no means obvious, and to illustrate this and to put the modern work and development in perspective it is worth glancing briefly at what two early pioneers of the subject thought about it. We have already attributed due recognition to both Leonardo Da Vinci and Sir Isaac Newton, but

Figure 7.1 The False Explanation of Lift

it is interesting to note the ways in which even these visionaries made fundamental errors in their assumptions. Leonardo Da Vinci, who died forty-five years before the birth of Galileo Galilei and so was not privy to any major scientific advances beyond the long-in-the-tooth theories of Aristotle (from the fourth century before Christ), believed that the way in which birds achieved lift was that, when they flapped their wings, they actually compressed the air beneath them increasing its density and thus its pressure. Although a very rational and natural assumption, we now know that one has to have the airspeeds associated with modern jet aircraft for compressibility to occur significantly, and that it doesn't dominate the issue until around the speed of sound – speeds out of reach of any birds of any era.

Sir Isaac Newton, on the other hand, who did have the benefit of living during the dawning of the scientific era, and who as we have seen was such a very major benefactor of mechanical science and mathematics and in many other areas, might have been expected to make more useful progress towards understanding the principles of aerodynamic force, which he certainly investigated earnestly. However, he applied his Third Law principle of action and reaction somewhat too simplistically, regarding the lift as being produced by the bombardment of a wing's lower surface by air molecules at a shallow angle. In other words, he thought that lift was purely a flat plate's reaction to bouncing a parallel stream of air particles off the lower surface. He had failed to appreciate that the change in momentum (mass times velocity) of the air particles accounted for by this approach paled into insignificance in the face of the constant random bombarding of the flat plate by vast numbers of particles arriving from all directions and at tremendous speeds, which we call air pressure.

However, Newton's work on aerodynamic lift was not in fact totally wasted. At extremely high altitudes, the density of the air is very low, and reaches virtually zero as we leave the Earth's atmosphere. At these heights, the air molecules have indeed become extremely few and far between, so that their total random momentum (which constitutes pressure) is also much smaller. Furthermore, the speeds of aerospace vehicles travelling in such rarefied air are normally in double figures of Mach numbers, (i.e. above ten times the speed of sound), speeds which are referred to as *hypersonic*, and so the momentum of the air particles in the stream-wise direction has increased until it is considerably closer to that of the random motion of the air particles. Interestingly, therefore, Newton's momentum theory of lift, although useless for the aerodynamics of conventional flight, actually comes into its own in modern hypersonic flight analysis!

So let's get down to business, and outline the structure of this chapter. We will start by linking back to the ideas of Chapter 5 where we introduced the potential flow method of analysis for inviscid airflow, and adding a few refinements. Although we were surprised that it gave us no drag, it was less surprising that it did not give us any lift, since we only developed the analysis on the basis of an object which, being symmetrical to the on-coming flow, would hardly have been expected to produce lift. We will look at a way in which the potential flow model may be enhanced so that it does predict lift, even surprisingly on our symmetrical circular cylinder, and this will introduce us to a most important concept known as *circulation*.

Through these new ideas we will be able to identify the essential features of an aerofoil, provide a formula for working out aerofoil lift, and develop the elements of the so-called 'lifting line' method for analysing and designing aircraft wings.

Although arriving at it from a completely different angle, this chapter will end at a very similar point to that at which the previous chapter ended, and we will find ourselves asking questions about the effects of the different types of boundary layers on the design and modelling of wings and aeroplanes. This will lead us naturally into the following chapter, on scale effect and modelling.

REFINING THE INVISCID MODEL

Although once again we remember that we are sworn to 'no mathematics', we are in this section talking about the development of a mathematical model, and as such we must deal with certain new mathematical concepts and ideas. But the nice thing about mathematics is that you never have to learn anything new from scratch; instead you are always just building on what you have already built, or climbing one more step of development on top of all the steps that you have ascended thus far. Each step on its own is fairly easy and painless provided you have properly reached the one below, but the achievement is not just in having mastered a single step but having reached a higher overall vantage point. Furthermore, if the step proves too difficult, you don't have to start at the bottom again, but just go back one or two steps to the point where you began to slip.

The point we had reached in our mathematical step-climbing at the end of Chapter 5 was that we had provided our mathematician with the continuity equation AV = constant, on the basis of which we were assured that he could provide us with equations for the flow streamlines. Actually, to do this, the mathematician would have had to employ some clever tricks, in order to incorporate the circular cylinder into his working. The usual equation of a circle is not suitable for the task in hand, because what we really need is the equation of the circle combined with the dividing streamlines on both sides of it: this is the streamline of fundamental importance, and it is equations of streamlines that we really need.

This need introduces us to a whole family of ingenious mathematical devices by which the equations of all sorts of flows may be produced, and also, as we will see, the equations of appropriate solid objects. They are all based on simply combining together (by methods of vector addition which are fully familiar to us) two or more flows to produce the required effects. The most basic flow, fairly naturally, is the uniform flow. Extremely useful in combination with this, for starters, is a flow called a source.

On its own, a *source* is simply a point in a two-dimensional plane at which fluid (air) enters the scene literally from nowhere! It is a bit like a tap with a tiny outlet and no visible means of supply or support. Bear in mind that this is a mathematical device, so the fact that you couldn't really make a source (any more than you could draw a perfect circle or square) is neither here nor there. Where does the fluid go to after entering the plane at the source? Since it is our own invention, it is not dependent on the laws of science, (if it were, it would probably swirl), and we may make it go any way we choose; the way we choose is radially outwards, so that the streamlines of the flow are straight lines radiating from the source in all directions. When the flow from the source crosses a circle of radius r, the cross-sectional area of the flow (assuming as earlier one unit of depth in the direction normal to the plane of the figure) is 1 times the circumference of the circle, i.e. $1 \times 2\pi r$. If the velocity in the radial direction at this radius is V, then by the continuity equation $V \times 1 \times 2\pi r$ is constant, so that Vr is also constant, which means that V is *inversely* proportional to r. As r gets bigger and bigger, (i.e. the flow gets further away from the source,) V gets smaller and smaller, until the effect peters out altogether. At each point in the plane we could draw a vector arrow representing the velocity at that point, V. All the arrows would point outwards, and the ones near the centre would be longer and those further out would be shorter.

Not very exciting on its own! But now let us superimpose a uniform flow onto the source flow. The velocity vectors of the uniform flow are, of course, simply arrows of equal length all pointing left-to-right (in our usual convention). Now all we have to do is to go to every point of the flow in turn and work out the vector sum of the two velocity vectors at each point. Their resultant will tell us the actual velocity at that point of the combined flow which results from simply superimposing the two separate flows, and we could draw in the vector arrow at each point to scale in the appropriate direction. We have all the necessary information to do this, i.e. knowledge of the magnitude and the direction of both of the velocity components at each point, so mathematically there is nothing to prevent us from going ahead – except that it would be a simply massive task!

Fortunately the mathematics delivers for us a convenient short cut, which is both intriguing and very instructive in the results that it produces. The set of equations resulting from potential flow analysis of every set of streamlines (e.g. of a source, or of a uniform flow) are all the same as each other for the whole set, except for one number which is different. This number is called the *stream function*, and actually represents the amount of air flowing between the streamline in question and one particular reference streamline. But that need not concern us. All we need to know is that each streamline can be designated by a specific number, and that this number is more than merely its position in a list; it actually emerges from the mathematics.

The really delightful bit is what follows. The flow which results from superimposing the two basic flows is, of course, a flow itself, and so has its own set of streamlines with its own set of equations. Although the shapes of these streamlines are like nothing you have seen in any elementary mathematics book, yet their equations turn out to be extremely simple, since we discover that they can be obtained simply by adding together the two contributory equations. Every point in the plane is an intersection of one of the streamlines of the uniform flow and one of the streamlines of the source flow. Let us consider the situation at any one such point of intersection. If the equation of the streamline of the uniform flow which passes through this point is of the form

[Expression for all uniform flow streamlines] = [The unique number, u, of this uniform flow streamline]

and if similarly the equation of the streamline of the source flow which passes through this point is of the form

[Expression for all source flow streamlines] = [The unique number, s, of this source flow streamline]

then the equation of the streamline of the new, resulting flow which passes through this point is simply obtained by adding together the two left-hand expressions to give the left-hand side, and adding together the two right-hand numbers to give the right-hand side, so that finally we have

[Expression for all resulting flow streamlines] = $[u + s]$.

Thus at each point in the plane, the unique number (the stream function) of the new resulting flow is simply the sum of the stream functions of the two contributory streamlines which intersect there. So we can construct our new flow pattern as follows, as is illustrated in Figure 7.2. We draw a set of horizontal uniform flow streamlines and give them numbers. A convenient numbering system is to number a central line 0 and number the rest upwards positive and downwards negative from the zero line. We have chosen to draw a total of 13 lines in Figure 7.2, from −6 to 6. We then choose a point on the 0-line as the location of our source, and draw a set of radial streamlines from it and give them numbers. We have started our numbering sequence at 0 on the 3 o'clock line and have numbered the streamlines (which have been drawn at 30° intervals) anti-clockwise from there. (The reason for these choices of numbers and intervals comes partly from the mathematics and partly from experience, but need not worry us.) We now look at each point of intersection on the drawing in turn, add together the numbers of the two streamlines passing through this point and write down the answer by the point. (Small print numbers have been used in the figure.) All that remains to be done is to draw smooth curves linking all the intersection points which bear the same number, and these curves are the streamlines of the resulting flow.

We have spent some time on this first example, since it demonstrates simply and graphically what the mathematics can do for us. We have restricted ourselves to a fairly small number of streamlines in Figure 7.2 for simplicity and clarity, and so we only get a picture of the central region of the flow, but if we were to take radial lines at a smaller angular interval and correspondingly more parallel lines, we could flesh out the picture with as much more detail as we wished, especially in the regions between radial lines 5 and 7, and 11 and 1. By taking different, new basic flows and simply adding them together like this, we can pro-

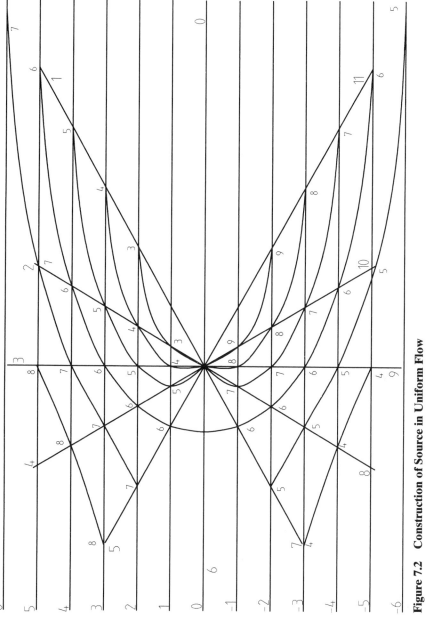

Figure 7.2   Construction of Source in Uniform Flow

duce virtually any flow pattern that we want, provided we can think up suitable new building block flows. Each flow, in addition to its form, has one or more measurable quantities related to it, (e.g. the magnitude of the velocity of the free stream flow, the flow rate emerging from the source), and by taking different quantities the scope of combining flows is expanded virtually endlessly. Before leaving this example, let us look carefully at the resulting figure, to see what it can tell us.

The free stream flow from the left is forced to spread out and divide around the source, and the flow from the source is swept away to the right. There is one streamline of the resulting flow which is of particular interest and significance, and that is streamline number 6. This is called the *dividing streamline*, because it totally divides the source flow from the free stream flow. Since no flow ever crosses a streamline, this dividing streamline acts exactly as if it were a solid body of the same shape. Its shape is called a *half-body* because it keeps getting wider and wider to the right and never closes up to form a closed body. We could dispense with the free stream and make a thin solid shell having the shape of streamline 6, and if we put a source inside the shell at the appropriate point, the resulting flow would be exactly the same as depicted by streamlines 3, 4, 5, 7, 8 and 9. But alternatively, and this is far more useful, we could put our thin half-body shell into a uniform free stream, and the flow would divide around it in exactly the same way as is shown by streamlines 4, 5, 7 and 8 (which have unfortunately been foreshortened owing to the frugal number of streamlines used to generate the flow).

The equation of the dividing streamline is thus the same as the equation of a surface of the same shape, a half-body. But it is even better than that for our purposes, since this equation does not *only* denote the half-body. It also denotes the two streamlines which form it, both that of the uniform flow which goes undisturbed from left to right and meets the front centre of the shape, and also that of the streamline which flows from the source in the 9 o'clock direction and strikes the front point of the shape from the inside.

The point where these two streamlines meet, the front point of the half-body, is a stagnation point, where as we have seen before the air velocity is zero. This arises naturally in the combined flow, since there must be a point at which the decelerating 9 o'clock direction source flow will have the same speed as the uniform 3 o'clock direction main stream flow[1], so that the resultant of the two flows is zero.

---

[1]The speed of a source flow as it leaves the source itself is infinity, and it reduces towards zero as its distance from the source approaches infinity. Thus at some point the speed must have every value between infinity and zero.

We have thus produced some sort of body with a flow pattern round it, a stagnation point as occurs in real flow and equations for all the streamlines, including most particularly an equation for the dividing streamline which is the same as that of the body. By combining this equation with the Bernoulli equation, it will be possible to discover the pressure distribution and thus to find the drag on the half-body. (Clearly d'Alembert's Paradox does not apply in this case, even though the flow is inviscid, because the body is not closed up at the rear and so has no rear stagnation point.)

Let us now develop these ideas, more briefly, in order to generate other shapes. The most obvious thing to look for first of all is a way to close the half-body up, and this can be done by introducing the idea of a *sink*, or a negative source. This is simply an imaginary plug-hole in the plane which swallows up air and behaves in exactly the opposite way from a source. Everything about it is identical, except that all the velocities are the negative of what they were in the source. If we place a sink in our left-to-right uniform flow of exactly the same *strength* as our source, (i.e. it swallows air at exactly the same rate as the source produces it,) the pattern that we get will be exactly the same as Figure 7.2, but reversed left-to-right. Now, if we were to place the sink to the right of the source in Figure 7.2 and then add together the *three* flow patterns in exactly the same way as we earlier added two, we would in fact find as we might reasonably expect that the sink would neatly swallow up all the air from the source, that the dividing streamline of the source flow would merge exactly into the reversed dividing streamline of the sink flow, and that a new rear stagnation point would occur to the right of the sink. We have succeeded in generating a closed oval body with our dividing streamline, which is doubly symmetrical, as shown in Figure 7.3.

Provided the sum of their strengths is zero (taking sinks as negative), many closed shapes can be created by arranging different combinations of sources and sinks along the horizontal axis, a principle developed by Rankine after whom the oval is named. William Rankine was a nineteenth century Scottish engineer and physicist whose main claim to fame was as one of the founders of the science of thermodynamics. But he was a very versatile engineering scientist, as demonstrated by his other major original contributions in fields as diverse as metal fatigue, soil mechanics and earth stability, propellers, streamlines and the lines of ships. Using the above method of combining sources and sinks, he devised a procedure for developing the contours of ships' hulls.

The similarity of the Rankine oval with the circular cylinder that we would like to be able to generate is striking, and it would seem a reasonable guess that, if we brought the source and sink closer together,

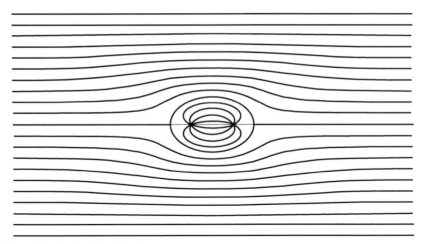

Figure 7.3 A Rankine Oval

the oval would get nearer to being a circle. This is in fact the case, but to get a true circle the source and sink would have to come right together into one point. There is a snag here: If a source and sink of equal strength are superimposed on top of each other, then obviously the sink will totally swallow up all the fluid being produced by the source, and there will be no flow pattern at all!

As ever, our ingenious mathematicians will not be beaten by mere trifles, and they come up with an improbable sounding solution which works a treat. They simply insist that the *strength* (i.e. the flow rate) of the source and sink (which are numerically equal to each other) should be continually increased whilst the distance between source and sink is being reduced, so that the product of flow rate and separation distance remains constant. Of course, this means that, when the source and sink eventually meet, the distance has shrunk to zero, and so the strength of each is required to have reached infinity. Not only does this not seem at all practical (which, we must remember, does not matter for a mathematical model), but it even sounds tricky mathematically. However, by a process of taking limits (i.e. observing how things are settling down as these limiting values of zero and infinity are being approached,) it can be made to work, and we obtain a Rankine oval which has become squeezed into a pure circle.

The converged source-sink pair, each member having infinite strength, is called a *doublet*. In passing, there is another intriguing feature of a doublet which is worth noting. We were always taught at school that, to define a straight line, you must specify any *two* points on the line. If you only know one point on the line, there is an infinite number of possible lines that you could draw through it. Now our doublet is undoubtedly one point, since the two points forming it have closed right in on each other until the distance between them is zero. But yet it has a direction of its own! Only if the source and sink approached each other parallel to the free stream flow do they create the desired flow pattern. If a source and sink are placed one above the other (in the drawing), normal to the free stream, the flow pattern produced is something totally different (and uninteresting), and if they are brought together from that orientation they do not create a circular dividing streamline. Thus a doublet is a most unusual phenomenon; it is a single point with a direction!

LIFT IN INVISCID FLOW

We have now demonstrated that we can represent our circular cylinder flow purely mathematically, but we still only have the symmetrical pressure distribution, 'no lift, no drag' model that we came up with at the end of Chapter 5. It would appear unlikely that real flow around a cylinder could ever produce lift, and so the following question might at the moment appear academic. Nevertheless, let us now ask ourselves whether there is any *mathematical* way in which we could make our cylinder model become a lifting model, regardless of whether such a thing is practically possible or not.

Looking back at the cylinder pressure distribution of Figure 5.10, we see that what is needed to produce lift (if for convenience we assume that we want to produce lift towards the top of the page) is further to reduce the pressure on the top surface (longer arrows, $C_p < -3$, i.e. larger numerically but negative) and/or to create less reduction of pressure on the bottom surface (shorter outward arrows, $C_p > -3$, i.e. smaller numerically, still negative; or inward-pointing arrows, C_p positive). In other words, we would like a pressure distribution rather like Figure 7.4.

One of the most tricky things about getting scientific and mathematical things right is not so much in finding numerical answers but in determining whether they are positive or negative (which often means which direction they act in), and whether changes in value are increases or decreases. The difficulty becomes even greater when we start talking about increases or decreases in quantities which are already negative, such as the pressure in a suction region, as the English language tends to become a little ambiguous. Some accelerations (such as gravitational and centripetal acceleration) compound the difficulty by naturally occurring in the direction which, intuitively, one would normally think of as negative, such as inwards or downwards. I believe that many people's aversion to mathematics stems partly from a subconscious feeling that, if I find simple plusses and minuses difficult, then I've got no chance at all when it comes on to real numbers! Such

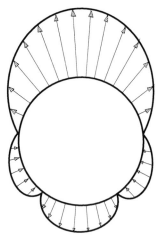

Figure 7.4   Circular Cylinder Pressure Distribution to Produce Lift

people should reflect on the fact that even the most sophisticated computers in the world work entirely by discriminating between two values, usually one and nought but it could equally well be plus or minus something. By doing nothing else but masses and masses of such discriminations in an ordered way, they can perform phenomenal feats of calculation. Understanding and handling positive and negative quantities properly is no puerile or trivial exercise, but is the essence of good mathematics, and so it is important to master it. Watch the use of the vocabulary very carefully, noting words which imply a negative such as 'suction'; remember that increasing a negative number means moving towards zero at first, i.e. into numerically smaller negative numbers, until you get to 0; and finally bear in mind the principle that a double negative (or an even number of negatives) affecting each other produces a positive outcome, and a single, triple or odd number of negatives produces a negative outcome. If in doubt about an ambiguity such as 'a retardation of –10 metres per second squared', you should enquire before making assumptions, because, as in this example, it may well be the author and not you who is at fault. (The acceleration in this example is almost certainly meant to be a retardation of 10 ms^{-2} or an acceleration of -10 ms^{-2}, and it is an incorrect use of a double negative.)

So how do we set about producing more suction on the top surface and less suction on the lower surface? By Bernoulli's Principle, more suction means more speed (and vice versa), and so we want to speed up the flow over the upper surface, and slow it down over the lower surface. Assuming that the free stream flow is from left to right, (and the flow direction does become significant now, even though the flow is inviscid), then there is already a left-to-right flow in both of these regions. What we would like to do is to superimpose on this flow an additional circular clockwise flow (centred on the centre of the cylinder) which we could perhaps do by stirring with a spoon or a paddle. Then above the cylinder we would have the vector sum of two velocities acting in the same direction, which would reinforce each other, and underneath we would have the vector sum of two velocities acting in opposite directions, so that the new, superimposed velocity would subtract from the left-to-right velocity, leaving a reduced resultant from left to right. (There is a case when the superimposed, right-to-left, component is actually greater than the initial left-to-right component, in which case the resultant velocity is actually reversed, but this does not often occur and we can safely ignore it for our purposes.)

The mathematicians quickly latch on to this concept and come up with a suitable mathematical model of the flow with extremely simple mathematics, as simple as that of the source. The model is called a *free vortex*, and consists simply of streamlines which are circles going round a central point, with no addition of new air into the flow. We saw earlier that a source's speed at any radius is inversely proportional to the radius, so that the product of speed and radius is constant. No relationship could be simpler than this, and conveniently an exactly similar inverse proportional relationship (Vr = constant) emerges for the speed of the vortex flow. This derives from an analysis of the pressure forces causing the centripetal acceleration of an element of air going around between two streamlines.

Since this relationship is derived (as briefly described above) on the basis of physical principles of fluid dynamics, all of which we have already met in this book, it will not come as a surprise to learn that the mathematical flow we have created closely matches fluid flows that occur naturally, such as in meteorological depressions (low pressure regions of the atmosphere) and in the water going down the plug-hole of a bath. However, there is one major difference, and that is in the region at the centre, where $r = 0$. Mathematically, the speed of flow would have to increase at the centre to infinity, in order to maintain a constant product of speed and radius. However, nature abhors infinity and always finds ways of avoiding it. In this case, what actually happens is that the flow speed in a naturally occurring free vortex (such as a tornado) can actually rise to an extremely high but finite speed, before the flow pattern breaks down and follows different rules. In the case of a liquid with a free surface such as water in the bath, the high centripetal force near the centre causes the water to be thrown outwards, leaving that characteristic funnel-shaped hole down the middle. In air, which has no free surface, what happens is that a small core region behaves according to a completely different rotational law. The streamlines are still concentric circles, but the speed is now *directly*, rather than inversely, proportional to the radius. This is in some ways a more natural sort of flow to understand, since it is synonymous with a solid rotating object like the turntable of a record player or a car wheel, but it is not the natural way for fluids to behave except in this exceptional core region.

We now have all the building blocks which we need to build, by superimposing flows, a flow satisfying our initial requirements: a uniform flow from left to right simulating our free stream airflow; a doublet (composed of a source and sink which have merged along a line parallel to the uniform flow) creating a dividing streamline in the form of a circular cylinder along with the airflow outside it, and now finally a free vortex which hopefully will do what we wanted and will speed up the top surface flow and slow down the bottom surface flow. We place the free vortex concentrically with the doublet and hence with the cylinder, and ignore the flow effect on the inside of the cylindrical dividing streamline. The velocity distributions of all of these flows are known to us (and are simple), and so it would be possible for us to work out all the contributory velocity vectors at any point, add them all together vectorially, and come up with the resultant velocity vector at that point; repeating the process for every point would give us the entire velocity distribution. But just as with the source in the uniform flow, this would be excessively tedious and it is much easier to express all the streamlines in terms of their stream functions (their identifying numbers), add all the streamline numbers at each point, and join the dots with corresponding totals as we did before. This exercise results in a flow pattern that looks like Figure 7.5.

So we have managed to create the desired effect on paper by dint of a few mathematical tricks. Although the flow direction and the vortex rotational direction were significant in producing the low pressure region above, rather than below, the cylinder and hence lift up the page, yet we have deliberately omitted any direction arrows so that it will be clear from the figure that we still have total left-right symmetry, and hence no drag at all in accordance with d'Alembert's Paradox. But we have managed, at least theoretically, to produce lift in a totally inviscid fluid flow.

CYLINDER LIFT IN REAL FLOW

The question now arises, is there any real flow equivalent to this rather idealistic concept? In other words, could we really produce a lift force on a physical circular cylinder in a uniform air flow? On the face of it, we might say 'yes, by spinning the cylinder clockwise', but if the fluid has no viscosity as the derivation assumes, there would be no adhesion between the cylinder and the fluid, and so the process of

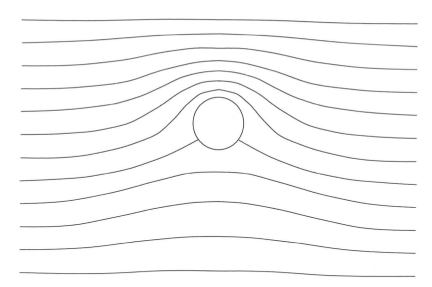

Figure 7.5   Vortex Flow Around a Circular Cylinder

spinning of the cylinder would be totally 'invisible' to the airflow, and would have no effect whatsoever. However in practice air *does* have viscosity, and so if we were to spin a real cylinder in a real flow, then it would pull the fluid around with it at least to some extent by means of the effect of the viscosity at the surface and in the boundary layer. This is called the Magnus Effect, after the nineteenth century German physicist and chemist who first observed and explained it. Surprisingly large amounts of lift can be produced in this way, giving rise to a number of interesting past and present practical examples, which are worth looking at.

This phenomenon of a circulating flow occurring around the cylinder is given the technical name of *circulation*. As we will see, there are a number of ways in which circulation can be produced, and however this is done circulation will always result in a lift force on the cylinder. Consequently, the concept of circulation is central to the production of lift, and so we will meet the term many times. Later in this chapter a section is given over to dealing with circulation in more depth, including its precise definition, but for the time being a general feel for the concept will suffice.

Around 1922 a German engineer Anton Flettner was inspired through work being done on rotating cylinders at Göttingen University. Although originally intending to construct ships with metal sails, he instead built a rotor ship, a vessel utilizing revolving cylinders for auxiliary power. The front and rear masts of the *Buckau*, a three-masted 960 ton displacement schooner, were replaced by shorter (42 feet high) stronger masts with bearings at the top and bottom to support vertical cylinders having approximately 9 feet diameters. To ensure that the cylinders operated as nearly to two-dimensionally as possible, the end effects were minimised by placing discs (of larger diameter than the cylinders) as top and bottom end caps on the cylinders. Spun by motors of 9 horse-power, the cylinders could spin at about 125 revolutions per minute, resulting in a speed of 60 feet per second at the periphery. This arrangement was found to produce 9 to 10 times the effect of an equivalent sized conventional sail. Sadly for posterity, although sea tests were said to have been successful, little was heard of the subject thereafter, but it seems that maintenance of the rotor machinery was the chief problem.

Exactly the same Magnus Effect principle applies to rotating spheres as to rotating cylinders. The actual mathematics would have to be modified, but yet the flow on a section taken through the centre of a spinning sphere parallel to the airflow would look much the same as Figure 7.5. This gives rise to the various effects created by spinning the ball in a number of ball games such as tennis, golf, cricket and football. The combination of the spin imparted by the player and the airflow over the ball resulting from its flight through the air will give rise to a force normal to the direction of motion. Depending on the direction of spin, a downwards force can be used to force a tennis or table-tennis ball sharply down onto the surface after crossing the net, an upwards force to keep a golf ball or football aloft for a longer flight, and left or right forces to make a ball veer in the air, such as when taking a corner-kick in football, or when wishing to cause the cricket ball to approach the batsman from an unexpected angle. Sometimes, as in the case of a hooked or sliced golf ball, the effect may be undesirable. This subject is excellently developed in C. B. Daish's book *The Physics of Ball Games*, published by Hodder and Stoughton, and you are now wise enough to see beyond his implication that the direction of the wake behind a ball determines its direction of flight. Finally, if you are familiar with the seam-bowler's technique in cricket and are wondering why it has not been mentioned either here or in the previous chapter on the boundary layer, do not fret, as this rather special technique will be covered at the end of Chapter 8 where it more naturally fits.

One notable application of the Magnus Effect in today's technology appears in the McDonnell Douglas 'NOTAR' helicopter. Traditionally, the side force required to prevent the fuselage of a single main rotor helicopter from spinning round in the opposite direction from the rotors (which is called the torque reaction) is provided by a sideways-mounted tail rotor, but this is not only a serious safety hazard when on the ground but is also inherently fairly wasteful of energy. The NOTAR helicopter, whose name stands for NO TAil Rotor, provides this side force by having a much thicker than normal cylindrical tail boom and no tail rotor. By using the downwash of the main rotor over it, combined with a circulating flow around it, a side force is produced which provides the needed torque reaction. However, the tail boom does not spin about its axis – there would be little advantage in this over having a rotating tail rotor – but the air is forced to circulate around the cylinder by means of jets of air squirting tangentially out from inside the cylinder, through slots parallel to the axis of the cylinder. This speeds up the flow on the side where the lower pressure is required, resulting in a flow pattern and force as shown in Figure 7.6. This principle is discussed again under the heading 'Boundary Layer Control' in Chapter 9.

On a conventional tail-rotor helicopter, directional control (i.e. 'yawing', or making the aircraft rotate about a vertical axis through its centre of gravity), is provided by varying the amount of side force that the tail rotor produces. In the case of the NOTAR, this system is replaced by opening left-pointing or right-pointing air jets in the tip of the tail cylinder, which has the same effect. Of course, all this air blowing requires quite a bit of power from the helicopter's main engine to compress the air in the tail boom, but on the other hand there is now no tail rotor to have to drive round.

So we appear to have struck on a rather good device for creating lift, a circular cylinder in a uniform airflow, with some means of super-

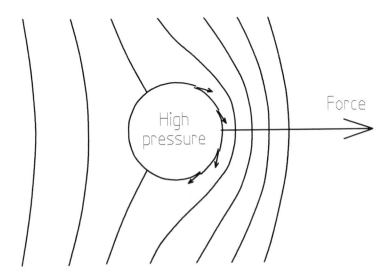

Figure 7.6   Magnus Effect on NOTAR Helicopter

imposing a rotational flow around it such as spinning it or squirting air jets. Could we use this device to produce the required lift to keep an aeroplane up in the air and to manoeuvre it? Presumably it would be possible to attach a pair of cylinders, sticking out on the two sides of a fuselage like wings; and furthermore one could either spin them round or supply them with compressed air for tangential jets, using some power source in the fuselage. Would this be a good idea?

Not really! Apart from the weight and constructional complication, and of course the form drag (which is not eliminated by the rotating air flow), we must remember that we also need a uniform flow for the method to work. Flettner's cylinders used the wind blowing sideways across the deck of the ship, the NOTAR helicopter uses the down-wash of the main rotors, and on our aircraft we will have to have an airflow from front to rear over the aircraft, which means that we still have to provide power to propel the aircraft forwards and overcome drag. We will shortly see that the suggestion of spinning cylinder wings is not as daft as it sounds, since this is exactly the idea on which the theory of wing lift is based. In practice, conceivably it would be possible – but let us see if we can find a better way forward.

The lifting flow pattern of Figure 7.5 can be produced on a real cylinder in a real fluid, as we have seen, by spinning the cylinder or by squirting air under pressure into the airflow at the right place in the right direction. Each of these methods requires the input of energy, as well as the design and manufacture of a relatively elaborate mechanical system with moving parts. Could the job be done passively, by simply modifying the cylinder in some way, with no compressors or moving parts or addition of power? Perhaps we could add a deflector to the flow either in front of the cylinder or behind it or both, to make the flow behave as required? Let us try adding a 'splitter plate', firstly in front of the cylinder at the position of the desired stagnation point, and secondly at the rear desired stagnation point.

This experiment reveals that a splitter plate at the front does not work at all well. What happens is that the flow is not significantly deflected in front of the splitter plate, but that the flow totally separates over the sharp front edge of the splitter plate. (We will look more closely at exactly what we mean by separation over a sharp corner like this a little later on.) Consequently we get a rather mucky flow with little if any sign of the effect we were looking for. However, when we place the splitter plate at the rear stagnation point, it actually does have very nearly the desired effect of producing rotational flow around the cylinder, as illustrated in the right-hand drawing of Figure 7.7. This figure is idealised to make a point, whereas in fact the flow will not be nearly as clean and inviscid-looking, but will have some boundary layer separation and some small regions of turbulence

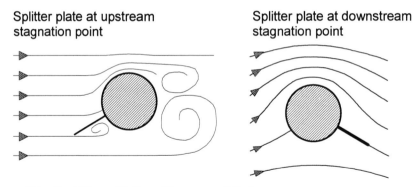

Splitter plate at upstream
stagnation point

Splitter plate at downstream
stagnation point

Figure 7.7   The Effect of Splitter Plates on a Cylinder

behind the cylinder. But even if not perfect, the idea of a splitter plate *behind* the cylinder does seem to work, giving us the inspiration that perhaps we would be able to produce a shape providing lift without having to use complicated contraptions.

So it seems to be the downstream end of our object which produces lift, just as earlier we saw that it was the downstream part of an object which was mainly responsible for drag. The main problem of the cylinder with a splitter plate at the rear is that there are still regions of separation and consequently lots of drag. Now that our cylinder does not have to rotate, (in fact we have ruled that out of the question by the addition of the splitter plate), we are no longer constrained to its circular form, and so we may consider whether we could modify the shape so that it would still force the airflow downwards behind it like the rear splitter plate, but would not have so much form drag. We need something that is pointed sharply at the rear, but nicely rounded at the front, whose surface gently curves in the region downstream of the widest (minimum pressure) point in order to keep the adverse pressure gradient to a minimum and thus to delay separation as long as possible. We might finish up with a progression something like the shapes in Figure 7.8.

Now the last of these figures is what we earlier called a streamline shape, because it is a good shape for minimising adverse pressure gradients and delaying boundary layer separation to almost the trailing edge. Therefore, provided that it is not so long that skin friction becomes excessive, it is a low drag shape. But by pointing it downwards at the rear like this, we find that it is also capable of generating the rotational flow pattern onto the uniform flow passing over it, and so of generating lift.

What we have evolved is the familiar shape of an aerofoil, although you may be surprised to notice that the shape we have here is symmet-

Figure 7.8   Development of the Aerofoil Shape

rical about a line from its trailing edge (which for our present purposes we will define as the point furthest from its trailing edge) to its trailing edge. We have not bent or *cambered* it at all (i.e. made the top surface curvature greater than the bottom surface curvature), in the way that is usually depicted in figures accompanying explanations such as that which we met at the beginning of the chapter. This is important. An aerofoil *may* be cambered, but it doesn't need to be. The crucial feature that gives an aerofoil lift is that it has a *sharp trailing edge* pointing *rearwards and downwards* if the free stream flow is horizontal and lift is to be generated upwards. An alternative way of thinking of an aerofoil is as if it were a nozzle deflecting a backwards airflow downwards from the aircraft, and receiving an opposite reaction (just like a fireman does when he holds a fire hose) which has a component upwards, which is the aerofoil's lift. We met this idea briefly before, towards the end of the section on Coefficient of Lift in Chapter 3.

THE NEED FOR VISCOSITY

Before we move on to examine in more detail how real aerofoils work and how they can be analysed, we must back-track a little and tackle some rather subtle questions which we may have overlooked. At the very end of our inviscid work in Chapter 5 we mentioned that the rigorous mathematical treatment which gave rise to d'Alembert's paradox could be extended to literally *any* cross-sectional shape in place of the circular cylinder, leading to exactly the same conclusion of 'no lift, no drag'. If the theory as we have presented it is applied to our aerofoil set at an angle to a uniform free flow – or rather, if we generate the shape of the aerofoil in the flow by some complicated arrangement of sources and sinks – and if we do not superimpose any rotational flow by means of the free vortex model, then the resulting streamline pattern which emerges looks like Figure 7.9.

As with the cylinder, there is a front and a rear stagnation point, and there is no overall deflection of the flow. Our eye is immediately caught by what appears to be going on near to the trailing edge. The potential flow theory as so far presented does indeed show the flow to behave like this, flowing up and round the very sharp corner of the trailing edge towards the stagnation point, rather as (less surprisingly)

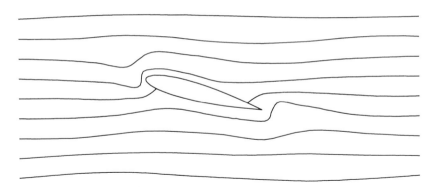

Figure 7.9   Inviscid Flow around an Aerofoil Shape

it does at the leading edge. But we feel that the theory is letting us down here, since the flow would be expected to flow straight off the trailing edge, and we would expect an overall downwards deflection in the flow, corresponding to a lift force on the aerofoil. This enigma merits some further investigation.

We recall how the potential flow method determines for us the equations of the set of streamlines that will occur around whatever object has been modelled in the flow. As we did with the cylinder, and also as has been done in Figure 7.9, we can get a good enough idea of the shape of the streamlines to be able to sketch them just by intuitively looking at where the flow has to go through narrow and wide passages and round sharp or gentle bends, and a reasonable approximation to the mathematically produced shape may be obtained. From either approach, we find that through narrow passages and round sharp bends the streamlines come close together, which implies a higher than free stream speed and a lower than free stream pressure.

At the leading edge, we have a very tight corner, which means that the streamlines come very close together, the speed is greatly increased, and the pressure greatly reduced, but only for a very short distance since the tightly curving leading edge region does not last for long. This short stretch of high speed low pressure flow then has to recover very quickly indeed back to a much lower speed, and consequent increased pressure, in an extremely short distance, which means that the flow is faced with an intense *adverse pressure gradient*. As we have seen, this would be of no concern in a totally inviscid flow since there is always just enough kinetic energy in the flow to allow it to recover the required pressure energy as it slows down; but all real fluids have some viscosity and thus a boundary layer, and this adverse pressure gradient is very liable to cause the boundary layer to separate. Real air, even though its viscosity is very low, still has a boundary

layer and hence cannot cope with the sudden retardation that is needed behind too tight a curve, and so there is a very strong tendency for
the flow to separate at this point. We will be looking at this so-called
leading edge separation or leading edge stall in Chapter 9, since it has
very important practical implications in wing and aeroplane design.

Let us now turn our attention to the trailing edge. Figure 7.9 shows
the flow smoothly flowing around the trailing edge towards a stagnation point on the upper surface which, as far as the pressure distribution is concerned, matches with the one below the leading edge. But
to get there the flow has had to negotiate the trailing edge, where the
streamlines are very tightly packed together, (as would have been
seen if many more of them had been drawn,) and the speed is consequently very high and the pressure is very low, just as we had at the
leading edge – only much, much more so now, since the sharpness of
the turn is now much greater. The sharpness of a turn is usually
referred to in terms of its radius of curvature, since this is precisely
quantifiable whereas 'sharpness' is rather vague. If the top and bottom
surfaces of the aerofoil meet as if they were two straight lines, then
the turn is razor-sharp and the radius of curvature is effectively zero.
In practice trailing edge radii may be of the order of one or two millimetres. But either way, the high speed, low pressure effect discussed
in the previous paragraph as occurring at the leading edge pales into
insignificance in comparison with what we would have now.
Consequently the adverse pressure gradient on leaving the sharp trailing edge is more of a pressure *step*, and no real flow could ever stay
attached around such a tight turn. This is why, for example, the leading edge splitter plate in Figure 7.7 would not work at all. The conclusion is that, in a real flow, we always get total separation at any sharp
corner of an object, including the trailing edge of an aerofoil.

… Well, not *quite* always. We have said that in aerodynamics we
only study steady flow conditions, but in the present context there is
one important exception to this statement. Rather than considering
our aerofoil to be immersed in a steady fluid flow as if it had been
experiencing this flow from the beginning of time, let us consider what
actually happens in practice when the flow initially starts. The aerofoil
of Figure 7.9, set at the same angle, is initially immersed in stationary
air and so there are as yet no streamlines. Either by moving the aerofoil through the still air (as in the case of an aeroplane beginning to
move on a runway), or by starting to blow the air over the fixed aerofoil (as if in a wind-tunnel,) the free stream speed starts to increase
from a speed of zero. Just for a split second the flow speed is exceedingly slow, scarcely more than zero. Let us zoom in to the region of
the flow very close to the trailing edge, and think about what is going
on here. If, as the potential flow method says, the flow were to flow

round the corner as shown in Figure 7.9, then a particle of air flowing around this corner is negotiating an extremely tight turn. Back in Chapter 2 we saw that, if an object is moving in a circular path, it has an acceleration towards the centre of the circle, and that this acceleration has to be produced by a force towards the centre (called the centripetal force). Although we had no need to quantify the acceleration at that juncture, it is instructive here to note that the acceleration towards the centre of the circle is given by the formula V^2/r, and so by Newton's Second Law the centripetal force on an element of mass m is mV^2/r where V is the tangential speed (in our case the speed along the streamline) and r is the radius of the curve, (in the present case the radius of curvature of the trailing edge). This centripetal force mV^2/r which is required to get the particle of air around the corner can only be provided by a pressure force from the air in streampaths further out – it could not be provided by viscous forces since these would be tangential to the flow.

At the trailing edge, the value of r is extremely small, and since r appears on the bottom of the formula for centripetal force, other factors being unchanged, the centripetal force required will tend to be extremely large. In normal flow conditions this large centripetal force is unavailable, and the flow does not manage to negotiate the corner but separates as we have already seen. But what happens as the flow starts from zero speed? For a brief moment, V is also very small, and so V^2 is even smaller.[2] Thus although the bottom of the formula for centripetal acceleration is very small, so (at least very briefly) is the top, and consequently the actual overall centripetal force can briefly be a reasonable value, and the surrounding pressure can be sufficient to satisfy this requirement and make the particle of air negotiate the tight bend. Thus, at the moment when the relative flow starts from rest, Figure 7.9 may in fact be a physical possibility, even with a real fluid with viscosity.

Careful experiments using cameras in laboratory-controlled conditions show that this actually is what happens around an aerofoil when

[2]It may surprise you that the square of a small number is even smaller, but try it out with any number less than 1: $(0.01)^2$ equals 0.0001 which is smaller, whereas 10^2 (a number greater than 1, squared) equals 100 which is larger. Sometimes this can be confusing. Consider a square of side 0.5 of a metre. Its area is $(0.5)^2$ or 0.25, which is smaller since 0.5 is less than 1. But if we express the square's dimensions in centimetres, the area is a bigger number than the length of the side: $(50)^2 = 2500$. What has gone wrong? The area can't be both smaller and bigger! No, the trouble is that we are trying to compare lengths with areas. We cannot say that an *area* of a certain size is bigger or smaller than a *length* of a certain size, as that is meaningless. The rule only works for numbers without units attached to them. But the resulting area is the same size, although expressed differently, by whichever route it is reached.

the flow starts from rest, but the situation doesn't last for more than a split second. Very rapidly the stagnation point moves rearwards from its starting point until the flow separates totally from the sharp trailing edge as already discussed, and as shown in Figure 7.10. But interestingly this is not quite all that happens. As the flow changes from the initial condition to the steady condition, a clockwise circulatory flow is being generated around the aerofoil as we have already seen. As a 'reaction' to this, another vortex, a swirl of air rotating in the opposite direction, is actually shed from the trailing edge of the aerofoil and is carried off downstream with the current, never to be considered again. This vortex is shown in Figure 7.10 and is referred to quite naturally as a *starting vortex*, and we will have occasion to refer to it again in Chapter 12 when discussing the drag of real wings which are not two-dimensional.

So it would appear that we have now succeeded in arriving at a suitable shape for an aerofoil, an object which is capable of producing a large aerodynamic force (lift) normal to the free stream flow direction whilst only producing a small force (drag) parallel to the free stream flow. But it only works, producing the lifting flow pattern of streamlines that we require, because the flow separates cleanly at the trailing edge; this only happens because of boundary layer separation; and the existence of a boundary layer presupposes the existence of viscosity. Thus we arrive at the very remarkable conclusion, not only that no drag could occur without viscosity, but also that no lift could be produced without viscosity. In other words,

Viscosity is essential for the production of any aerodynamic force whatsoever.

This raises an interesting field of speculation which you might find entertaining to think about, and to discuss with friends over a drink: what sort of a world would this be if air had no viscosity? Or, extending this further, if all fluids had no viscosity?

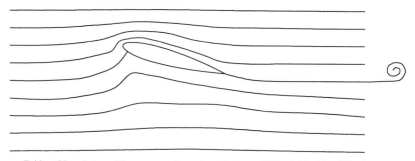

Figure 7.10 Circulatory Flow around an Aerofoil, and Shed-Starting Vortex

Although Figure 7.10 looks superficially like a potential flow diagram, with neat attached flow everywhere, we must remember that actually it is not: it is a modification of the potential flow solution that was illustrated in Figure 7.9, where the air flows round the trailing edge to a stagnation point on the top surface. So once again our mathematical model has failed to live up to our requirements of predicting lift forces and analysing the lift of aerofoils, even though it has got us very near to it. Undoubtedly Figure 7.10, a real flow diagram, is very much closer to Figure 7.9, an inviscid flow diagram, than the real separated flow around a cylinder is to the ideal flow depicted in Figure 5.8. This makes us wonder whether the mathematician might not once again be able to come up trumps and produce some trick to bridge the gap. In fact a mathematician named Kutta has done exactly this; but before we can finish the story, we must introduce another new concept, that of circulation.

CIRCULATION

We have talked a lot about the lifting effect of superimposing a rotating or swirling flow around our object, be it cylinder or aerofoil, and have shown that it can be conveniently mathematically modelled by means of a free vortex. Although the need for varying and hence measuring the strength of this vortex is obvious, we have so far avoided considering how this may be done. But if we are going to be able to make use of the mathematical model in our further discussion, it is essential that we now remedy this omission and consider how to measure and quantify the strength of the rotating flow around a lifting body.

Returning to the free vortex of earlier, we recall that Vr is constant: let us say $Vr = k$. Thus k is a measure of the strength of the vortex. (At a fixed radius, a larger value of k implies a larger vortex speed.) However, the mathematicians do not in fact find this value k the most convenient, but prefer to define a new quantity which is closely related to k, is called *circulation* and is usually given the symbol Γ, the Greek capital letter gamma.

The basic definition of circulation is somewhat abstruse, but it will quickly make sense when we have applied it a couple of times. To evaluate the circulation around any body, start by drawing *any* closed loop completely enclosing the body. It could be a circle, or a rectangle, or a free-hand shape. Cut it up into lots of little lengths and approximate each of them to a straight line. Then evaluate the velocity vector (both magnitude and direction) of the flow at the middle of each of these line segments, and calculate the component of this velocity in the direction of the little straight line element, (i.e. tangential to the loop,) going clockwise around the loop. (Some books may choose anticlockwise instead – just be consistent.) For each segment multiply the magnitude of the velocity component by the length of the little line segment. Add all the answers for all of the line segments. Provided that the line segments have been taken small enough so that treating them as straight lines gives a reasonable approximation to the closed loop, the answer will be the circulation Γ around the shape. Each term, and hence the total circulation, is the product of a speed and a distance, and hence it is a purely kinematic quantity which does not relate to the mechanics (i.e. forces) of the system.[3]

Let us apply this idea to free vortex flow. The easiest choice of closed loop will be any circular streamline of the flow. The loop *happens* to be a streamline, but bear in mind that there is no need for the loop to be a streamline – it could equally well have been an equilateral triangle if that would have been more convenient. But being a streamline, it means that the velocity of the flow at any point on it is also the velocity in the direction of the tangent, which is what we require, so that we will not in this case have to resolve the vector to find the appropriate component. At each point on the loop the tangential velocity is in fact V. Now since V is the same all the way round, the sum of all the terms $V \times$ [element length] is the same as $V \times$ [circumference], and if the radius is r the circumference is $2\pi r$. This gives us the circulation:

$$\Gamma = V \times 2\pi r$$

We have already said that $Vr = k$, and so we conclude that k and Γ are related by the formula $k = \Gamma/2\pi$, and thus the circulation around a vortex is directly related to its strength. If we had chosen, say, a square loop, we could still have evaluated the circulation by adding together lots of little products of velocity and length, but each element would have involved a considerable amount of work, and the answer would only have been approximate.

Notice that it did not matter *which* circular streamline we took for the calculation of circulation: the answer was always going to be the same, since Vr is constant. Furthermore, if the vortex is superimposed onto a doublet in a uniform flow, the result will still be exactly the same, since the doublet and the uniform flow on their own have no lift and hence no circulation. In this case we can conveniently use the surface of the cylinder itself as the closed loop, and so the velocity on this

---

[3]For the benefit of readers with a knowledge of Calculus, the mathematical definition of circulation is $\Gamma = \oint v \cos \theta \, ds$, integration being carried around the closed loop C, where θ is the angle between the flow velocity vector and C at that point and s is the distance round the closed loop.

surface is the velocity of the dividing streamline in the potential flow model, or the actual speed of the periphery in the case of a spinning cylinder such as Flettner's cylinders.

KUTTA CONDITION

At the turn of the century and the early days of the era of flight, there was so much enthusiasm and powerful motivation to establish a sound scientific and mathematical basis for the aerodynamics of flight, that a number of completely independent people were working to solve the same problems at the same time. Three of them (Frederick Lanchester in England, Wilhelm Kutta in Germany and Nikolai Joukowski in Russia) simultaneously came up with substantially the same answer to explaining lift by means of the concept of circulation, and their names along with others are closely intertwined with the development of the subject. One particularly important break-through was attributed to Kutta, and was named the Kutta Condition.

The problem to be solved is this: potential flow theory applied without adding circulation to an aerofoil shape produces a flow pattern like that of Figure 7.9, which in normal conditions is unrealistic and not very helpful. A real flow over an aerofoil looks much more like Figure 7.10, and nature takes good care to ensure that the flow does indeed separate at exactly the sharp trailing edge and nowhere else, for the reasons that we have discussed. We know how to model mathematically the pattern of Figure 7.10 – we simply superimpose a vortex onto the flow and hence add circulation to the flow; but the question remains as to exactly how much circulation is needed to be added to the flow in order that the flow will stream off exactly at the trailing edge and will not merely form a new stagnation point somewhere else on the surface. The Kutta condition applies a delightfully obvious and commonsense answer to this question: it says that, just as nature adds exactly the right amount of circulation to ensure separation at the trailing edge, so mathematically the determining factor must be exactly the same. The potential flow mathematical model was thereupon enhanced so that it incorporated exactly the right amount of circulation to ensure that separation took place at the one *singularity* that was allowed on the surface of the object, that singularity simply being the mathematician's name for the sharp trailing edge.

So the mathematicians have succeeded in modelling the lifting flow of an aerofoil, a well streamlined object with a sharp trailing edge. To do this they must model the actual form of the aerofoil itself and the streamlines of the flow round it, by suitable use of the source and sink building blocks in a uniform flow, and then add a vortex for circulation. But it seems now that the idea of circulation provides such a powerful model of the flow system round an aerofoil, that maybe the model is more than merely an allegory or parallel of the flow, maybe it actually provides a scientific physical description of what is really happening. To explain the rather subtle difference, compare the ideas of a source and a free vortex. A source is a nice mathematical idea, but it can't exist naturally in the real world. A free vortex, however, is equally neat mathematically, but its mathematical derivation is actually based on the principles of science and how the real world behaves, rather than how we might like it to behave for our convenience. If you want to make a source work, firstly you must totally contravene the principle of conservation of matter and the continuity equation in order to provide a steady supply of fluid from nowhere. Secondly, the pressure difference between centre and outside needed to cause the radial flow would in fact tend to produce not a radial flow but a swirling flow, rather like the wind flow *along*, rather than *across* the isobars of a weather map. This happens because nature adheres to the so-called principle of conservation of angular momentum, a principle based on Newton's First Law, which is what makes the flow towards the centre of a vortex go round faster than the flow further out. These two principles are both laws of nature, or principles of science, and as such mathematicians cannot alter them. The *mathematical* idea of a source is extremely useful, but has no basis in the real world. However, the idea of a free vortex is *both* mathematically valid *and* represents very closely something that actually happens in the natural world. It is therefore doubly useful.

At the beginning of this chapter we posed the question, 'How can an enormous weight like an airliner be supported up in the air by its wings? – or, more tersely, how is lift generated?' The answer, we have now discovered, is that:

> **Lift is generated by the production of circulation around the wings, by which some velocity is added to the stream-wise velocity over the top of the wing, and some is subtracted from the velocity beneath the lower wing surface. By Bernoulli's principle the resulting speed difference produces a lower pressure on the top surface than on the bottom surface, and the consequent pressure distribution produces lift.**
>
> **The circulation is generated by means of separation of the flow at the sharp trailing edge of a streamlined shape called an aerofoil, and this flow separation occurs because the fluid possesses some viscosity, and thus has a boundary layer which separates because of the strong adverse pressure gradient around the sharp corner of the trailing edge.**

To do sums on lift, it is very often convenient to ignore the fact that the wing cross-section is an aerofoil, which is mathematically a rather unwieldy shape to deal with, and to pretend instead that it is a circular cylinder sticking out of the side of the aircraft, just as we earlier rather facetiously suggested for the design of a real wing. Although physically it would make a clumsy and inelegant wing, yet for the purpose of analysis it provides the most powerful and elegant simplifications, since (as we have seen) the fundamentals of the lifting circular cylinder model are all very simple indeed. Therefore most analysis of lift is based on the neat idea of substituting a vortex for a wing. The axis of the vortex coincides with the axis of the wing, and the vortex flow is rotating so that the top of it flows backwards and the bottom of it forwards relative to the wing.

In fact we can take this simplification one clever stage further still. Remembering that the circulation of a vortex is found to be the same, no matter which streamline we work it out along, we might as well use the most convenient streamline. If we use a tiny (but finite sized) streamline which is just big enough to encompass the axis of the vortex, we get the same value of circulation, and so anything larger is surplus to requirements. Doing this, the vortex becomes reduced to just its axis, or the line down the middle of it. So all we need for modelling the wing is just a straight line sticking out from the fuselage, which represents a vortex, which in turn represents the wing! This is precisely the way we usually do things, and this rather sophisticated and neat modelling method is known as *lifting line theory*. In Chapter 12 we will look at what happens when we get to the wing-tips, and we will discover that, far from failing us when we have finite rather than infinite wings, the lifting line model actually comes even more into its own.

We have laid all the essential foundations for mathematically analysing lift, and so we might reasonably expect to be rewarded by being told something of the mathematical conclusions that can be derived from these inputs and ideas. The potential flow with circulation gives us one absolutely key result which is the foundation of all subsequent work in the field, and that is a formula for the lift of our two-dimensional object in a uniform flow with circulation. The delightful thing is that, despite the undoubtedly high powered mathematics that is required to reach this conclusion, yet we really could not wish for a simpler formula to emerge than the one which we get. It is this:

$$L = \rho V \Gamma$$

where L is the lift per unit length of the two-dimensional shape, be it aerofoil, circular cylinder, lifting line or anything else, ρ and V are the density and the speed of the free stream airflow and Γ is the circulation around the object in this flow. As a quick validation exercise of this formula, we can quickly check out that it is homogeneous, i.e. that the dimensions are the same on each side. The dimensions on the left are those of force per unit length, which is mass times acceleration divided by length, i.e. ML/T^2L which cancels down to M/T^2. On the right density has dimensions M/L^3, speed L/T and circulation (found by multiplying distance by speed) $L \times L/T$. Multiplying these three dimensional fractions together, we have $\dfrac{M}{L^3} \times \dfrac{L}{T} \times \dfrac{L^2}{T}$ which cancels to M/T^2 as we required. Proving that an equation is homogeneous like this is of course a far cry from proving the equation itself, but it is a good way of increasing your confidence in the validity of a formula if you think you have remembered it right but are not quite sure. In this case, the formula may have looked just too good to be true, so that a dimensional check can be helpful to those of little faith!

So if we know the length of an aircraft wing and the circulation it produces, together with the airflow conditions around it, we can now work out completely the lift produced, which certainly makes life sound very easy. The concealed difficulty in this is, of course, finding the actual amount of circulation that the aerofoil produces, and a large portion of the subject of aerodynamics is involved with doing just that. Furthermore, since real wings have wing-tips, the circulation and hence the lift falls away towards the wing-tips, so that circulation is not even a constant for the whole wing but a rather complicated variable. Never mind, the mathematics has brought us thus far, and as we will see in Chapters 12 and 13, it can take us much further.

So we have declared our faith in nice neat water-tight mathematics for designing our aerofoils, and hence our aircraft. But this inviscid approach failed us lamentably when we tried to apply it to finding drag, because of the effects of viscosity. In this chapter on lift, our only mention of viscosity has been in an entirely favourable light when raising the phenomenon of flow separation at a sharp trailing edge, and we said that without viscosity lift would be totally impossible. Of course, it is not really true that viscosity has no adverse effects on lift, as a cursory reading of this chapter might be inclined to imply, and so in the next two chapters we will take a good hard look at some of the realities that we have so far not fully investigated.

CHAPTER 8
Physical Modelling and the Effect of Scale

INTRODUCTION

The designing and improving of aeroplanes is by no means a neat, clinical job that can be done purely by using computers and clever mathematical ideas. The sort of analytical methods that we have been considering in Chapters 5 and 7 are capable of expanding into very powerful tools, but on their own they are not enough. All analytical methods depend on certain presuppositions which are usually approximations to the truth, and sometimes (as in the case of viscosity) the presuppositions made may prove to be untenable in certain circumstances. The ideas have to be tried out in real life, the departures from the theoretical answers which occur in practice have to be investigated, and modifications to the original design have to be tried out to see whether they have the desired effects.

So far, our investigations have been very heavily biased towards the theoretical methods. In this chapter we will turn our attention to the subject of practically testing out the ideas, which means making actual aeroplanes or bits of aeroplane, either full-size or scale models, and testing them in actual airflows, either the real airflow of flight or the controlled airflow of a wind-tunnel.

If one wants to investigate questions about how an aeroplane is going to behave in flight, it is clear that test flying the aeroplane for real, being direct, is the most reliable way of getting the right answers. Although this may be a feasible approach for modifying existing types of aircraft, for a newly conceived aircraft design such an approach is clearly fraught with problems. The aeroplane does not yet exist except on paper, and so a prototype must be built. With the cost of modern technology, this is clearly going to be an extremely expensive exercise which can normally only be considered once, and so one must be certain of getting it substantially right first time. Essentially this means that the designers must be pretty certain of the correctness of most major aspects of the design before it is committed to prototype construction. Mistakes could be extremely costly, not only in production costs but also in human life.

The history of test flying often makes dramatic and classic literature. Perhaps the greatest era of exciting test flying was in the post Second World War period and the early 'fifties, when the challenge of 'breaking the sound barrier' was being tackled. In order to fly at supersonic speeds, it is unfortunately necessary to start from subsonic speeds and fly through the speed of sound itself, which presents formidable problems. In this inhospitable flight regime, shock waves begin to appear and these can cause severe and sometimes catastrophic control and other problems. The two distinctly different theoretical approaches for subsonic and supersonic aerodynamics turn out to be incompatible at around the speed of sound and no theoretical model naturally fits. Furthermore, the problems of building transonic[1] wind-tunnels had not by that time been overcome, and so it was not possible to test aircraft, or even models, in wind-tunnels at the crucial speed before building and flying prototypes. The only way at that time to investigate how an aircraft would behave at around the speed of sound was for a test pilot to dive his aircraft deliberately into this speed regime and observe what happened as he rapidly and sometimes uncontrollably approached the ground. Many lives were tragically lost, but the quest was pursued relentlessly until eventually the problems were resolved.

Although test flying of a prototype is the most direct method of testing, some of the quantities that are required to be measured are not directly measurable on an aircraft in flight. We mentioned earlier one or two of the many complications that arise, for example, in the measurement of the airspeed of an aircraft. Furthermore, the difficulty can be imagined of trying to measure the flight forces (lift and drag) on an aircraft in flight, and these are some of the most important quantities that we need. It is for these reasons that the idea of testing in a wind-tunnel is particularly attractive, since the aircraft is captive and the airflow is under close control. There are six forces and moments[2] (three of each) on an aircraft or a model, and the model may be mounted on a force and moment measuring balance which is capable of measuring all six of the forces and moments on the aircraft at once.

Of course, if a wind-tunnel is big enough, there is no reason why a full-size aircraft should not be mounted and tested in it. Many relatively small full-size aircraft in the past have been wind-tunnel tested in extremely large wind-tunnels in this way. But of course as the air-

---

[1] The word transonic merely refers to operating in this awkward regime at around the speed of sound.

[2] A moment is the turning effect of a force, and is a force times the length of its moment arm or lever arm. There are three primary moments on an aircraft, about three mutually perpendicular axes, just as there are three primary forces along these axes. This will form the basis of the stability and control work covered in *Flightwise: Aircraft Stability and Control*.

craft size and flight speeds increase, so the wind-tunnel would have to be ever larger and ever more powerful. The construction difficulties and costs, and also the operating costs, eventually become out of hand. It is very natural then to consider turning to the use of a small scale model, in order hopefully not only to save a large amount of time, cost and perhaps risk to life, but also to have a laboratory-controlled environment in which we can carefully take lots of accurate measurements of most of the quantities that we require to know. It will also be possible to simulate in the wind-tunnel situations which in real flight would involve operating outside the normal margins of safety.

THE PROBLEM

Before we can rely on getting meaningful and accurate results from using the technique of scale model testing for estimating the values of full-size flight forces, we will need to find out how the forces on the full-size prototype (which will obviously be much larger than those on the small scale model) are related to the test result forces, so that we will know what to do to scale-up the answers: do we just multiply by the scale factor, or is something else required? But before we can tackle that question, there is a much more fundamental and tricky question to be resolved, which might easily get completely overlooked, and it is this: can we be sure that the very process of scaling down the prototype is not in itself going to produce any unexpected effects whereby the model aeroplane performs fundamentally differently from the full-size one? How can we have confidence that the model will behave in all essential respects in a manner which corresponds with the full-size prototype which we are trying to emulate, but which we have not yet built? We will tackle this last question first. Doing so will involve some fairly intense logical thinking, during which we will meet the very important principle of dynamic similarity and will take a deep hard look at the meaning of a quantity called the Reynolds number. So if a cup of coffee helps the concentration, now might be the time to go and make one.

When we were considering the theoretical inviscid flow pattern over a circular cylinder, we did not need to specify the diameter of the cylinder or the speed of the free stream, since the flow pattern turned out to be geometrically similar[3] regardless of either. Because of the incompressible assumption the density was a constant, and hence dropped out of the continuity equation so that the equation

---

[3]If two shapes are geometrically similar, they have exactly the same shape as each other but not necessarily the same size, like photographic enlargements or scale drawings or scale models.

(AV = constant) became purely kinematic. Thus the flow pattern turned out to depend purely on the geometrical shape of the object. Objects other than the circular cylinder (such as that in Figure 7.9) 'look' different to the approaching free stream flow when set at different angles to it, and in such cases the shape of the flow pattern will also depend on the orientation of the object to the flow, but still on nothing else. Thus in inviscid flow, provided that we keep the shape and orientation of the object the same in scale model and prototype, the streamline pattern, and hence the pressure coefficient distribution, will be indistinguishable for all values of free stream speed and density and object size. The pressure distribution and the streamline shape are each both cause and effect of the other, so that the force effect of the object, like the streamline pattern around it, depends only on its shape and orientation. Thus we can conclude that, if air flow were in fact inviscid, we would need to have no qualms at all about our confidence in testing scale models, since all the important ingredients would automatically be to scale.

It was only at the end of Chapter 6 (Figure 6.9) that we saw different flow patterns occurring, and this was as a direct result of viscosity and the boundary layer behaviour; specifically, of boundary layer separation. It is this, and to a much lesser extent the thickness of an attached boundary layer, that dictates the nature of the flow pattern around an object, and these depend substantially on whether the boundary layer is laminar or turbulent.

BOUNDARY LAYER TRANSITION

There is one key and crucial question about boundary layers which we have not yet tackled. Although we have talked about the relative characteristics and merits of both laminar and turbulent boundary layers, we have not so far considered what factors determine which type of boundary layer will exist in any particular situation. Every boundary layer starts its life laminar, and at some stage it degenerates into a turbulent boundary layer. The laminar motion is orderly, but tending towards being unstable. The point on the surface at which the laminar boundary layer collapses into disorder and becomes turbulent is called the *transition point*. It must not be confused with the separation point, which is very different.

The actual distance of the transition point behind the starting point of the boundary layer depends on a number of factors each of which, one instinctively feels, might be expected to tend to interfere with the orderliness of laminar flow. To help our thinking about what is going on, let us think of the air within the boundary layer as a number of columns of marching soldiers in close formation, all marching in orderly straight lines, in step, close together (side to side and front to rear) but not quite touching each other. The column closest to the wall is going very slowly, the next column out a little faster, and so on out to the full speed of the 'free stream'. This is quite difficult for them to do, and inevitably there is some strain and emotional friction amongst them, which eventually may overcome their good discipline and force their ordered laminar motion to degenerate into chaos and turbulent motion.

What factors might provoke this to happen sooner rather than later? One possible answer is their overall speed: if they are marching 'at the double', their orderliness will be less stable than if they are quick marching; if quick marching, less stable than slow marching. Another is their degree of discipline and camaraderie obtained through training: the more disciplined they are, the more stable will be the formation. Another factor will be the amount of spacing between them: the less densely packed they are, the less jostling there will be. Then there is the condition of the surface that they are marching over; a well Tarmacadamed road will be more conducive to good order than a muddy, pot-holed track. If they are having to march up-hill, things are more difficult than if they were marching along a level or down-hill. And finally, if all of them were alcoholically inebriated, their motion would already be unsteady before they even started the exercise, making disorder liable to occur earlier than otherwise.

Each of these six points has a direct parallel in the fluid boundary layer situation. The greater the speed of free stream flow, the shorter will be the distance from the beginning of the boundary layer to the transition point. The greater the fluid's viscosity (analogous with the soldiers' discipline), the later transition will occur. The greater the density, the more jostling will occur and the earlier transition will occur. A rough surface (i.e. the pot-holed track), or an adverse pressure gradient (equivalent to marching up-hill), will both be conducive to early transition. And being drunk before they even started is rather like the presence of a certain amount of turbulence in the free stream flow before the boundary layer even begins.

Of these six quantities, only the speed, density and the viscosity are essentially properties of the fluid or of the flow. The surface roughness and the adverse pressure gradient both depend on the nature of the object interacting with the airflow, and any free stream turbulence is also due to some feature within the physical system being considered. We could therefore class the speed, the density and the viscosity as the system-independent quantities of interest. Furthermore, they are all convenient quantities which can be expressed in numbers and units, whereas the others are not.

In passing, if we are to talk about the distance d to the transition point of a boundary layer in an invisible fluid such as air, we will need some means of physically identifying where this transition point is. If a pitot tube (which we discussed in Chapter 4) having a diameter much smaller than the boundary layer thickness is placed pointing upstream in the lower reaches of the boundary layer, it is clear from Figure 6.4 that it will detect a considerably greater pitot pressure in the turbulent boundary layer, because of the profile fullness, than in the laminar boundary layer. Thus as the pitot tube is moved slowly along close to the wall in the stream direction, a sudden increase in the pitot pressure will indicate the presence of the transition point. (The other side of the pressure-measuring device may be connected to any constant pressure source such as the static pressure of the free stream.) Since only a *change* in conditions is required rather than a numerical value, the pressure-measuring instrument may be replaced by an ordinary medical stethoscope connected to the pipe from the pitot tube. Because of the increase in turbulence at the transition point, there will be a change in the nature of the sound transmitted to the operator's ears as the pitot tube is moved downstream through the transition point.

DYNAMIC SIMILARITY

We were posing the question, how can we be certain that the model under test accurately represents, to some scale, the conditions on the prototype that it represents? We could put this another way: what test could we apply to find out whether the lift and drag force components of the model total reaction are proportional to the lift and drag components of the total reaction in the full-size case? Working backwards, this test must show that the vector triangles of lift, drag and total reaction for the two situations would be exactly similar to each other. Taking the prototype flight direction and the wind-tunnel longitudinal axis as our reference directions, this requirement simply means that the two total reactions must be equally inclined to their reference directions, or, if drawn on the same piece of paper, parallel to each other.

The total reaction was obtained by drawing a vector polygon of all the little elemental forces around the surface in 'daisy-chain' fashion, and these consisted of a set of pressure forces and a set of viscous forces, one pair at each little element of the surface. Although clearly not the only way in which we can get the total reactions to be parallel to each other, one fool-proof way to do so would be to insist that the two vector polygons were exactly similar to each other; in other words, that every pressure and viscous elemental force of the one was parallel to and directly proportional to the corresponding elemental force on the other.

We will quickly tire of reading the recurring phrase 'parallel to and directly proportional to' when referring to vectors, so let us agree that 'proportional to', when applied to vectors, will have this meaning in the present section.

So we have come up with a *sufficient* (although not *necessary*[4]) condition that the model is behaving in an exactly representative way of the full-size situation. The condition is that every elemental force (pressure and viscous) acting on the scale model should be proportional to the corresponding elemental force acting on the prototype. It is not *necessary*, because it is conceivable that a completely non-scale model or some other system could be devised that would satisfy the requirement of model and full-size total reaction being proportional to each other, but this is a mere technicality. We are concerned with accurate scale modelling, and so we can take it that the condition specified above is the absolute requirement for proper representation.

The elemental forces that we have usually considered are those which act on the surface itself, since they are the ones which produce the required aerodynamic total reaction on the object. But of course there also exist elemental forces at every point throughout the flow field, acting on each particle of air. It is these elemental forces acting on any specific particle of air that precisely dictate the motion of that particle, in accordance with Newton's Second Law. Fore and aft forces will cause the particle to speed up and slow down (resulting in stream paths becoming narrower and wider), and sideways forces will cause the paths of the particles to be curved. Without such forces the particles would simply travel in straight lines at a constant speed, as in a uniform flow, in accordance with Newton's First Law. Consequently, the streamline pattern of the flow is totally and solely dependent on the distribution of elemental forces throughout the flow field.

It is therefore possible to step back one pace further and to stipulate the condition for representativeness in another way:

> **IF (1) a model is accurately made to scale and (2) it is orientated to the airflow at the same angle as the prototype that it represents, and (3) the streamline pattern around the model is exactly similar to (i.e. identical in shape with) the streamline pattern around the prototype, THEN the model's elemental forces will be proportional to those of the prototype, and thus the model lift and drag forces will be proportional to the prototype lift and drag forces.**

If this condition is satisfied, it is said that the two systems possess *dynamic similarity*, and

> **only if the two systems are dynamically similar can we be certain that the model properly and accurately (to scale) represents what would be happening on the full-size version.**

---

[4]*Necessary* and *sufficient* are a pair of words that are used technically by mathematicians, but their technical meaning is exactly identical with their everyday meaning, so that they should present no problem.

It is relatively easy to check a model for geometrical similarity, by measuring it carefully to ensure that every aspect of it, even down to fine detail like the radius of curvature of sharp corners and the roughness of the aerodynamic surfaces, is as closely as possible exactly scaled-down from the full-sized version that it represents. It is also relatively easy to measure the orientation of the model to the wind-tunnel airflow, and to specify that the test only applies to the same orientation of the prototype to its airflow (which is not so easy to measure in flight). It is far less easy, but equally essential, to check the geometrical similarity of the streamline patterns of the two systems, since they cannot be seen. Even if they could, they would be extremely difficult to chart accurately on the model, and probably impossible around the aircraft in flight. But all three of these conditions must be met in order to ensure dynamic similarity.

As we have seen, in ideal (inviscid) flow dynamic similarity pertains all the time since the flow pattern depends only on the system geometry, but in real flow this is not the case. Flow patterns are also dependent on boundary layer behaviour and are thus variable, even when the shape and orientation of the object in the flow is fixed. This is something that it is very easy to overlook. Although we can see the object, and we probably know the free stream flow direction even though we cannot see it, (it is parallel to the flight direction in flight and to the wind-tunnel walls in a model test,) yet we normally cannot see the airflow around the object. If airflow patterns were visible, then I venture to suggest that driving a car on a busy road would be a very different experience from that with which we are familiar. At junctions and at roundabouts in particular, driving would be a quite traumatic experience!

REYNOLDS NUMBER

The late nineteenth century English engineer and fluid dynamicist Osborne Reynolds developed a theory which helps us in investigating dynamic similarity and thus answering our question about modelling confidence. He showed that there exists a special number formed by combining the distance d to the transition point, the free stream velocity V, the density ρ and the viscosity μ in a certain way, that is directly related to the position of the transition point, and hence to the nature of the flow at all points on the surface. This number, which is called the *Reynolds number* (Re), is given by the formula

$$Re = \frac{\rho V d}{\mu}$$

(An alternative form, in which μ and ρ are replaced by the kinematic viscosity ν where $\nu = \mu/\rho$, is sometimes used, which gives us $Re = Vd/\nu$. We however will stick to the first form.) There are of course other ways of altering the transition point's position, such as roughening the surface or inducing free stream turbulence, and these are aspects of the flow which do not appear directly in the Reynolds number. We will return to look at this point again at the end of this chapter, in the section entitled 'transition fixing'.

Reynolds number is without doubt one of the most important and ubiquitous ideas in the whole of fluid mechanics and in the theory of flight. It is fairly easy to obtain a certain virtuosity in bandying around the term Reynolds number and values of it deftly and with a modicum of correctness, yet to understand the concepts that it encapsulates is a lot more difficult. In the tradition of Flightwise we will not flinch from the task, but be prepared that, however good an explanation you are privy to, it may take more than one reading, and probably reading from more than one source, to understand the concepts fully. Do not therefore be discouraged if you find this next couple of sections challenging, and rest assured that you *will* be able to cope with the subsequent sections even if your initial grasp of Reynolds number ideas is tentative.

We have established that dynamic similarity is required to ensure the representativeness of our model, but we have also had a brief insight into the difficulty of checking on this condition. Following fairly closely in the footsteps of Osborne Reynolds in developing his approach, we will now go back and look at the intricacies of the forces in the flow field, and unravel the ingenious method that he has provided us with for ensuring that we obtain dynamic similarity.

Let us consider the forces acting on a particle of air moving along a curved streamline in a flow field, as illustrated in Figure 8.1. The force labelled 'resultant pressure force' in the main drawing is itself the vector sum of the two parts of the pressure force on the particle, as shown

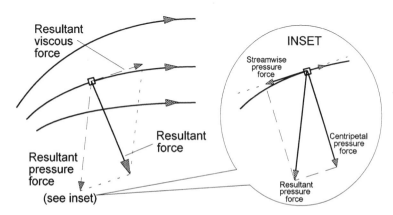

Figure 8.1   Forces on an Air Particle, for Derivation of Reynolds Number

in the inset: (i) the streamwise pressure force due to the pressure difference *along* the streamline slowing the particle down, (we know it's slowing down because the streamlines are getting wider apart in the flow direction,) and (ii) the centripetal pressure force due to the pressure difference *across* the streamlines from the outside of the curve towards the inside, causing the particle's path to be curved. Transferring back now to the main drawing, the force labelled 'resultant viscous force' is tangential to the streamline, and is the difference between the viscous force due to particles below our particle pulling our particle forwards and the particles above pulling it backwards. (We know that the particles below are going faster because the streamlines there are closer together, and vice versa for the ones above.) Of course, these relative directions and magnitudes only apply to the specific situation illustrated, but dealing with it in this way may help to make clear the nature of the forces. Incidentally, the vector diagram is not even remotely near being drawn to scale, as it shows the resultant viscous force to be of the same order of magnitude as the pressure forces. We know that the viscous forces are very much smaller than the pressure forces, so much so that, in the free stream and away from any solid boundary, we can safely ignore the viscous forces altogether. However, distorting the vector diagram like this is useful for our present purposes, and in no way invalidates the arguments.

Now if the flow of Figure 8.1 is to retain dynamic similarity when any features such as size or air-speed change, the geometry of the flow pattern must remain unchanged. If the resultant forces on all the elements changed proportionately to each other in magnitude but remained unchanged in direction, then the shape of the flow pattern would be maintained, but if the direction of any one or more of these resultant forces were to change then the flow pattern would immediately be corrupted. We require therefore the condition such that the *directions* of all the elemental resultant forces such as the one shown in Figure 8.1 remain unchanged.

Each of these resultant forces is the diagonal of a parallelogram, whose sides represent a pressure force and a viscous force. If one of these were to change in magnitude (i.e. length) and the other didn't, the direction of the resultant would be changed, but if the magnitudes of both were to change in proportion to each other (i.e. they were each multiplied by the same factor as each other), then the direction of the resultant would not be affected at all. We have therefore reached the following conclusion:

> **In order that dynamic similarity may be ensured following any changes in the flow system, the ratio of the magnitude of the pressure force to that of the viscous force at each point in the flow must remain unchanged.**

Now of course we cannot actually find the specific resultant pressure and viscous forces at each point. (Even if we could, it would be an infinitely long task for an infinity of particles.) Instead we would like to find a mathematical formula to represent the crucial *ratio of the pressure force to the viscous force* acting on a particle of the air, in terms of measurable quantities of the system. What we will develop will be a formula that says that the ratio of the forces at the point in question is directly proportional to a unique number that is the same for the whole system. If we move our attention from point to point in the flow when no flow changes are happening, the thing that varies is not this special system number, but rather the constant of proportionality which relates each point to the special system number. If the system is changed in any way at all, then provided that the change does not cause the unique system number to alter, the force ratio at each point, and hence the dynamic similarity (i.e. the similarity of the streamline pattern) will be maintained.

We could now obtain such a formula to give us a system number. But in fact the way that this has been traditionally done, as introduced by Reynolds, is slightly different from that suggested above. If we were to go ahead independently now we would achieve a correct but unconventional result, which would be rather a waste of effort. In order to conform with convention and with Reynolds' approach, we will not choose to use the ratio of pressure force to viscous force at each point, but another closely related ratio. We will consider this slight change in approach now.

We have been referring to the vector sum of the pressure and viscous forces as the resultant force. By Newton's Second Law we can say that this resultant equals the mass of the air particle times its acceleration, and this acceleration on this mass is the effect of the force. The system of forces acting on the particle is not in equilibrium, since there is a resultant force and consequently a resulting acceleration. However, there is a very effective little trick that was introduced into the general study of mechanics by our old friend Jean d'Alembert, by which any problem in dynamics involving a resultant force acting on a mass and causing it to accelerate can be simplified for the purposes of analysis into an equilibrium or static system, i.e. one with zero resultant force and consequently no acceleration. The trick, as illustrated in Figure 8.2, is simply to add to the force system a new pseudo-force whose magnitude is the mass of the object acted on times its acceleration, and whose direction is exactly opposite to the resultant of the real force system. When this device is used in aerodynamics, the new pseudo-force is given the common-sense name of *inertia force*, but it should always be remembered that this is not a new real force, but simply a convenient way of expressing the resultant of the set of real forces in terms of its accelerating effect on the air.

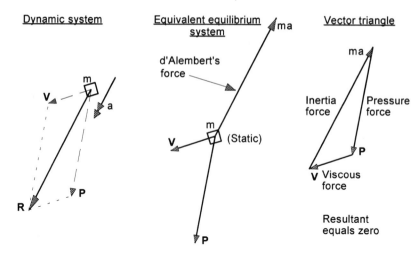

Figure 8.2   Using d'Alembert's Force to Represent a Dynamic System by an Equilibrium System

If we want to specify how the whole of something is divided up, we usually use fractions or percentages of the whole. For example, '40% or 2/5 of the students were female and 60% or 3/5 were male', and the sum is 100% or 1. Note that we do not so often specify the ratio of the sub-components to each other (e.g. 'The number of female students is 2/3 of the number of male students'), although this would be a perfectly legitimate and correct way of expressing the same relationship. A somewhat similar situation arises in our present case of three forces, one of which is effectively the 'sum' of the other two. However, with vectors, the sum of two vectors is not normally their algebraic sum but their resultant. For example, the 'total' force in the previous paragraph is the inertia force, but its magnitude is not the sum of the magnitudes of the pressure force and the viscous force but something smaller.

For our present purposes we are after a relationship between just the *magnitudes* of pressure force and viscous force acting on an air particle, but it would seem sensible to express each of these in turn as its relationship with their effective total, the inertia force. Thus

it would seem quite sensible to use the ratios $\dfrac{|\text{Viscous force}|}{|\text{Inertia force}|}$ and

$\dfrac{|\text{Pressure force}|}{|\text{Inertia force}|}$, where the vertical bars mean 'the magnitude of'.

These two fractions will not add up to one, because the tops are only the magnitudes of vectors whose *vector* sum is the inertia force, but they are more closely in line with normal practice (e.g. the use of 2/5 and 3/5 in the above example) than $\dfrac{|\text{Viscous force}|}{|\text{Pressure force}|}$, which is like the 2/3 of the example.

There is another good reason for using one of these new ratios to express the required relationship. Other types of force than pressure and viscous forces crop up in some fluid mechanics problems outside aircraft aerodynamics. Gravity force becomes significant if a free surface with waves is involved, such as in the case of ship design or coastal defence work. Where slow trickles of liquid with a free surface are involved, another force, the surface tension, will become significant and enter the picture. The inertia force on each fluid particle will be the vector sum of all the contributory elemental forces, and so it would be convenient to express the magnitude of each as a fraction or proportion of the 'total' inertia force. By this means the method that we are discussing in the present section can be very greatly expanded to cover a host of very diverse aspects of fluid mechanics, and so we will be working on a sound basis if we follow the general convention, and relate each of our forces to the inertia force.

There is one further little snag, or rather, inconvenience. Fractions in ordinary arithmetic with the total on the bottom will always be less than 1, and so must be expressed either as decimal numbers or as fractional parts in some other way. Nothing wrong with that! But whole numbers greater than one are generally easier to handle than fractions less than one, and so the approach that has been adopted, by Reynolds and by all subsequent workers in the field, is to turn the fraction upside down, and always put the inertia force on the top and the other force of interest on the bottom. However, bear in mind that it is possible in some circumstances for the magnitude of the sum of two vectors to be *smaller* than the magnitude of either of them separately, in which case our answer by the new method will turn out to be a fraction less than 1. Numbers less than 1 are not therefore impossible, but in our present application numbers greater than 1, usually enormously so, are more commonplace. Negative numbers cannot arise, since the numbers are ratios of the magnitudes of two vectors, and the magnitude of a vector is always taken as positive.

So we have a choice. Shall we use $\dfrac{|\text{Inertia force}|}{|\text{Pressure force}|}$ or $\dfrac{|\text{Inertia force}|}{|\text{Viscous force}|}$ as our criterion for dynamic similarity? Since in aerodynamics these are the only two forces involved, we could use either. However, the pressure force is also influenced by compressibility which we are temporarily ignoring, and so we are inclined to choose the second ratio. Furthermore, since dynamic similarity is intimately tied up with boundary layer behaviour, which in turn depends on viscosity, we must incorporate viscosity into our formula, and so the accepted practice is to adopt the ratio $\dfrac{|\text{Inertia force}|}{|\text{Viscous force}|}$ as our criterion for dynamic similarity. It is this ratio that leads us to the Reynolds number.

So how does this ratio relate to the formula for Reynolds number that we briefly met earlier? We have already seen that, provided we have dynamic similarity, any quantity relating to a fluid particle (force, velocity, etc.) is directly proportional to all other quantities of the same type anywhere in the fluid field, and so we will express the top and bottom of the ratio in terms of quantities which are amenable to measurement. Remember in the following discussion that 'is proportional to' means 'equals a constant times', and note that the constant of proportionality in each case is a constant *for the particular point in question*, but will have a different value for each other point.

The magnitude of the inertia force acting on the fluid particle equals the particle's mass times the magnitude of its acceleration in the direction of the force. The mass is equal to the density ρ times the volume, and the volume is proportional to ℓ^3, the cube of any chosen reference length ℓ which is characteristic of the system[5], and so the mass is proportional to $\rho\ell^3$. The magnitude of the acceleration of the particle is a rate of change of speed, and so is proportional to any chosen speed of the system divided by any chosen time period t of the system. For a speed we will normally choose the magnitude of the free stream velocity V. There is no obvious time period which is characteristic of the system, but we can invent one by dividing a length by a speed – what better than ℓ/V? Thus for the magnitude of the inertia force on top of the fraction we have (simply re-stating the above in mathematical short-hand)

---

[5]If you find this statement tricky to follow, consider the following simplified argument. In any system, if the length (or any convenient measurement) of a fluid particle under consideration is ℓ, then its volume will consist of a formula of the form $k\ell^3$ where k is a constant. (E.g. the volume of a sphere of diameter d is $\dfrac{\pi}{6}\,d^3$ which is a constant times d^3.) If a system consisting of the flow around an aerofoil is replicated at twice the size, then all distances are doubled. The elemental length ℓ is doubled, and so the volume of the element becomes $k \times (2\ell)^3$ or $8k\ell^3$. The chord length c (a length which is representative of the size of the aerofoil) is also doubled, and so, like the elemental volume, the value of c^3 is increased by a factor of 2^3 or 8. Thus the volume of the fluid element is directly proportional to the cube of any chosen length, such as ℓ or c.

$$|\text{Inertia force}| = ma = (k_1 . \rho\ell^{\,3})\left(k_2\,\frac{V}{t}\right) = k_1 k_2 (\rho\ell^{\,3})\left(V \div \frac{\ell}{V}\right)$$

$$= k_1 k_2 (\rho\ell^{\,3})\left(\frac{V^{\,2}}{\ell}\right) = k_3 \rho\ell^{\,2} V^{\,2}$$

where k_1, k_2 and k_3 are constants of proportionality and $k_3 = k_1 \times k_2$.

The magnitude of the viscous force on the bottom of the ratio will be the shear stress (F/A) multiplied by the area A over which it acts. The area A is proportional to the square of the characteristic length, ℓ^2. (F/A) can be expressed in terms of other quantities by using the defining formula of viscosity $\mu = \left(\dfrac{F}{A}\right)\Big/\left(\dfrac{dV}{dY}\right)$ as introduced in Chapter 6, from which $\left(\dfrac{F}{A}\right) = \mu\left(\dfrac{dV}{dY}\right)$. Now this rate of strain term comes, you will recall, from a consideration of the slope of a velocity profile, and even if we are not near a wall there is no reason why we should not still draw a velocity profile to show how the flow rate varies across the flow. If we did, then the velocity gradient at each point, like the streamlines and like the force vector diagram, would have to remain unchanged with changes of scale if dynamic similarity is to be maintained, and so the dV and the dy of the rate of strain must respectively be proportional to the characteristic speed V and to the characteristic length ℓ. Thus, again summarising this in mathematical notation,

$$|\text{Viscous force}| = \left(\frac{F}{A}\right)(A) = \left(\mu . k_4\,\frac{V}{\ell}\right)(k_5 \ell^{\,2}) = k_6\,\mu V\ell$$

where k_4, k_5 and k_6 are constants of proportionality and $k_6 = k_4 \times k_5$. It follows that

$$\frac{|\text{Inertia force}|}{|\text{Viscous force}|} = \frac{k_3 \rho\ell^{\,2} V^{\,2}}{k_6\,\mu V\ell} = k_7\,\frac{\rho V\ell}{\mu}$$

where k_7 is another constant of proportionality and is equal to k_3/k_6.

The number $\dfrac{\rho V\ell}{\mu}$ is the all-important system number that we have been looking for, and it is called the system's Reynolds number. The last equation above states that the ratio of the forces at the point in question is directly proportional to the system Reynolds number.

Having got thus far, let us make sure that our thinking is on the right track. We are *not* saying that the ratio of |Inertia force|:|Viscous force| is the same at every point in the flow field around the object. That would be patently absurd, since the particular circumstances contributing to the form of the vector diagram in Figure 8.1 are obviously different at each point of the flow and around the object. Rather, what we are talking about is what happens at *one point* if the nature of the flow should change. We are saying that, if any two or more features of the flow system (including scale size, air density and viscosity, and speed) should change in such a way that the new resulting Reynolds number of the flow system remains unaltered from its value before the change, then the ratio of the inertia force to the viscous force at that point, being the same constant k_7 times the same Reynolds number, will be unchanged. If true at one general point as discussed here, then it follows that this is true at every point in the flow field, and consequently the flow system is dynamically similar to what it was before the change. To summarise,

> **If two geometrically similar systems possess the same Reynolds number, then the systems are dynamically similar, and the forces of one are directly proportional to the corresponding forces of the other.**

So now we have determined the condition for our model to be valid, which is that the model and prototype systems are dynamically similar, and we have also established a simple test to find out whether dynamic similarity exists. If it does, we are set to answer the final question: How do the model forces compare in magnitude with the prototype forces? How should we scale-up our test force measurements?

SCALED FORCES

In Chapter 3 we introduced at some length the idea of dimensionless aerodynamic coefficients to express forces, pressures and other quantities. Our treatment at that point was deliberately introductory as appropriate to our needs at that time. However, the concept of dimensionless aerodynamic coefficients really comes into its own now that we are considering the problem of scaling, and so we must pick up from where we left off in Chapter 3. A glance back to the section entitled 'Aerodynamic Coefficients' in that chapter might prove beneficial before reading on. We will have to go through a little bit more dimensional analysis in the way that we did in Chapter 3, but although the mathematics will be beneficial to you if you can follow the argument, do not worry if you can't, as you will be able to pick up again at the statement $C_F = f(Re)$ following the mathematical development below.

We can tackle the question posed at the end of the previous section by asking ourselves what quantities a force depends on. From our discussion of this question in Chapter 3, with the addition now of viscosity which we omitted there for simplicity, the answer is that an aerodynamic force F depends in some way on the free stream flow speed V, the size of the object which we can represent by a characteristic length ℓ, the air density ρ and its viscosity μ.

We will introduce a useful bit of mathematical notation here, the function notation. Suppose we have a set of experimental data for two related quantities, say x and y. We can plot a graph of y (on the vertical axis) against x (on the horizontal axis), and we get some sort of curved graph line – it doesn't matter what shape. All that this tells us so far is that y depends in some unknown way upon x, or putting this into mathematical jargon, y *is a function of* x. The mathematician's shorthand for this is simply $y = f(x)$. It is not as strong a statement as 'is proportional to', which specifies a particular type of relationship. Notice that in this notation the f is not a variable multiplying the bracket, but is an *operator*, which effectively says 'If you do the operation which is called f on the contents of the bracket, x, the result will be y.' If the values of y do not depend only on x but also on some other quantity, say z, then we say that y is a function of both x and z, and write this in shorthand as $y = f(x,z)$.

Now in the current situation we have the force F being dependent in some unknown way on four different quantities which we have identified, and so we can say that F is a function (f) of all four quantities together; or in shorthand:

$$F = f(\rho, \mu, V, \ell)$$

The dimensions of the left-hand side are $\dfrac{\mathbf{ML}}{\mathbf{T^2}}$, and so for the equation to be homogeneous each term of the right-hand side of any resulting formula for F must also have the dimensions $\dfrac{\mathbf{ML}}{\mathbf{T^2}}$.

The right-hand term(s) will be composed of some combination of the quantities listed in the brackets, raised to some as yet unknown powers, since this is the only way that the dimensions of the left-hand side can be matched.

Thus $F \triangleq \rho^a \mu^b V^c \ell^d$ where $\triangleq$ means '. . . has the same dimensions as . . .', and so

$$\frac{\mathbf{ML}}{\mathbf{T^2}} = \left(\frac{\mathbf{M}}{\mathbf{L^3}}\right)^a \left(\frac{\mathbf{M}}{\mathbf{LT}}\right)^b \left(\frac{\mathbf{L}}{\mathbf{T}}\right)^c (\mathbf{L})^d$$

The second bracket on the right-hand side contains the dimensions of viscosity which we haven't had before, but they can quickly be verified just by considering the defining formula for μ, noting that the dimensions of (dV/dy) are those of V/ℓ, i.e. $1/\mathbf{T}$.

Equating coefficients of **M**: $a + b$ $= 1$
Equating coefficients of **L**: $-3a - b + c + d$ $= 1$
Equating coefficients of **T**: $-b - c$ $= -2$

Here we have three equations in four unknowns. When we met this approach in Chapter 3 we had the same number of equations as unknown quantities so that we could solve the equations to find the three unknown powers, but we cannot do that on this occasion. Instead, we will simply assume that one of our four unknown quantities is in fact a known quantity, and just solve the three equations for the other three unknowns. Of course, the one which we treat as known is going to crop up in our answers for each of the others so that the problem is not totally solved, but it does give us a way forward. Based on the experience of others, we will choose b to be the 'known' quantity, and solve the equations for a, c and d. The three equations give us, in order,

$$a = 1 - b$$
$$-3a + c + d = 1 + b$$
$$-c = -2 + b$$

The first of these gives us $a = 1 - b$
The last of the equations gives $c = 2 - b$

Substituting these values for a and c into the second equation and manipulating it gives

$$-3(1 - b) + (2 - b) + d = 1 + b$$
$$\therefore \quad d = 1 + b + 3 - 3b - 2 + b \text{ so that } d = 2 - b$$

We now substitute the values of a, c and d (which are all in terms of b) into the dimensional equation $F \triangleq \rho^a \mu^b V^c \ell^d$ above, which gives us $F \triangleq \rho^{1-b} \mu^b V^{2-b} \ell^{2-b}$. We note from the rules of powers

that ρ^{1-b} is the same as $\rho \times \dfrac{1}{\rho^b}$, V^{2-b} may be written

$V^2 \times \dfrac{1}{V^b}$ and ℓ^{2-b} equals $\ell^2 \times \dfrac{1}{\ell^b}$. Now rearranging the

order of the factors and combining together those containing a b in the power, we get

$$F \triangleq \rho V^2 \ell^2 \cdot \left(\frac{\mu}{\rho V \ell} \right)^b$$

If we now divide both sides of this equation by $\rho V^2 \ell^2$, we have

$$\frac{F}{\rho V^2 \ell^2} \triangleq \left(\frac{\mu}{\rho V \ell} \right)^{-b}$$

Finally turning upside down the contents of the bracket whilst inserting a minus sign into the power (in accordance with the rules of powers), we have

$$\frac{F}{\rho V^2 \ell^2} \triangleq \left(\frac{\rho V \ell}{\mu} \right)^{-b}$$

The bracket on the right looks familiar! But we'll come to that in a moment. First of all, you may recognise the expression on the left of the equation as being almost the same as the force coefficients that we introduced in Chapter 3. In Chapter 5 we looked at the easy way to develop and write down force coefficients – on top of a fraction line we put the force, and on the bottom the dynamic pressure $\frac{1}{2}\rho V^2$ multiplied by the reference area which we called S. To get our present equation into this form, we can proceed as follows: first of all, we multiply the bottom of both sides of the equation by $\frac{1}{2}$, which has no unbalancing effect since we are doing the same thing to both sides; secondly, since ℓ^2 is an area that is proportional to any reference area S, we replace ℓ^2 by kS where k is the constant of proportionality. Thirdly, we multiply both sides by k so that it disappears from the bottom on the left and appears on the top on the right. After performing these three steps we have

$$\frac{F}{\frac{1}{2}\rho V^2 S} \triangleq \frac{k}{\frac{1}{2}} \left(\frac{\rho V \ell}{\mu} \right)^{-b}$$

Now the left-hand side is our familiar form of an aerodynamic dimensionless force coefficient such as the coefficient of lift or coefficient of drag. We may replace the F by any such force as appropriate, but in its general form as we have it here we will write it just as a general force coefficient C_F.

The right-hand side of the equation looks like a bit of a hotch-potch, but we immediately notice that, amidst all the clutter around the outside of the bracket, the contents of the bracket is in fact the Reynolds number. Now we have no means of finding the value of k, and neither do we know anything at all about the value of the power $-b$, and so in a sense we can go no further in developing this formula mathematically. In any case, we should remember that what we have is not a normal equation but merely a dimensional equation which says that the dimensions of the two sides are equal. Thus even if we did know k and b, this dimensional equation would still not specify the precise relationship between the two sides. In fact, what we have done is to manipulate the dimensional equation into a form such that the dimensions on each side totally cancel out, leaving dimensionless quantities on both sides.

Although we don't know anything about the nature of the relationship between the force coefficient on the left-hand side and the

Reynolds number on the right-hand side, what we do now know for certain is that the dimensionless group on the left-hand side, the force coefficient, depends for its value *only* on the Reynolds number of the system, since there is nothing else on the right-hand side which is system-dependent. (*k* and *b* are both constants.) In the function notation introduced earlier, we say that the right-hand side is a function of the Reynolds number, or *f(Re)*. (This is not the same function *f* as we had before. The letter *f* is used generally to mean any function.) So finally we can write our original relationship very simply as

$$C_F = f(Re)$$

or in words,

> **Any aerodynamic force coefficient is a function of the Reynolds number *and nothing else.***

If the Reynolds number is a constant (our condition for dynamic similarity), then the force coefficient is a function of a constant. Provided you always apply the same function or operation (whatever it may be) to a constant, the result, the force coefficient, will always be the same. It is those few words *'and nothing else'*; which are really the all-important ones, and unfortunately this message does not come out clearly from the pure mathematical representation of the result.

What does this apparently rather innocuous and perhaps trivial-looking equation tell us? It actually gives us the full answer to the question with which we started this section. It tells us that, when we make and aerodynamically test a scale model of an aircraft or an aircraft component at the same orientation to the airflow as the full-size version, then

> **provided the Reynolds number of the scale model system is the same as that of the full-size aircraft system, the coefficients of lift and of drag (or of any other forces chosen) will be the same in the full-size version as in the model.**

So it is not the force itself that is the same on model and prototype, but the force coefficient. For example, let us suppose that we are measuring lift force on an accurate scale model of a light trainer aircraft in a wind-tunnel, and we have managed to ensure that the Reynolds number is the same for the model as the full-size version. Having measured the lift force on the model by use of the wind-tunnel balance, we may obtain the coefficient of lift from $C_L = L/\frac{1}{2}\rho V^2 S$ by dividing the lift by $\frac{1}{2}\rho V^2$ and by S, where V, ρ and S are speed, air density and wing plan area of the wind-tunnel and model. Now we may use the same equation written as $L = C_L \frac{1}{2}\rho V^2 S$ to find the lift force on the real aircraft at any speed and at any height (i.e. value of air density), simply by inserting the *same* value of C_L and the full-size value of S. C_L is therefore the lifting effect of the aircraft wing *when set at the same orientation as that of the model*, and its value can be used at a number of different flight conditions to give the actual lift in each case.

THE MODELLING PROBLEM

On the face of it, it would appear that we now have the makings of a very workable system for analysing flight forces by means of wind-tunnel tests – just check for dynamic similarity, measure a force, convert it to its coefficient form, and use it at any other scale size or flight condition to predict the force in those circumstances. But as soon as we try to do this, we come across some very serious snags, which we must consider now.

Let us take, as an example, a Piper Tomahawk which was illustrated in Figure 5.4. This is a two-seater basic trainer aircraft with a span of 34 feet and (at 75% power) a cruising speed of 125 mph at 8,800 feet altitude, and we would like to do some wind-tunnel tests on a model representing the aircraft flying in this condition. In order to ensure dynamic similarity and thus validity for our test, we must first of all look at the Reynolds numbers of both systems and try to match them, remembering that

$$Re = \frac{\rho V \ell}{\mu}$$

For interest (although we will not actually need its value in the present discussion) the Reynolds number of the full-size Tomahawk at the flight condition specified, based on using the wing chord length as the reference length, is approximately 3,500,000. The density of the air at the cruise flight altitude is about 80% of what it is in the wind-tunnel, and the viscosity is about 95%. If we were wanting to be very accurate about our Reynolds number matching we would have to take these variations into consideration, but conveniently we do not normally require such accurate values of Reynolds numbers, since the kind of differences we meet between Reynolds numbers in different situations tend to be of the order of powers of 10 rather than smaller numbers. Therefore for the sake of the present discussion, as very often in similar circumstances, we will ignore the changes in density and viscosity, and only consider the more significant quantities V and ℓ.

Let us suppose that we decide to make a 1/10-scale model; its span would be 3.4 feet, which would be fine for testing in a wind-tunnel with a test section about 5 or 6 feet wide. (In fact, some correction will be required because of the fact that the tunnel walls actually modify the flow pattern around the aircraft to some extent compared with an aircraft flying in the unconstrained atmosphere, but that is not our concern here.) If nothing else were to change, this scale factor would have the effect of reducing the Reynolds number by a factor of 10, which decidedly *is* a significant change from the full-size value and will mean that our test will be unreliable and invalid. Since density and viscosity are dictated to us by the air conditions, the only thing we have left to adjust, in order to restore the Reynolds number, is the speed, and in order to restore the original flight Reynolds number we will need to increase the speed ten-fold to 1,250 mph. What are the implications of this?

Apart from this being an extremely high speed for constructing and operating a wind-tunnel (of the size needed), and therefore excessively expensive for the sort of work in mind on a low cost basic trainer, there is a much more fundamental problem. The speed of sound is about 660 mph, and so 1,250 is approaching twice the speed of sound! All of our work so far has been firmly based on the assumption that the air is 'incompressible', and in Chapter 5 we discussed this concept thoroughly and showed that we could only reliably make such an assumption at speeds below about 30% or 40% of the speed of sound. Soon, (in Chapters 10 and 11) we will break out from this constraining straight-jacket of incompressibility and introduce supersonic and transonic aerodynamics, but at the moment all we can say is that the entire scene changes very drastically indeed, and a whole new way of looking at things is required, once we approach or exceed the speed of sound. The forces and their coefficients have to be worked out in new ways, and the incompressible approach would give force results which were not even remotely near to being correct.

So what has gone wrong with our nice tidy expression $C_F = f(Re)$, which told us that the force coefficients only depended on the Reynolds number, and that provided the Reynolds number was the same the force coefficients would be the same? The answer is that the expression $C_F = f(Re)$ is an over-simplification which has arisen out of our attempt to introduce things one at a time, but now we are forced to stretch out once again and incorporate yet another concept in order to explain what has gone wrong. Earlier in this section we stated that any aerodynamic force F depended on the four quantities ρ, μ, V and ℓ, which was a development from our ideas of Chapter 3, where we had only included three of the quantities and had omitted μ. However, we are now being made aware that there is yet a fifth quantity on which aerodynamic force depends and which therefore we must include in this list for total completeness and accuracy, and that is the speed of sound a. We will not tire you with going through the mathematical development this time, which involves solving three equations for five unknown quantities, and treating two of them as 'known'. Suffice it to say that the outcome of this exercise would be an extended version of the formula $C_F = f(Re)$ that we developed above, namely

$$C_F = f(Re, M)$$

where M is the Mach number, which is simply the speed of the freestream airflow V divided by the speed of sound in air at the same conditions, a, or in mathematical shorthand $M = V/a$. The Mach number is another dimensionless number like the Reynolds number, and in words the above modified equation now reads 'Any force coefficient is a function of both Reynolds number and Mach number, and nothing else.' Thus for the force coefficients to be the same in the model and in the full-size situation, it is necessary for both the Reynolds number and the Mach number to be constant, i.e. the same in both situations.

So the condition for ensuring dynamic similarity is not quite as simple as we had been led to believe. Rather than just one number, there are in fact two numbers, Re and M, that must both be matched in the model and full-size situations, and annoyingly it is usually impossible for these numbers both to be made equal in both systems at the same time. Fortunately all is not lost, since at low ('incompressible') speeds the Mach number is far less significant than the over-riding Reynolds number, and so the Mach number requirement can be ignored. At supersonic speeds, boundary layer separation is not the same problem that it is at subsonic speeds because what were adverse pressure gradients become favourable pressure gradients, for reasons that we will look at in Chapter 10. Consequently at supersonic speeds the Mach number becomes the all-important criterion for dynamic stability and the Reynolds number can usually be ignored.

Coming back to the Piper Tomahawk example, the full-size aircraft is operating comfortably within the incompressible speed zone, and so Mach number matching can be ignored. But if we are forced to increase the wind-tunnel speed to about twice the speed of sound, the model system is in the regime where the Mach number dominates, and clearly there is no hint of compatibility between the two systems.

We have not solved our problem of matching the model Reynolds number to that of the full-size aircraft. The problem is that we cannot scale down without unacceptably reducing the Reynolds number, and there is no obvious way of restoring this. Clearly the ideal is to keep to full-size, or if forced to scale down to do so as little as possible. But even if we use a model which is half of full-size, we will still need to double the speed to restore the Reynolds number, and if the full-size aircraft's speed is, say, 30% of the speed of sound or Mach 0.3 which can be regarded as incompressible, twice this speed is Mach 0.6, which is by no means in the incompressible regime. Furthermore, one of the chief purposes of scale modelling, to save the expense of making an extremely large scale model or full-size prototype, is lost, not to mention the colossal size of wind-tunnels that would be required.

Recalling the formula $Re = \dfrac{\rho V \ell}{\mu}$, are there any other ways in which we could restore the full-size Reynolds number to compensate for a reduction in ℓ? Increasing V turned out to be abortive, but we are left with the quantities ρ and μ. First of all, let us investigate the possibility of varying the air density ρ. This would have to be increased in the wind-tunnel by a factor matching the scale factor, i.e. 10 in our example, to maintain the same Reynolds number, and this would involve building a compressed-air wind-tunnel, in which the entire wind-tunnel and not just the working section would have to be maintained and operate at a pressure of about 10 times atmospheric pressure.

The history of aviation has been paralleled by a similarly intriguing but less heralded story of the development of the wind-tunnel. In 1921 the above approach of increasing the air density so as to match flight Reynolds numbers was adopted very successfully by NACA[6] at its Langley laboratory in the building of the first Variable Density Tunnel, as illustrated in Figure 8.3. Although the test section was only 5 feet diameter and test section maximum air speed only 50 mph, yet by dint of raising the pressure, and hence the air density, to 20 times atmospheric conditions in the tunnel, flight Reynolds numbers could be achieved. The Variable Density Tunnel was used for testing models of all manner of aircraft including Zeppelins, at Reynolds numbers close to those of aircraft flight at that time. In 1933 a NACA Technical Report was published containing a very authoritative and accurate set of tests carried out in the tunnel on seventy-eight aerofoil sections, using a Reynolds number of 3,200,000. This is about the same as the 3,400,000 of our small and slow Tomahawk trainer, and so it was a Reynolds number typical of the small, low-speed aircraft of that time. It was the first time realistic flight Reynolds numbers had been achieved in a wind-tunnel.

In 1939, NACA took a further step in the development towards more advanced variable density tunnels by building at Langley a 19

[6]NACA stood for the National Advisory Committee for Aeronautics, which was the precursor of the USA's National Aeronautics and Space Administration of today.

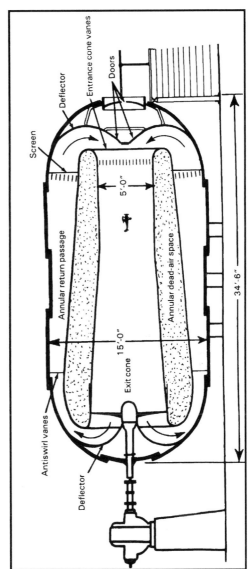

Figure 8.3   The NACA Langley Laboratory's Variable Density Wind-tunnel

feet (working section diameter) Pressure Tunnel. Much more massive than the first, the working airspeed could also go much higher, to 300 mph, so that even with the far more modest $2\frac{1}{2}$ atmospheres of pressure considerably higher flight Reynolds numbers (which were becoming needed) could be achieved. Being so large, it was not desirable to allow the tunnel to decompress between tests, and so operators, like deep-sea divers, had to enter and leave their working quarters through a decompression chamber, staying there for a considerable time at the end of a working shift to avoid getting 'the bends'.

Such solutions as we have so far considered, increasing tunnel speed, size or air density in any combination, all proved to be prohibitively costly for coping with the high Reynolds numbers of large modern commercial and military aircraft, which almost without exception operate near or in the transonic regime. There is still one other way in which test Reynolds numbers might be increased, and that is the possibility of reducing the air's viscosity on the bottom of the Reynolds number formula. We recall that the viscosity of air increases with increasing temperature, and as might consequently be expected it also reduces with reducing temperature. Wind-tunnels designed to operate on this principle run full of super-cooled gas (usually nitrogen) and are called *cryogenic* wind-tunnels, the word being based on the Greek word *kryos*, meaning frost. However, the cost and complication of achieving very high Reynolds numbers at transonic Mach numbers by this means have proved to be both excessively expensive and problematic, and cryogenic wind-tunnel testing has not yet taken over as mainstream technology.

TRANSITION FIXING

So it looks as if the quest to match perfectly the Reynolds numbers of flight in wind-tunnel tests is virtually a lost cause in most practical instances. However, it is clear that accurate and dependable wind-tunnel test results are a very important part of the overall aircraft design and development scene, and so we must look for alternative approaches. In doing so, let us recall the fundamental cause of the problem, as outlined early on in this chapter, that of separation of the boundary layer.

Departures from dynamic similarity of two geometrically similar systems occur as a result of a difference in flow patterns, and such differences depend almost entirely on where the boundary layer separates from the surface. This separation point in turn is very strongly dependent on the nature of the boundary layer: if it is turbulent, the boundary layer will stay attached much longer and will separate considerably further back, than if it is laminar. Once the boundary layer has become turbulent, then the degree of turbulence and the thickness of the boundary layer will also have a substantial (but secondary) effect on the position at which the boundary layer separates.

Thus the thing that we must attempt to control if we wish to influence the position of the separation point is where the boundary layer changes from being laminar to being turbulent; in other words, we need to fix where the transition point occurs. This is called *transition fixing*.

In the section on boundary layer transition near the beginning of this chapter, we considered an analogy of marching soldiers, and came to the intuitive conclusion that the position of the transition point depends upon speed, density, viscosity, surface roughness, free stream turbulence and adverse pressure gradient. So we have six possible handles by which we might be able to manipulate the transition point. However, we have already investigated and exhausted the first three, which all come within the scope of the Reynolds number. There is little that we can do about the adverse pressure gradient, since it depends directly on the shape of the object, which we can only alter at the expense of losing our fundamental geometrical similarity. If we did that, we would not be testing the original object at all, but something else. As for free stream turbulence, yes, we can introduce free stream turbulence into our wind-tunnel airflow, and yes, it will bring forward transition, which is the same effect as increasing the Reynolds number. But the trouble is that every tunnel has some free stream turbulence, and the amount is uncontrollable. Furthermore, doing the same tests on different wind-tunnels invariably produces different results simply because of the level of free stream turbulence. It is therefore extremely important to reduce the level of free stream turbulence as much as possible, and certainly it is not something that we want to encourage, because of its uncontrollability.

There is only one thing left, and that is the roughness of the surface. It is by physically roughening the surface (e.g. on an aerofoil at or near to the leading edge) by means of a strip of sandpaper or a layer of fine glass beads called Ballatino balls fixed with glue, that wind-tunnel testers actually persuade their models to behave *as if* the Reynolds number were higher than it actually is. An alternative technique is to use a thin trip-wire along the surface just where the transition point is required to be.

This is a fine idea in essence. But the problem is that, if we are trying to get the model to behave exactly like an un-built prototype in order to predict how the prototype will behave, then how can we possibly decide in advance where the transition point on the model should be? We need to know what we are trying to model before we can know what modification is required. Very much a chicken and egg issue! The problem is real enough, but the solution, not entirely satisfactory, is simply to rely on the accumulated wisdom and experience of, and data generated by generations of expert wind-tunnel operators. They have no better solution, so that is how it is done.

CRITICAL REYNOLDS NUMBER

It may have struck you that we have actually used Reynolds number in two slightly different ways in this chapter. Latterly we have taken the ℓ in the formula to represent some arbitrary length which is characteristic of the system, such as an aerofoil chord length or the diameter of a circular cylinder. But at the beginning of the chapter the length in the Reynolds number formula (which we called d) was the distance back from the leading edge of a semi-infinite[7] flat plate to the transition point. How can we reconcile these two essentially different approaches to defining Reynolds number, the first a system constant and the second a system variable?

First of all, it must be noted that, in the case of the flow over a semi-infinite flat plate, we have no other choice, since there does not exist any length which is characteristic of the system independently of the flow. A photograph of a semi-infinite plate which included its leading edge could contain no detail at all which would indicate the scale of the photograph, because no such detail exists. Therefore if Reynolds number is to have any use or meaning in this context, it must be a distance to *something* downstream from the leading edge, and since the Reynolds number gives us information about the transition point's location, what better choice than the distance to that point? Using this length, the Reynolds number is called the *critical Reynolds number*, and sometimes designated Re_{cr}.

Consequently, this critical Reynolds number is directly proportional to the distance to the transition point. But it is not a variable number, since the transition point is fixed by the combination of five of the contributory factors already referred to, (not adverse pressure gradient, since the plate is flat). The critical Reynolds number for flat plate flow is in fact found to be approximately 500,000 (give or take 100,000 to allow for the factors of surface roughness and free stream turbulence which do not appear in its evaluation). If we define a new, variable Reynolds number for the plate flow based on x, the distance back to *any* point in the flow, which we will call Re_x, then if Re_x is greater than

---

[7]Who but an aerodynamicist would introduce a term like 'semi-infinite'? Half of infinity is still infinity! But it does prove handy for describing a flat surface which begins at some finite point but from there on extends in the flow direction indefinitely. By comparison, a fully infinite plate would be one that had started at infinity upstream, but that is not particularly useful in aerodynamics, since the boundary layer will have grown to be infinitely thick by the time it reaches the observer.

500,000 we can expect probably to be behind the transition point and in a region of turbulent boundary layer; if less than 500,000, probably in the laminar flow region in front of it.

Let us move on now to consider a circular cylinder in a uniform flow. In this case, in contrast to the last, there *can* exist a uniquely defined Reynolds number for the system under particular flow conditions, since the object size, specified by its diameter which we use as the characteristic length, is system-specific. Does this new concept of a critical Reynolds number have any significance in this case? A glance back to the very end of Chapter 6, and especially at Figure 6.9, will suggest that the answer is probably 'yes', since there is some critical situation above and below which the form drag is markedly different because of the change in boundary layer separation point. We simply said in Chapter 6, without referring to the transition point, that a laminar boundary layer produced early separation and consequently high form drag, and that a turbulent boundary layer produced late separation and consequently low form drag. But how does this now relate to the transition point?

To answer this, let us consider what happens in a very low-speed flow over the circular cylinder. The transition point would occur very late on the cylinder because of the very low speed, and the boundary layer would be laminar almost everywhere. Therefore this transition point will never occur, because the boundary layer will separate whilst still laminar, before it gets to the hypothetical transition point. As the speed increases, so this hypothetical transition point moves upstream along the surface, until it reaches a point just upstream of what had been the laminar boundary layer separation point. The boundary layer flow at the point where separation had been occurring now becomes turbulent, so that suddenly the boundary layer separation point moves in a big jump much further downstream, and the pressure distribution changes from that on the left of Figure 6.9 to that on the right.

While this process of speeding up of the flow was going on, all the other Reynolds number factors, (density, viscosity and cylinder diameter) were remaining constant, and so the Reynolds number was rising proportionally to the speed. As we would expect, there is a speed, and hence a system critical Reynolds number, that coincides with the change from early to late separation. Of course the speed is system dependent, but the critical Reynolds number is not. The results of many experiments brought together show that the critical Reynolds number for a circular cylinder based on diameter is in the range of about 200,000 to 500,000. You may be inclined to think that, with a spread of values of 300,000 which is roughly the same as the mean value, such a statement is laughable and useless. But when you remember that Reynolds numbers don't just come in the hundred-thousands, but that they range over many decades (i.e. over many powers of 10), from numbers less than 1 to numbers as great as 10^8 or 10^9, then you will realise that the range 200,000 to 500,000 is in fact remarkably small, and, relative to the complete Reynolds number range, may be regarded as approximately constant.

Let us call this number Re_{cr} rather than having to quote it at length. If the system Reynolds number based on diameter is greater than Re_{cr} then we would expect late separation, a narrow wake and low form drag; and if less than Re_{cr}, early laminar boundary layer separation, a broad wake and much higher form drag. Incidentally, the change in form drag is not trifling but very substantial, with the value of the coefficient of drag falling from about 1.2 at subcritical Reynolds numbers to 0.35 (less than a third as much) at supercritical values. But what happens if the Reynolds number is slightly less than Re_{cr} and we then force early separation by transition fixing, i.e. by roughening the front of the cylinder with sandpaper or something similar? The presence of the sandpaper does not itself have any effect on the Reynolds number, but yet the cylinder behaves *as if* its Reynolds number had increased above Re_{cr}. But there is a more convenient and common way of putting this somewhat clumsy concept. Rather than saying that the effect is as if the Reynolds number had been increased above Re_{cr}, the alternative is to say that Re_{cr} has itself been *reduced* to below the system Reynolds number (which is, in fact, the case, although we are not measuring Re_{cr}). Thus, using this terminology, we say that the effect of using transition fixing is to *lower* the critical Reynolds number of the system.

How does this idea of critical Reynolds number apply when we are thinking of aerofoils? Although for some very thin aerofoils with fairly sharp leading edges (as we shall see in Chapter 9) there is a sudden and dramatic movement of the boundary layer separation point from a point near to the trailing edge to a point close to the leading edge, with very sudden and drastic consequences, this is invariably related to a small change in aerofoil orientation (and hence adverse pressure gradient), rather than one of the factors affecting the Reynolds number.

In fact, we do not usually relate the idea of a critical Reynolds number with aerofoils at all. In practice, to a fairly good approximation, the behaviour of most aerofoils at 'flight Reynolds numbers', which of course range over a fairly large numerical range, is fairly consistent with no funny jumps or sudden changes. This is extremely convenient, because it means that, as far as aeroplanes (but not models) are concerned, the coefficients of lift and of drag may be regarded as totally independent of Reynolds number, and only dependent on aerofoil shape and orientation. Pilots, then, never need to be concerned with Reynolds numbers, since the changes involved have insignificant effects.

Between the low Reynolds numbers of typical wind-tunnel tests and flight Reynolds numbers, however, there is a considerable change in performance of aerofoils, affecting both lift and drag coefficients, and this cannot be ignored. However, there is not a clear-cut 'critical' Reynolds number as there was in the case of the circular cylinder, above and below which the flow characteristics are suddenly different. Rather, the changes from one regime to the other tend to occur gradually over a range of Reynolds numbers, so that, when presenting technical data based on test results on a particular aerofoil, it is necessary to carry out the tests over a range of different Reynolds numbers and to present each result separately. Such data are particularly important for designers of devices other than aircraft (e.g. wind turbines and helicopters) where the aerofoils may have to operate at a variety of different Reynolds numbers. But fortunately from our point of view in studying aircraft flight, we can largely ignore Reynolds number effects.

BALLS

To close the chapter, let us take a third and final look at the subject of ball games. At the end of Chapter 6 we saw how dimpling a golf ball reduces its drag, and we now have a better understanding of the mechanism involved there. Near the beginning of the section in Chapter 7 on Cylinder Lift in Real Flow, we talked about the use of the Magnus effect on spinning balls, and we promised to return to cover the cricket bowler's technique of seam bowling in this chapter, which is where we come in now.

The seam bowler uses a combination of the Magnus effect and the existence of a critical Reynolds number to produce a sideways force on a ball, in order to make it swerve in the air. Although he incorporates some spin, this is not for aerodynamic reasons, as we will see. Figure 8.4 shows a cricket ball flying through the air from right to left, being viewed downwards from above. The bowler bowls the ball in such a way that the seam of the ball remains orientated at the same angle to the on-coming flow throughout the ball's flight as shown. If the speed of the ball is such that the ball's Reynolds number (based on diameter) is slightly below the critical Reynolds number (which is about 160,000 for a sphere, a little less than that of the cylinder), then the smooth side of the ball (which the bowler has meticulously polished on his flannels) will have a laminar boundary layer and the flow will detach early. However, the roughness of the seam on the other side of the ball will have the effect of tripping the boundary layer into transition and hence reducing the critical Reynolds number on that side to below the flight Reynolds number, and as a result the turbulent boundary layer will stay attached until more than half way around the

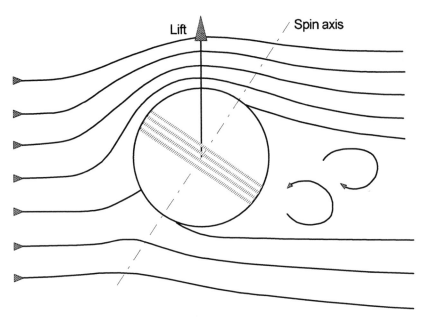

Figure 8.4 Cricket Ball Bowled by a Seam Bowler

ball. If the 'smooth' side has got rough through excessive play of the ball, then the laminar boundary layer cannot be retained despite the bowler's best attempts at polishing the ball, and in this case the effect cannot be achieved until a new ball is produced for play.

The result of this differential separation on the two sides of the ball is to produce a circulation around the ball as shown in Figure 8.4, and hence a sideways lift as illustrated by the arrow. But the clever bit is how the bowler can possibly ensure that the ball stays correctly orientated throughout its twenty-two yards or so of flight through the air. It would only need to rotate a quarter of one rotation during this flight for the effect to be completely lost or even reversed, and to prevent such a small rotation occurring would seem to be virtually impossible. The answer is that the bowler imposes spin on the ball, but this time not to create circulation. The ball is spun about the axis perpendicular to the plane of the seam, as shown by the dashed and dotted line in the figure, and this produces in the ball a gyroscopic stability, keeping the ball correctly orientated throughout its flight just like a gyro compass in an aircraft.

Being no cricketer myself, I am full of awe and admiration that any bowler can conceive of, and then execute, such a complex and demanding delivery of the ball. I wonder if they understand what is going on!

CHAPTER 9
Practical Aerofoils in Real Flow

INTRODUCTION

Having worked hard at establishing a sound understanding of both the theoretical and the experimental methods by which aircraft designers can ply their trade, we can at last begin to reap some of the rewards of our efforts by looking at the real outworking of these ideas in practice. In this chapter we will consider the behaviour of real aerofoil sections that have been developed, and will also discuss ways in which their performance can be modified by the pilot for particular requirements whilst flying the aeroplane.

We will at last begin in this chapter to get a feel for the real business of flying. We will be talking about pilots, about controls, about hazards and about real accidents. However, even now bear in mind that we haven't reached the end of the story yet. We are still in this chapter basing our discussion on the two assumptions that, firstly, the wing is two-dimensional and so is infinitely long with no wing-tips, and secondly that the speed of the airflow everywhere is well below the speed of sound. In the subsequent four chapters we will rapidly demolish the need for both of these assumptions, but we will for now carry on learning to walk before we try running.

Although we have been able to establish the basic horizontal teardrop form of the aerofoil shape from careful logical considerations, yet there can be a literally endless range of different profiles encompassing this fundamental form. A mathematical method exists (a little beyond our scope) for creating a special group of these which exactly match the circular cylinder flows on which they are based, so that their circulation, that all-important quantity which tells us about the lifting effect of the aerofoil, may be readily calculated. However, in the world of real flow, they are not in fact very practical since they have arisen out of pure inviscid theory. Instead of using these, experimenters and developers (more recently with the help of sophisticated computer-based methods) have given us an enormous range of aerofoil shapes for practical use as aircraft wings or for other purposes, together with a wealth of accurate working data generated by careful wind-tunnel tests according to the principles discussed in Chapter 8.

AEROFOIL TERMINOLOGY

If we wish to talk about the performance characteristics of different aerofoils, first of all we will need to establish some form of language, or terminology, by which we can fairly precisely describe the particular features of the shape of the aerofoil which give rise to the different aerodynamic effects. Real aerofoils do not have nice simple and tidy mathematical equations describing their shapes, and so these shapes are in fact usually presented as a set of (x, y) co-ordinate data, like the points of a graph. To generate the aerofoil shape, all the points are plotted and joined with a smooth curve except for the trailing edge, which is a sharp corner. But this string of number pairs is scarcely a convenient form in which to carry on a meaningful discussion about the effects of the actual features of the aerofoil shape. We need a language of words.

The general terminology which is applied to aerofoils is fairly universal and standard, but the precise definitions of some of the terms differ from one aerofoil source to another. We will therefore use one old and very well established and respected system as the basis of all our discussion in this chapter, that offered by the USA's National Advisory Committee for Aeronautics (NACA, predecessor of today's NASA). Not only will we use NACA's established terminology, but we will also discuss the effects of aerofoil shape as they are revealed through wind-tunnel data of some of the NACA family of aerofoils. Although today many newer aerofoils are also in use, the NACA family has stood the test of time very well and members of it are still to be found in very many applications.

Figure 9.1 shows a stereotypical aerofoil section with its important features labelled. The basic frame of reference for all other terms is the chord line, and all lengths and distances are quoted in terms of the chord length (usually just referred to as the chord) of the aerofoil. It is therefore a first priority to define the chord line of the aerofoil, and since this must be a straight line its definition requires the specification of two points. We conveniently have one natural point, the trailing edge, but we need another point somewhere at the front which we can

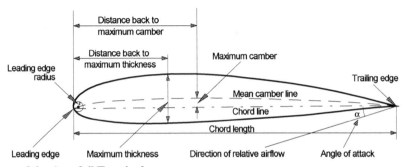

Figure 9.1   Aerofoil Terminology

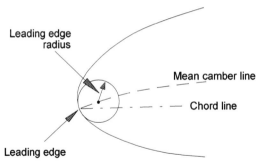

Figure 9.2   Leading Edge Detail

refer to as the leading edge. Unfortunately there is just a smooth (although quite tight) curve passing through this region with no unique point obviously shouting at us 'I am the leading edge', so we must somehow define a leading edge reference point on this curve.

You may think that this is a trivial matter, but a glance at the enlarged leading edge detail in Figure 9.2 will show that this is not the case. One possible definition of the leading edge might be the point furthest away from the trailing edge, which is the extreme left point of the envelope[1] in Figure 9.2. It is clear from the figure that this point is appreciably higher than the point labelled 'leading edge' (which we still have to define). There may be an angle of a degree or two between the lines joining each of these points to the trailing edge, and although this is a small angle in absolute terms it is quite considerable in terms of change in angle of attack and aerodynamic effectiveness, as we shall see later in this chapter. Therefore different choices of leading edge definition may make an appreciable difference to the way in which the aerodynamic characteristics of the aerofoil will be expressed.

So how should we define the leading edge point of the aerofoil in order to provide a front anchor point for the chord line? To help us out, it will be useful to reflect on the philosophy on which the NACA family of aerofoils was based. This consisted of a logical two-stage process whereby the important characteristics of thickness and camber were distinguished from each other and treated separately before being combined. A thickness distribution on its own (i.e. top and bottom surfaces equally distributed about a chord, a straight reference line) will produce the basic symmetrical aerofoil shape that we met in Chapter 7. If this shape is then taken and metaphorically bent across your knee, then the top surface will have increased curvature, (i.e. will

---

[1]An envelope is simply a curve containing a shape, in this case the curve of the aerofoil surface.

be more humpy), the bottom will have decreased curvature (i.e. will be flatter), and the line through the middle that was originally the straight chord line will itself become arched, or 'cambered'. Its new path, which is called the *mean camber line,* provides a means of measuring the camber (or amount of bending) that has been applied to the aerofoil.

This now gives us a good clue as to the most logical way to define the leading edge. It should be the same point on the aerofoil surface as it was before the aerofoil was metaphorically bent over your knee. Thus we *define* the leading edge of an aerofoil as the point at which the mean camber line meets the aerofoil envelope. But of course this begs the question as to precisely how do we define the mean camber line for a cambered aerofoil, which we must consider now.

Remembering that the mean camber line is derived from the chord line before camber is applied, let us consider a symmetrical aerofoil section, and imagine a series of equally spaced points along its chord line. Now in your mind's eye draw lines normal to the chord line at each of these points, to intersect the aerofoil envelope at both top and bottom surfaces. The distance up each one of these lines from the chord line to the upper surface is equal to the distance down to the lower surface, because the aerofoil is symmetrical.

Now as before, mentally bend the aerofoil over your knee. What will happen to all the short lines perpendicular to the chord line? They will fan out as the top surface stretches and the bottom surface shrinks. But they will all remain perpendicular to the newly curved chord line, which is now the mean camber line, and the distance along each short line from the mean camber line to the top surface will still be equal to the distance from the mean camber line to the bottom surface, just as it was before.

We can therefore *define* the mean camber line as the locus of points half way between the upper and lower surfaces, as measured perpendicular to the mean camber line itself. This line automatically defines the leading and trailing edges as the points where it intersects with the surface, and hence we can define the chord line as the straight line joining these points. The *chord* (or chord length) is defined as the distance from leading to trailing edge measured along the chord line.

The chord is used as a reference for all other lengths, which are all given as a fraction or a percentage of the chord, so that the geometrical characteristics may be applied to the aerofoil scaled to any overall size. As shown in Figure 9.1, lengths referred to in this way are the maximum camber and maximum thickness (both measured perpendicular to the chord, now it has been defined), the distances back from the leading edge of these two measurements, and the radius of curvature of the leading edge.

The chord is used for another very crucial purpose, that of defining the *angle of attack* of the aerofoil. This angle, designated α, is defined as the angle between the chord line and the direction of the relative airflow in the free stream, the latter being represented by a straight line going to the trailing edge. There are a couple of important things to notice about this. Firstly, this line representing the free stream velocity direction is not a streamline, and it does not represent the *local* airflow around the aerofoil, since that has different directions at all points in this region. Rather, it represents the undisturbed direction of the stream that is responsible for creating the flow field around the aerofoil and thus the lift and drag forces. Secondly, the angle of attack is only one of a number of different angles that are used to relate the aircraft's attitude (nose up or down) to the airflow or to the horizon. We will not confuse things by introducing at this point other angles which are not relevant here, but would just remind you that α, the angle of attack, is simply a relationship between the aerofoil (as represented by its chord line) and the relative airflow. It has nothing to do with the longitudinal reference line of the aircraft fuselage, or the way the wings are attached to the aircraft, or the orientation of the aircraft to the horizon, or whether the aircraft is climbing or descending.

Referring back to Figures 9.1 and 9.2, the leading edge radius requires a little explanation. Most aerofoils have a small region of the leading edge in the form of a circle, but this region may be very small indeed if the curvature is continuously changing around the leading edge. Either way, a circle can be fitted into the 'nose' of the aerofoil whose curvature exactly fits that of the aerofoil at the leading edge point. If this circle is thought of as remaining in place when the aerofoil is bent over the knee to apply camber, the result will be as shown in Figures 9.1 and 9.2. The length of the circle's radius is the same as the radius of curvature of the envelope at the point where they touch – in fact, the radius of curvature of a curve at a point is actually defined in this way, as the radius of the circle that exactly fits the curve at the point. The length of the radius in this case is referred to as the *leading edge radius*.

It can be shown from its definition that the mean camber line is perpendicular to the envelope at the leading edge. The mean camber line curves on its way from here, whereas a radius of the circle drawn from this point would be a straight line perpendicular to the circle and to the envelope. Thus a radius of the circle drawn through the leading edge will be tangential to the mean camber line at the leading edge. The radius, of course, goes through the circle's centre, and so the mean camber line, being curved, veers off from going through the centre of this circle. Thus the mean camber line does not quite pass through the centre of curvature of the leading edge, as a number of text books would have you believe.

A Caution

The literature on the subject tends to be either dismissive of the problems of definition or else very confusing. If you take any of today's leading aerodynamics text books and look up 'aerofoil nomenclature' or 'aerofoil terminology', there is a high chance that you will find a diagram almost identical to Figure 9.1, accompanied by a very brief apology of a definition (if any) of the crucial words such as chord and mean camber line. Most books totally fail to acknowledge that there is a problem of comprehension and rapidly gloss over the issue to talk about the aerofoil characteristics. The chord line is usually defined correctly as the straight line connecting leading and trailing edges, but the leading edge is frequently not defined at all. Typical of definitions of the mean camber line is 'the locus of points midway between the upper surface and the lower surface, *as measured perpendicular to the chord-line*' (my italics), which, as we have seen, is incorrect. A glance at that part of the mean camber line in Figure 9.2 which is ahead (left) of the centre of curvature of the leading edge will immediately make it clear that the distances from any point on this camber line vertically upwards and downwards to the aerofoil surface (i.e. in directions perpendicular to the chord line, which is here horizontal) are certainly not equal, the upward distance being considerably greater. Furthermore, the mean camber line cannot be defined in terms of the chord line, since the chord line cannot itself be defined until the mean camber line, and hence the leading edge, has been defined. The argument is cyclic and unsustainable.

You may feel that I am being unduly pedantic about the definitions of the aerofoil nomenclature. After all, it is only at the very leading edge that things get tricky, and over the majority of the aerofoil surface the difference between alternative explanations or definitions is very small and may safely be ignored. If you feel this way, be warned! It is true that approximate definitions will do over most of the aerofoil, but it is very far from true that the leading edge region may be tritely brushed aside as too small to be important. It is at the leading edge that many of the most striking aerodynamic features of the aerofoil occur. In this region, by far the highest and lowest pressures occur, flow speeds change rapidly from zero to extremely high values and back to low values again, and the aerofoil surface is so tightly curved that the directions of the pressure or suction forces range through about 180° over a very short region of the aerofoil. Also in this region very severe adverse pressure gradients occur, which can cause sudden total flow separation resulting in a leading edge stall, with dramatic and sometimes catastrophic effects. It's all happening at the leading edge!

AEROFOIL CHARACTERISTICS

In order to gain an insight into the actual performance of different aerofoil shapes as wings for aircraft, we will consider and compare with each other just a small selection of NACA aerofoils. In general we will be interested in their lifting characteristics, their drag characteristics, and also in the ratio of lift:drag. Let us start by looking at lift.

The lifting characteristics of aerofoil sections are most conveniently represented in the form of a graph of the lift coefficient C_L against the angle of attack α, and this graph is referred to as the *lift curve*. We saw in Chapter 8 that for a given aerofoil at a given angle of attack (for incompressible flow), the coefficient of lift depends only on the Reynolds number, a relationship which we expressed as $C_L = f(Re)$. It was also observed there that for most flight purposes Re can be regarded as constant, (which we will assume in this present section,) so that a given aerofoil at a given angle of attack has a constant lift coefficient. From this it follows that, when dealing with just one aerofoil shape, the lift coefficient depends only on the angle of attack. We can therefore plot a graph of C_L against α for a given aerofoil and get some sort of curved or straight line which will inform us of the precise relationship. What is the nature of this relationship?

Recalling our earlier work on inviscid, potential flow theory, we saw that the circulation produced by an aerofoil is directly proportional to the direction in which the trailing edge is pointing relative to the free stream direction, or in other words that the circulation is proportional to the angle of attack ($\Gamma \propto \alpha$). We also met the equation expressing lift per unit span in terms of circulation and flight conditions, $L = \rho V \Gamma$, which shows that, for given flight conditions, lift per unit span is proportional to circulation ($L \propto \Gamma$). Note that we are here using L to mean lift per unit span and not total lift. Finally, in the well-established equation $C_L = (\text{Total lift})/\frac{1}{2}\rho V^2 S$, if we divide both (Total lift) on top and S on the bottom by the span, we obtain the form $C_L = L/\frac{1}{2}\rho V^2 c$ where c is the chord. Thus for a given aerofoil size and flight condition C_L is proportional to the lift per unit span ($C_L \propto L$). Remembering that this is based on ideal flow theory, we may combine these three proportionalities showing us that

$$C_L \propto \alpha$$

Furthermore, although we will not prove it here, it can be shown from the ideal flow theory that, if the angle is expressed in radians, the constant of proportionality in this relationship is 2π, so that we may write

$$C_L = 2\pi\alpha$$

This means that our graph of C_L against α would (in ideal flow conditions) be a straight line through the origin, and that the slope of the

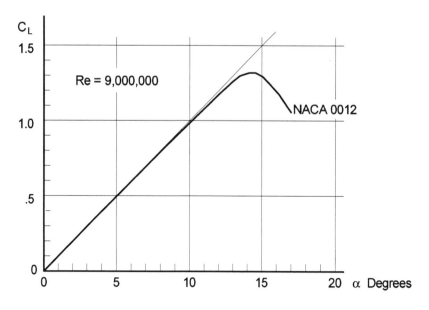

Figure 9.3   Approximate Ideal Lift Curve Compared With NACA 0012 Lift Curve

graph (known as the *ideal lift curve slope*) would be 2π. To make life easier, 2π is approximately equal to 6, and 1 radian is roughly equal to 60°. If C_L increases by 2π in one radian, then it increases by about 6 in 60°, or 1 in 10°, as shown by the thin graph line in Figure 9.3

Now a real aerofoil in real flow unfortunately does not behave quite like that. Figure 9.3 presents approximately the real lift curve of a symmetrical NACA aerofoil (NACA 0012 – the first zero means zero camber) alongside the ideal lift curve. The similarity over the first 13° or so of angle of attack is remarkable, greatly enhancing our faith in the potential flow model which has produced a theoretical line so closely resembling what happens in real life. But at this point the real lift curve fairly suddenly breaks down and keels over, and as the angle of attack increases further the lift coefficient fails to respond and actually falls off rapidly. The aerofoil has stalled. The adverse pressure gradient somewhere over the top surface has defeated the boundary layer's penetration power, and the boundary layer has separated, resulting in a major breakdown in the smooth lifting airflow behind this point.

Let us look now at a number of different features of typical aerofoils and at the aerodynamic effects of these features. Figure 9.4 shows the lift curves of a selection of five NACA aerofoils, plus a dashed straight line passing through the origin at a slope of 2π per radian, the ideal lift curve slope, for comparison.

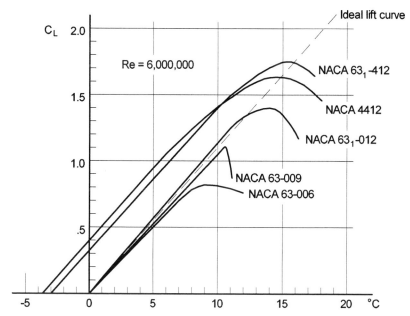

Figure 9.4   Lift Curves of Some Typical Aerofoil Profiles

Camber

The lift curves of three of the aerofoils depicted pass through the origin, and so they have no lift when they are set at zero angle of attack. These three are therefore all symmetrical, and this is indicated in their NACA code numbers by the zero following the hyphen[2]. The aerofoil NACA 0012 whose lift curve is shown in Figure 9.3 is also symmetrical, as indicated by the two 0s at the start of its four-figure code number, and has frequently been used in the past for helicopter rotor blades in order to avoid introducing twisting moments in the blade, since a symmetrical aerofoil normally produces no pitching moment about a particular fixed point.[3] Symmetrical aerofoils are also usually used for aircraft vertical tail fins, since they are as likely to be required to produce a lift force in one direction as in the other.

The other two aerofoils of Figure 9.4 both have positive camber, and hence produce some positive lift at zero angle of attack. This is

---

[2]Strictly this figure after the hyphen specifies the 'design lift coefficient' which is defined as the lift coefficient when the foremost part of the mean camber line is parallel to the airflow. However, since the mean camber line is synonymous with the chord line in a symmetrical aerofoil, the zero here implies no camber.

[3]The pitching moments of aerofoils will be covered in some detail in *Flightwise: Aircraft Stability and Control*, under the topic of longitudinal static stability.

because if a cambered aerofoil is set at zero angle of attack, i.e. so that its chord line is parallel to the free stream air flow, then the camber (the bending downwards of the rear part of the aerofoil relative to the front) causes the trailing edge to point downwards relative to the free stream direction, resulting in the circulation which produces lift. Camber contributes significantly to profile drag (boundary layer dependent drag) as well as to lift, and so aerofoils with little or no camber are used in applications in which high values of C_L are not required, such as fast transport aircraft.[4] However, as is very evident from the figure, the cambered aerofoils are capable of producing very much higher values of C_L than the symmetrical ones before they stall, and consequently they are particularly valuable for large load carrying applications where drag is not so important.

Lift curve slope

As we commented about Figure 9.3, so very strikingly in Figure 9.4, all the symmetrical aerofoil lift curves have a straight portion which lies very closely indeed to the theoretical lift curve, until they deviate as flow separation occurs. Furthermore, the two curves representing the cambered aerofoils likewise have a straight portion up to near the stall, which can be seen to be parallel to the dotted ideal line. Thus, before separation occurs, all the aerofoils (and this is typical of most conventional aerofoils produced) behave in very good agreement with the potential flow theory and have a lift curve slope which is very close to the ideal theoretical value of 2π per radian (or about 0.1 per degree).

In Chapter 6 we introduced the idea of rate of change and the Leibeniz notation. Using those concepts, the lift curve slope may be expressed as $dC_L/d\alpha$. This is a very important quantity since it is the constant of proportionality between C_L and α (for the symmetrical aerofoils). Using it in the appropriate relationship, we can predict the pre-stall behaviour of an aerofoil very accurately by purely mathematical means, but once the curve starts deviating from this relatively ideal straight line the mathematics lets us down, and we have to depend on experimentation and measurement.

Thickness

The last two digit pair on each of the NACA code numbers in Figure 9.4 represents the aerofoil thickness as a percentage of the chord, the thickness ranging from 6% of the chord (for the lowest curve) to 12% (for the top three). Notice that the thinner aerofoils have lower maximum C_L values. In Chapter 11 we will discover that these aerofoils

---

[4]We will have to modify this assertion in Chapter 11 when we consider design for aircraft flying close to the speed of sound.

were well suited for use on high subsonic speed aircraft where it was required to make sure that the speed around the aerofoil nowhere rises to the speed of sound. However, we will also see in that chapter that a new breed of 'supercritical' aerofoil has been developed, making these very thin conventional aerofoils virtually obsolete today.

An aircraft wing is not merely an aerodynamic device, but is also a structure, which has to be designed to be capable of withstanding all the forces that are to be imposed on it. Being fixed at only one end (at the fuselage), it is in fact a cantilever. It is the material at the extreme top and bottom of a cantilever that has to withstand the greatest forces when the cantilever is loaded, and these forces are best withstood if the distance between the top surface and bottom surface is as great as possible. This is achieved by having a deep cross-section, which means a thick wing. If for some reason (such as aerodynamics in the case of a wing) a cantilever has to be less deep than would for structural reasons be desirable, compensation may be made to some extent by adding more material to it. But this makes it much heavier, and ultimately the available strength will probably be limited by the depth that can be allowed.

It is therefore clear that thin wings are not good news from the structural point of view. At the dawn of manned flight aerofoils were thought to require predominantly camber to produce lift, which they were given at the expense of thickness by making the lower surface concave. Aircraft wings consequently tended to be very thin. The early designers got around this problem by using biplanes, in which the struts and bracing wires effectively made for a (structurally) very deep wing indeed, and a very strong, light structure. Unfortunately, however, the biplane had some serious aerodynamic limitations. Firstly there was the very substantial drag produced by the struts and bracing; secondly, the low pressure region being created over the bottom wing constantly pulled downwards on the top wing, tending to cancel out its lifting effect, and thirdly – but we will look at that one in the subsection later on on boundary layer control. Once it was realised that much thicker wings could in fact be used without any aerodynamic disadvantage, the extra cantilever depth available meant that designers could move towards the monoplane configuration that is prevalent today.

Leading Edge Stall

You will observe that NACA 63-009 lift curve has a very abrupt down-turn at just under 11° of angle of attack, whereas the lift curve closely matched the ideal straight line right up to more than 10°. Let us suppose that you are flying straight and level and fairly fast in an aircraft with this wing. Your C_L is less than the maximum value available, which is about 1.1. If you now slow down, whilst remaining in straight level flight, you will need more and more C_L in order to maintain an amount of lift equal to the aircraft's weight. (We will be considering this a little more closely later in this chapter, under the heading of 'lift augmentation'.) You obtain this additional C_L by increasing the wing's angle of attack, achieved by using the tail controls to push down on the tail (but you do *not* climb). The slower you fly, the more angle of attack you will need, until suddenly and without any warning, the stall angle will be exceeded, and the lift will fall off very suddenly and steeply.

This undesirable aerofoil characteristic is called a leading edge stall. A little later in this section, after looking at the drag characteristics of aerofoil sections, we will give closer attention to what goes on at various kinds of stall, but for now let us just say that in a leading edge stall the boundary layer totally separates immediately behind the leading edge, leaving no lifting flow over the entire upper surface. It is characterised by the very sudden down-turn of the lift curve.

Supersonic wings have to be thin, and are in fact often as sharp at the leading edge as at the trailing edge, for reasons that we shall see in Chapter 10. The early high subsonic speed wings were also thin for reasons to be covered in Chapter 11, so that their leading edges had small radii of curvature. This meant that in both cases aircraft were prone to leading edge stall, and since maximum C_L values were not high the level flight stalling speed was extremely high, and so landings had to be carried out at very high speed.

As we have seen, leading edge stalls are particularly associated with sharp leading edges (small leading edge radii), which are an inevitable consequence of having very thin wings. The early thin and highly cambered aerofoils referred to in the last sub-section certainly were prone to leading edge stall, which caused numerous crashes for Sunday afternoon aviators of that era. The thinnest aerofoil in Figure 9.4 (at 6% thick) might have been expected to demonstrate a leading edge stall, but surprisingly according to its lift curve this appears not to be the case. It would have been prone to leading edge stall if it had reached a high enough angle of attack, but as can be seen its performance falls off prior to this for some other reason. A premature trailing edge stall (as discussed below) is probably being induced by the presence of the very sharp leading edge and lack of surface curvature.

Trailing Edge Stall

It would appear from Figures 9.4 and 9.3 that, to be certain of avoiding the leading edge stall characteristic, an aerofoil should be both reasonably thick and cambered, as are NACA 63_1-412 and NACA 4412. (The first 4 of the four-figure number represents the maximum camber as a percentage of the chord and the second 4 is its distance from the leading edge to the maximum camber in tenths of the chord. The 4 of NACA 63_1-412 actually represents the design lift coefficient of the section, but it is in effect a good indication of camber. Note that it is the only thing that distinguishes this aerofoil's code from that of NACA 63_1-012 which is symmetrical.) Each of these thick cambered aerofoils demonstrates a trailing edge stall, a characteristic very far removed from the leading edge stall, and the lift curve of each begins to deviate early and very gently from the direction of the ideal lift curve (especially NACA 4412). Over the top of the curve, there is only a very gradual falling off of C_L, at a very much enhanced C_L value. The pilot of an aircraft with wings of one of these sections can expect to receive plenty of advanced warning that a stall is imminent, because the separation commences from the trailing edge and gradually creeps towards the leading edge as the angle of attack is increased further.

C_D/α and C_L/C_D Curves

Important as lift is, it is only half of the overall story, and the designer must be equally concerned with the drag characteristics of the aerofoil sections he may choose to use. We saw in Chapter 3 that the main purpose of an aerofoil is to achieve a high lift:drag ratio, and therefore we must expect our drag coefficient values to be one or two orders of magnitude[5] smaller than lift coefficient values, perhaps clustered around 0.01 rather than 1 as in Figure 9.4.

When looking at the drag characteristics of aerofoils, it is important to realise that so far we have only considered boundary-layer generated drag (skin friction and form drag). When we are dealing with actual aircraft with wing-tips rather than theoretical two-dimensional aerofoil sections, there is another equally important form of drag known as lift induced drag, which we will be considering thoroughly in Chapter 12. What we are looking at here are purely two-dimensional aerofoil section drag characteristics, and although these are very important they do not give the complete picture.

When we were looking at lift characteristics just now, we were able to compare the experimental results with theoretical results obtained

[5]I must not attempt to define 'orders of magnitude', since the usefulness of the term arises directly from its deliberate vagueness. (Aerodynamicists tend to delight in this sort of language!) It simply implies relative concepts of bigness. Sometimes an increase (or decrease) by an order of magnitude is regarded as roughly multiplying (or dividing) by 10, e.g. from something sensibly measured in inches to something sensibly measured in feet (or vice versa). A time period sensibly measured in years might be regarded as perhaps an order of magnitude more than a period of months, and two or three orders of magnitude more than a period of days.

by ideal flow theory. But recalling d'Alembert's paradox, there is no way we can predict any drag force other than zero by means of ideal flow theory. Therefore all graphs of aerofoil section drag coefficients are purely experimental and cannot be compared with ideal flow theoretical results at all.

Aerofoil drag coefficients, like lift coefficients, are dependent on Reynolds number. But fortunately once again it is found that this dependence becomes very much less marked once we are firmly in the region of real flight Reynolds numbers, and so we can (to a good first approximation) ignore the Reynolds number dependence, which is what we will do here. This is not of course the case if we are trying to compare small scale model situations with full-size wings.

Figure 9.5 takes a representative NACA aerofoil section and shows the behaviour of each of the quantities C_L, C_D and C_L/C_D as they vary with α. Aerodynamicists sometimes choose instead to plot C_D values against C_L values rather than against α, but that is rather more difficult to interpret. Note in passing that the NACA 2412 of Figure 9.5 is another of the 12% thick NACA four-figure series of aerofoils, which are the oldest. We have met the symmetrical one in Figure 9.3, the 4% cambered one in Figure 9.4, and now the 2% cambered one in Figure 9.5. All have the same thickness distribution, and only differ from each other in that each has been bent a different amount over the knee.

The important thing to observe from Figure 9.5 is that over an angle of attack range from about $-5°$ to $+6°$ the drag remains very low – so low that the steadily rising value of C_L in this range divided by an approximately constant drag gives a lift:drag ratio which steadily rises from zero to near its maximum value of around 100. However, as the angle of attack increases further, the C_D curve gets much steeper and the drag rises rapidly. Clearly the most efficient operating range for low drag purposes will be at the lower angles of attack, and it must be remembered that there is always a significant drag penalty (which is not necessarily always a problem, as we shall see) for flying at high C_L.

Notice that the C_L/C_D curve rises rapidly to a maximum point and then falls less rapidly at higher angles of attack. There is always such a point of maximum lift:drag ratio, and the aircraft being designed for economy will normally be designed so that most of its operations are carried out in the angle of attack region of the maximum lift:drag ratio. The maximum value reached in Figure 9.5 of around the 100 mark confirms our discussion about lift:drag ratios and glide angles in Chapter 3, under the heading 'The Aerofoil'.

The four NACA aerofoils of Figure 9.4 whose codes begin with the Figures 63 are members of a widely used family of aerofoils known as the '6-series' laminar flow aerofoils, which were developed during the

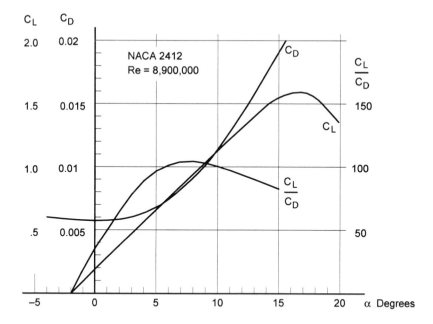

Figure 9.5   Typical Lift Coefficient, Drag Coefficient and C_L/C_D Curves

Second World War. In the code number the initial 6 designates the series; the second digit is approximately the distance back to the thickest point, 30% in all those depicted in Figure 9.4. As we have said, the figure after the hyphen indicates the camber, and the last two specify the thickness. These so-called laminar flow aerofoils were developed out of a desire to design wings that could cruise with a laminar boundary layer over most of the surface in order to minimise profile drag.

You will recall that skin friction drag is minimised in a laminar boundary layer, but that laminar boundary layers are very prone to separation at the slightest provocation, resulting in high form drag. Ultimately the only cause of boundary layer separation is an adverse pressure gradient, which there always must be towards the rear of any object in an airflow, and it is only this cause that can be taken account of in the geometric design of the aerofoil section. The technique used was to design an aerofoil such that adverse pressure gradients were kept as gentle and as small in area as possible. One technique was to place the point of maximum thickness further back than was otherwise desirable, typically at 50% chord, so that their code numbers were of the form 65-xxx (not depicted in Figure 9.4) and these were perhaps the most ubiquitous aerofoils of the period. The effect on the C_D/α curve was as shown in Figure 9.6.

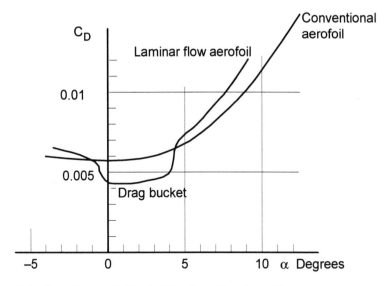

Figure 9.6   Drag Curve of a Typical Laminar Flow Aerofoil

Provided the smooth-surfaced aerofoil was only operated over a very limited angle of attack range so that the flow could remain attached, the reduced skin friction made for a substantial reduction of profile drag (the so-called 'drag bucket') compared with that of a turbulent boundary layer. However, once outside this range the form drag resulting from the inevitable boundary layer separation was greater than for a conventional aerofoil, whose shape was designed to cope with a wider range of conditions. The sudden change was the result of the boundary layer separation point moving very rapidly from the trailing edge to the point of maximum thickness once the critical angle of attack was exceeded.

Nowadays all fast or large (or both) aircraft have flight Reynolds numbers which are substantially above the critical Reynolds number. Transition to turbulence in the boundary layer thus inevitably occurs near to the leading edge, and so laminar boundary layer flow is not naturally attainable on aircraft surfaces. But at the time when the '6-series' aerofoils were being generated flight Reynolds numbers were still around the critical value, so that the attempt was worthwhile. However, in practice, although the aerofoils performed very well in laboratory tests, they did not normally show any substantial operational advantages, largely because of the impossibility of maintaining a smooth and clean enough surface that would not trip the boundary layer into turbulence.

STALLING

We have distinguished between two kinds of stall, but what actually happens to the aircraft, to the pilot and to the passengers when an aircraft stalls? Is it dangerous? What does the pilot have to do to recover from it? Are there any types of stall from which recovery is not possible? Let us answer some of these questions now.

Effects

A stall happens when the pilot 'pulls' too much angle of attack, through trying to get too much lifting effect from the wings. This may happen in straight level flight, as we have seen, if the speed is progressively reduced and the aircraft's nose is pulled higher and higher until the stalling angle of attack is exceeded. Alternatively, and probably more commonly, it can occur during any manoeuvre where more lift than usual is temporarily required, such as during a turn or a pull-up. The slowing down scenario is quite likely to occur during preparation for landing, when the aircraft is near the ground and there is very little vertical room for manoeuvre without hitting the ground. Stalls during manoeuvring are tricky to deal with, because of course the pilot is already pre-occupied with carrying out the manoeuvre, so that stall recovery is that much more demanding of him. Of course, if the manoeuvre is being done near to the ground, such as a final turn before landing, the problems are compounded, and things can be tricky.

The first effect of a stall is that lift *reduces* rather than increasing if the pilot applies more angle of attack (which is normally the intuitive thing to do to get more lift). This follows from the downward plunge that we have seen in the lift curves of aerofoils. Secondly, there is an extremely large increase in aircraft drag, which of course aggravates the situation by slowing the aircraft even more, so that even more lifting is required (but is unavailable) from the wings. Thirdly, there is likely to be some intense buffeting of the aircraft, especially those parts behind the wings. The smooth flow that the tail depends on to provide control may be seriously disrupted, so that the control surfaces needed for pitch control may become very much less effective than usual, or at the very least may be seriously shaken about. Furthermore, if the region of the wings towards the wing-tips is also stalled, (a subject we will talk about at length in Chapter 13,) then it is likely that roll control, essential for carrying out normal turns, will also become sluggish or ineffective.

Recovery

To recover from the stall the pilot needs more speed, so that he may obtain sufficient lift to equal the aircraft's weight whilst using less angle of attack. This speed may partially be provided by increasing the thrust of the engines, (provided spare thrust is available and can be obtained quickly) but being stalled, the drag of the aircraft is exceedingly high and will often exceed the available thrust. The required additional speed may be most effectively provided by allowing gravity to pull the aeroplane 'down hill'. To achieve this, the aircraft must be deflected downwards from its horizontal flight path, and for this it must temporarily produce *less lift*, so that the excess of weight over lift may deflect its flight path from horizontal to downwards. Then gravity will speed the aircraft up as it flys 'down hill'. Professional pilots are taught to recover from a stall by first of all increasing the throttles to maximum thrust, and then *gently* pushing the pitch control forward to lower the nose just sufficiently to recover without losing more height or gaining more speed than is necessary.

There is of course a loss of lift naturally occurring as a result of the stall. Furthermore, the position of the point of action of the total reaction on the wing (which is called the centre of pressure) usually moves rapidly towards the trailing edge of the wing when the stall fully develops, so that the remaining lift tends to pitch the aircraft nose down as required. Furthermore, when flying normally the downwash behind the wing (which will be discussed in Chapter 12) impinges on the tailplane, pushing it downwards and consequently holding the nose up. When the wing stalls, this downwash largely disappears, and so does the downward force on the tailplane, so that the nose is free to pitch downwards. Thus in many cases an aircraft will recover unaided from a stall.

But sometimes through some design quirk this may not happen, or it may simply happen too slowly so that the pilot would rather do something about it instead of just waiting. In this case the pilot must push his control column forward, which will deflect the elevator (the control surface at the back of the tailplane) downwards, thus providing more camber and hence upwards lift to the tailplane. This results in the aircraft being pitched (or tipped) nose down, so that the angle of attack is reduced substantially to well below the stalling angle, a lot of wing lift is given up, lift is now less than weight, the aircraft is deflected into a descending path, the speed increases, hence lift increases at a smaller angle of attack, and the aircraft can be recovered into level flight again. This action of the pilot also has the desired effect of raising the tail above the wings, so that the tail will follow the wings 'down hill' in an orderly fashion. If you like, the effect of the tail is like that of the flight of a dart thrown at a dart board; it will keep the aircraft pointing in the direction of flight.

Deep stall

Thus a normal stall, provided that it does not occur so near the ground that there is not sufficient height left for recovery, is a very safe and fairly innocuous event in the hands of a competent pilot. There are, however, a couple of special types of stall which call for particular attention. The first of these is called the deep stall.

Many aircraft designers, whether designing airliners, fighters, commuter aircraft or sailplanes, have recognised the potential advantages of putting the tailplane at the top of the tail fin (the so-called 'T-tail'), rather than more conventionally on the fuselage at the bottom of the tail fin. This is a particularly attractive option if it is required to mount engines at the rear of the fuselage. It is also done in order to keep the tailplane out of the direct wake of the wing, since this wake can sometimes be very turbulent, especially in the case of flying close to the speed of sound, as we will see in Chapter 11, and it is obviously most important that the tailplane control surfaces work effectively at all times.

There is an in-built danger in the use of a T-tail, and it is the possibility that the aircraft will enter a so-called *deep stall*. If the aircraft enters a normal stall, the high tailplane is brought virtually into the line of airflow from the wings as a result of the large angle of attack. Of course the separated flow over the wings creates a very thick turbulent wake, and the tailplane's job, as discussed above, is now to provide an upward force to pitch the aircraft's nose down for recovery. However, the long fuselage ahead of the wings is also inclined upwards in front of the high tailplane, and it sheds a pair of large, powerful vortices. Within these vortices, the air flows downwards close to the fuselage and upwards further out. Unfortunately it is the strong downward flow close to the fuselage that can catch the high tailplane, and apply a downward force on it, effectively sucking it down into the turbulent wake behind the wings. Elevator control is therefore drastically diminished, and cannot overcome the effect of the vortices which are still pushing the tail downwards. Eventually the tailplane will get pushed right out of the bottom of the turbulent wake, by which time the wing angle of attack has reached around 45°, in a flight direction which is probably steeply downwards. Now that the tailplane has emerged from the wake, the clean airflow tries to push it back into the wake, but the wake and the vortices keep making sure that it can't get back in again. Consequently the aircraft 'flies' on and downwards in an inexorable stable flight condition at about 45° angle of attack, with absolutely no recovery action possible. If (typically) its descent path is about 45° down from the horizontal, then the aircraft's wings and fuselage will be approximately horizontal. The inevitable outcome is a continued descent in this attitude until the

Figure 9.7   Hawker Siddeley Trident

aircraft hits the ground. None of the aerodynamic controls can have sufficient effect in this condition to bring about a recovery, and even the engines are unlikely to be available to produce more thrust, since their intakes may also be embedded in the turbulent wake behind the wing, and they may consequently have been extinguished or have 'flamed out'.

A memorable example of exactly such a catastrophic event once occurred just outside London Heathrow Airport. A Hawker Siddeley Trident (Figure 9.7) of British European Airways, bearing the unforgettable code name Papa India, was climbing out to the West of Heathrow, and in the normal course of events the captain raised the flaps when he thought that the aircraft speed was high enough. (The purpose and use of flaps are covered in the next section.) Apparently the speed was not in fact high enough when the captain did this, and an audible stall warning ensued. The flight crew repeatedly came to the conclusion that the stall warning system was giving a spurious warning, and cancelled the alarm. However, the aircraft entered a deep stall in the manner described in the previous paragraph, and descended very smoothly and stably, defying all attempts at recovery, to crash just outside Staines killing all on board.

Spinning

In the early days of aviation getting an aircraft into a spin used to be regarded as the kiss of death to heavier-than-air flight, the dreaded and fatal phenomenon that should be avoided at all costs. Nowadays, with all but a few high-performance combat aircraft (typically with short, swept wings,) a spin is a fairly routine training manoeuvre in small aircraft and something that can safely be recovered from by appropriate use of the controls.

Spinning is really a subject which might better fit under the category of stability and control, the substance of *Flightwise: Aircraft Stability and Control*. However, it is appropriate to mention spinning whilst dealing with stalling, and so the next few paragraphs will look 'through a glass, darkly' and will draw on aircraft control and stability phenomena which are not fundamentally covered in the present volume. If you find this glimpse of interest, perhaps it will whet your appetite for the companion volume.

Spinning is a possible outcome of a conventional stall, and it is a particular hazard when turning an aircraft near the ground when lining it up for a landing, especially if the speed is low. To understand the phenomenon we will start from considering an aircraft that is in straight and level flight, whose speed has been reduced and whose wing angle of attack has been increased to such an extent that it is on the verge of stalling, but hasn't quite stalled yet. Let us suppose that in this condition some small passing disturbance in the air tips one wing (let's say the right wing as viewed by the pilot) downwards, so that the left wing tips upwards. The downwards-moving wing is moving down into the air around it, so that the local airflow to that wing comes up at it from below. Consequently, without changing the orientation of the wing aerofoil section at all, the angle of attack of the down-going wing is increased. This effect is more pronounced the further out you look along the wing towards the tip, since the tip (moving in the arc of a larger circle) moves downwards faster than points further inboard. Remembering that the aircraft wing was already on the point of stalling before it started to roll, this increased angle of attack may be just enough to take the right wing-tip region beyond its stalling angle and cause it to stall. It then loses some of its lift (when what it really needed was a bit of extra lift to make it recover automatically) and the right wing therefore continues to descend.

Whilst this is happening, the other wing-tip is moving upwards, so that the relative airflow to it comes from above its original direction, causing the angle of attack there to be reduced. Thus this wing-tip, which had been on the point of stalling, is now given a reprieve from stalling so that the high lift that it is achieving is maintained and consolidated. Its lift will in fact fall a little as its angle of attack falls in the straight line region of the lift curve, but if the loss of lift on the stalled right wing-tip is greater then the net effect will be to roll to the right.

As the aircraft rolls, the stalled, down-going right wing experiences considerably more drag than the other wing, since as we have seen the drag of a stalled aerofoil is greatly increased. As a result, the aircraft begins to do a turn to the right, (clockwise viewed from above,) about an axis normal to the plane of the wings and the fuselage. This motion is called *yawing*, to distinguish it from pitching or rolling. The aircraft is now both rolling and yawing.

When the aircraft has rolled a little, it will begin to *sideslip* to the right, or move down a sideways slope in a direction at right angles to its flight direction, just as your car may slide sideways down the camber of a straight road if you drive over a sheet of ice on the road surface. This sideslipping phenomenon is one of the chief characteristics of the motion of an aircraft which distinguishes it from most land vehicles, which are normally restrained by rails or tyre friction to continue in a straight line forwards. As the tail fin sideslips with the rest of the aircraft, the airflow relative to the tail fin will come at it from the right, so that it generates an angle of attack and consequently a lift force to the left. (Remember that 'lift' doesn't mean 'upwards'.) Since the tail fin is behind the aircraft's centre of gravity, this will result in the nose yawing to the right, or down the sideways slope in the direction of the sideslip, thus adding to the yawing motion produced by the high drag of the stalled wing.

As a result of the aircraft's yawing motion, the left wing is travelling forward faster than the right wing, and so will generate more lift still than the right wing, exacerbating the situation arising out of the right wing stalling. As a result the tendency to roll to the right is increased, followed as before by an increased tendency to side-slip and consequently to yaw clockwise (as viewed from above).

So the aircraft enters a spinning motion, which is basically the combination of a rolling motion and a yawing motion. The sideslip, which is not a rotation but a translation (i.e. a linear motion), only indirectly contributes to the rotational motion of the spinning aircraft, but it does contribute to its rate of descent, which although not as high as if the nose had pitched down into a dive, can be fairly rapid.

The natural temptation in trying to recover from a spin might be to try to roll the aircraft the other way by using the control column to move the ailerons[6]. However, since the wing-tip which would require more lift to achieve this (the right wing) is already stalled, the deflection of its aileron will only serve to enhance its stall, and will not achieve the desired effect. In some aircraft it is found that the most effective way to recover from a spin is to apply full rudder in the direction which would normally cause a yaw in the direction opposite to that in which the aircraft is yawing in the spin, and once the yawing motion is arrested to use elevator to push the nose down and so recover speed. However, aircraft of different types and shapes display markedly different stalling characteristics, which depend not only on the aerodynamic shape but also on how the mass is distributed around the centre of gravity. Consequently the recommended recovery procedure varies greatly from type to type. In some aircraft a drogue parachute must be deployed from the tail to enable spin recovery, and certain aircraft cannot be recovered from a spin at all.

---

[6]Ailerons are the roll controls placed at the outer ends of the wings.

MODIFICATION FOR FLIGHT – LIFT AUGMENTATION

An aerofoil once designed is a very permanent shape, whereas the requirements of an aircraft in flight are constantly changing for a multitude of reasons. Right from the earliest days of aerofoil and wing design some in-flight modification of the shape of wings was possible, such as wing warping by pulling strings, in order to control the aircraft or produce required aerodynamic effects. We will concentrate on the need of the pilot, during flight, to be able to re-configure the wings, by means of what are called *lift augmentation devices*.

In straight level flight, and also in nearly level flight such as on a shallow approach to land or climbing away gently from the airfield after taking off, the lift produced by the wings must be approximately equal to the aircraft weight. During the few moments of flight being considered, we can assume that the weight of the aircraft is constant, since the amount by which its weight reduces due to fuel consumption during this period is small compared with the total weight of the aircraft. We can therefore use our 'lift formula' once again, and will write it in the following form:

$$\text{Lift} = \text{Weight} = C_L \tfrac{1}{2} \rho V^2 S$$

Now let us consider an aircraft which is able to fly at a maximum speed of 500 miles per hour at sea-level. Putting $V = 500$ and appropriate values of ρ, S and Weight into the lift formula will enable us to calculate the aircraft's high speed C_L value, and this will be very small since the speed is large and the formula contains the square of the speed. Thus for high speed an aircraft does not require a very 'lifty' aerofoil section, and so a thin, scarcely cambered section may be chosen in order to keep the high speed drag as low as possible. However, in order to be able to land safely on runways of a sensible length, the aircraft must also be capable of level flight at, let us say, 100 miles per hour. If $V = 100$ is substituted into the formula, the other terms on the right-hand side remaining unchanged, the lift would be reduced by a factor of 25 (because V is squared), but for level flight the lift must remain unaltered. It is thus necessary to boost the other terms of the right-hand side by an overall factor of 25, if landing and take-off at a sensible speed is to be possible.

Clearly air density cannot be varied at will, and S is *defined* as the aircraft wing area and is thus a constant. This leaves only the possibility of varying C_L, and so the aircraft requires a large C_L range. As we have seen, C_L is normally varied by altering the wing's angle of attack, but the C_L range available in this way is limited by the stall conditions, and for a thin aerofoil the maximum value of C_L is low because of the sharp leading edge and the tendency of the boundary layer to separate there.

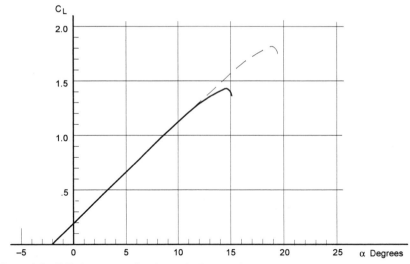

Figure 9.8   Lift Augmentation by Delaying the Stall

For this reason aircraft wings are designed to be modifiable in flight between the shape of a high-speed low drag aerofoil section for efficient high-speed flight, and a high-lift aerofoil section for low speed, especially for landing. The lift augmentation devices used to bring about this transformation are based on two fundamentally distinct approaches, which we will now consider separately.

The first approach is by delaying the stall to higher angles of attack. Normally C_L is increased by increasing the angle of attack, but this is limited by the stall. If some way could be found of preventing, or at least delaying, the stall, then the angle of attack, and hence C_L, could be increased further, thus extending the straight-line portion of the lift curve, as in the dashed portion of Figure 9.8. Briefly, this is most commonly achieved by the use of a leading edge device called a slat, which is a small, highly cambered aerofoil placed slightly ahead of the main aerofoil leading edge, as illustrated in Figure 9.9. The aerodynamic theory of how this works is complicated and somewhat obscure, but it may be simply thought of as causing a higher speed air flow by venturi action in the slot created between the slat and the main aerofoil. This flow is directed tangentially into the main flow boundary layer at the very point where without it the boundary layer would be on the point of separating because of the very strong adverse pressure gradient just behind the leading edge. We will come back in a few minutes to look at this and other ways of controlling the boundary layer in a little more detail.

There is one rather serious problem related to this approach to aug-

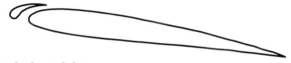

Figure 9.9   Simple slat and slot

menting the lift coefficient. Since lift augmentation is usually required during landing and taking off, it is at a time when the pilot requires to have a good field of view in front of him, below the horizon, so that he can see the airfield and the runway. But if he is forced to tip the nose of his aircraft high up in the air in order to achieve the necessary large angle of attack needed to provide sufficient coefficient of lift, it is likely that his downward visibility will be seriously impaired. A very clear example of the seriousness of this seemingly rather trivial problem emerges in the design of the Concorde supersonic airliner, which also depends on very large angles of attack (for slightly different reasons). The remedy in this case was to incorporate a 'droop snoot', in which the entire portion of the fuselage ahead of the flight deck hinges down from its normal flight position to improve the pilot's view. There are some aircraft (such as, for example, the Nimrod maritime reconnaissance aircraft based on the Comet jet airliner) which, if landed without flaps, have to have such a nose-up attitude that it is impossible for shorter-than-average pilots to see out over the instrument coaming to get a safe view of the runway, and so the Royal Air Force has to impose a minimum height restriction for pilots to operate such aircraft.

Even if the pilot visibility problem can be overcome, the conventional shape of aircraft creates another serious design problem arising out of the need for too much nose-up attitude on landing. Nose up means tail down, and if the tail is too low on landing it will strike the ground before the rest of the aircraft. This can't simply be fixed by placing a wheel at the back end of the fuselage, since if such a wheel were in place, once it touched the ground there would still be an appreciable height to descend before the main undercarriage wheels would touch the ground. During this period of pivoting nose-downwards about the tail wheel, the angle of attack of the wings would be rapidly reducing, and so the aircraft would lose lots of its lift before the main wheels had reached the ground. There would then be no way of preventing the main weight of the aircraft from falling to the ground at an uncontrollable rate, resulting in a very heavy bump with every landing. The only solution would be a main undercarriage designed along the lines suggested in Figure 9.10! Some airliner undercarriage legs (e.g. on the Boeing 767) are very long, partly for this reason.

Figure 9.10   The Design Problem of Landing with a Very High Angle of Attack

The second approach to obtaining lift augmentation is to alter in some way the camber of the aerofoil section of the wing, rather than attempting to obtain an extended angle of attack range with the natural aerofoil section. This can be crudely achieved by hinging the trailing edge portion of the aerofoil so that it can be drooped, and such a device is called a flap. The use of a flap does not extend the straight line portion of the lift curve, but rather pushes the entire curve upwards, as shown by the line labelled 'With Flap' in Figure 9.11.

Flaps are usually power operated, and move from the fully up to the fully down position in a very few seconds. Looking at Figure 9.11 we can work out what the effect of this will be. Let us suppose that the aircraft is flying fairly slowly and consequently at a fairly high unstalled angle of attack, say 11° as shown by the vertical dashed line in Figure 9.11. If the pilot then selects flaps down and nothing else changes, the operating point on the graph will immediately move straight up the dashed line at 11° to the new, higher value of C_L on the 'with flap' curve, which is not desirable since the instantaneous additional lift will place the aircraft in a pull-up manoeuvre as discussed in Chapter 2. Instead of this, the pilot must simultaneously reduce the angle of attack to about 5° in the case illustrated, so that the lift coefficient does not suddenly increase drastically. By doing so the operating point moves from right to left along the horizontal dashed line on the graph. Subsequently the pilot has the extended range of the 'with flap' lift curve available to use, by gradually adding more angle of attack, and the maximum C_L obtainable before stalling has increased from about 1.4 to over 1.9.

This pitching downwards of the nose conveniently often tends to occur automatically, since one effect of putting the flap down is to move the centre of pressure, the point on the aerofoil at which the aerodynamic total reaction acts, further back, and this in turn tends to cause the nose to pitch downwards as required. But this is not always

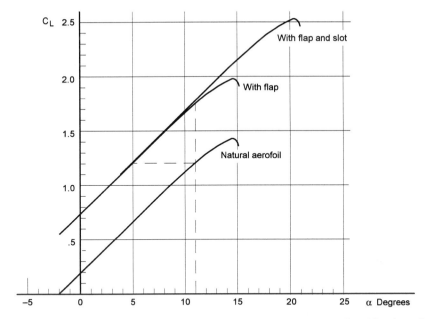

Figure 9.11   Lift Augmentation by Increasing the Camber, and in Combination with Slat and Slot

so. In the case of the Jetstream turbo-prop business aircraft, the tailplane is mounted in an unusual position between the top and the bottom of the tail fin, and this has the effect of placing the tailplane strongly in the downwash flow of the wings when flaps are applied. The nose-up pitching moment caused by this down-force at the rear of the aircraft is greater than the nose-down moment created by the flaps themselves, and so the aircraft's response to having its flaps lowered is to pitch its nose *upwards*. The pilot must therefore take immediate compensatory action to prevent a tricky flight condition ensuing.

The lift augmentation devices installed on modern aircraft can be extremely elaborate, consisting often of combinations of a number of moving surfaces and combining both of the two approaches to lift augmentation discussed. Thus lift curves may be doubly modified as shown in Figure 9.11 by the curve labelled 'with flap and slot', and sometimes maximum C_L values may be as high as 3 or more. However, the use of such sophisticated mechanisms is not without its hazards in flight. Lift augmentation devices are neatly tucked away out of sight and out of mind during cruising flight when they are not required. But when the aircraft is at a low air speed, near the ground with little vertical space for recovery from mishaps, and is necessarily engaged in tight and complicated turning manoeuvres in preparation for landing, and when the flight crew work load is at its highest, this is the phase of flight in which these complex devices must be deployed and must work reliably first time. Furthermore, since they must work simultaneously on both wings, if any asymmetric failure should occur it can be even more devastating, as the example of the Tristar crash referred to below will illustrate.

Airline operators find that one of the things that most disturbs passengers is sudden and unexpected noise, and usually the deployment of lift augmentation systems a little while before landing creates sounds that many passengers would prefer to do without. But if the noise alone can be alarming, how much more terrifying it can be to a perhaps elderly passenger at a window seat with a view of the trailing edge of the wing. Accompanying the sounds of the deployment mechanisms, large chunks and slabs of metal appear to come out from the rear of the wing, revealing gaping holes in the wing, and apparently being attached to the wing by very tenuous connections. The sight of the aircraft apparently breaking up around one can scarcely be conducive to an atmosphere of trust and faith in the safe landing of the aeroplane!

BOUNDARY LAYER CONTROL

Having considered the basic needs and mechanisms by which lift augmentation can be achieved, it will be informative for us to investigate a little deeper the practical outworking of these ideas. We will start off by considering just the approach of delaying the stall and extending the lift curve to higher C_L values, but whilst doing so we will also come across some other related applications of technology that have been developed initially for this purpose.

We have already mentioned that the most common method of delaying the stall is by use of the slat and slot as illustrated in Figure 9.9. The full name of this device is the Handley Page Slot, after the British aircraft designer and pioneer Sir Frederick Handley Page. Formerly an electrical engineer, he became interested in the problem of flight and founded the first British aircraft construction company Handley Page Ltd in 1909. In the early barn-storming days of Sunday afternoon leisure flying in the open biplanes of the day, one of the greatest dampers to enjoyment and constraints to further development was the ever-present fear of stalling ones aircraft and uncontrollably plummeting to the ground. Stalls were typically of the sudden and severe leading edge variety, a consequence of the sharp leading edges that at the time were regarded as a necessary characteristic of wings with sufficient camber for the required lift. Handley Page's invention of the slat and slot and its application to these biplanes transformed flying overnight from what had been becoming a discredited furore into a carefree and desirable pastime. This in turn opened the door to further aeronautical development. One major advance was the thickening of the aerofoil section as we mentioned earlier, making possible the natural development from biplane to monoplane.

Interestingly, the arrival of thick leading edges meant that the leading edge stall problem largely disappeared as the much safer trailing edge stall superseded it. This rendered the use of slats and slots virtually obsolete for a number of years, until they came into their own again with the arrival of very much thinner aerofoil sections as higher and higher air speeds were sought.

It would not be desirable in high performance wings for the slats to remain deployed when they are no longer needed, since they would create a considerable amount of drag at high speed with no benefit at all. Therefore the slats are nearly always designed to be retractable. At first slat retraction was made automatic. The slats were mounted on arms extending forward from the wing leading edge, and normally the slats were held retracted by springs. But when a large angle of attack was reached by the wing, a very substantial suction peak occurred over the leading edge, and this suction would pull the slat forward from the wing against its spring on its extending arms, bringing it automatically into action. In nearly all cases nowadays slats are extended or retracted by internally powered systems.

The Lockheed 1011 Tristar is a wide-bodied three-engined jet airliner of over 50 metres span. It has one engine mounted on a pylon beneath each of its wings, and the third buried in the root of the tail fin. A fatal crash once occurred to a Tristar during take-off. Having just left the ground, and being still over the runway, one of the wing mounted engines separated from its pylon and fell right away from the aircraft wing. One might naturally conjecture that, following such an event, the large unbalanced weight of the remaining engine would cause the aircraft to roll over with that wing going downwards.

Surprisingly what actually occurred was exactly the opposite. The aircraft did indeed roll over, which sadly proved to be catastrophic, but rather than rolling in the direction expected, it actually rolled with the wing still carrying an engine going upwards, and the engine-less wing descending! It was discovered later that the probable cause of this occurrence was that the control lines to the leading edge slats on the wing which lost its engine were severed as the engine was torn away from the wing, and subsequently the now uncontrolled slats retracted automatically under the influence of their retraction springs. As a result, this wing stalled, whilst the other wing's slats were still properly configured so that it remained unstalled. The extra wing lift of the wing still having its engine was thus much greater, causing the aircraft to roll to its destruction.

The concept of the slat and the slot is also used extensively in slots around the camber-enhancing lift augmentation devices, to ensure that air flow remains attached to the flaps around quite tight corners. We will meet this more fully a little further on when discussing aircraft flap systems.

Although the concept of slat and slot has undoubtedly proved high-ly successful, it is limited in its effectiveness by the amount of energy available in the free stream for injecting into the boundary layer over the leading edge. Certain requirements such as landing on aircraft-car-rier decks require large lift coefficients, often from aircraft that have fundamentally been designed for speed rather than high lift, and the use of slats and slots has insufficient range of operation. In this case, the slat and slot may be replaced by high pressure air being forced out through thin tangential slots just behind the sharp leading edge. This does essentially the same job as the slat and slot but with a greater amount of power available in the air flow. The power to compress the air is provided by the aircraft's engine(s).

A notable example of using boundary layer control by blowing, as this is called, occurs in the case of the Hawker Siddeley Buccaneer, a strike and reconnaissance aircraft (Figure 9.12). Designed in the 1960s to operate at speeds above Mach 0.9 (nine-tenths of the speed of sound), for reasons that will become apparent in Chapter 11 it had very thin aerofoil sections for its wings and tailplane. Being also des-tined for use with the Royal Navy on board aircraft-carriers, very short landing and take-off runs were essential. Not only was boundary layer blowing used on the upper surface of the wings, but also on the lower surface of the tailplane, in order that the tailplane could achieve

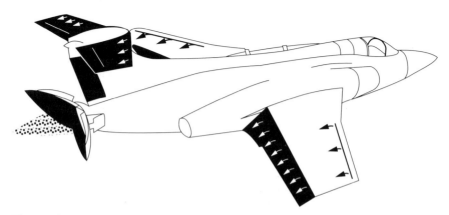

Figure 9.12 Buccaneer with Boundary Layer Control by Blowing

the down-force required for pitching the aircraft against the large nose-down pitching moment of the wing.

Although a very successful idea, the main problem associated with boundary layer control by blowing is that the lift of the wings is directly dependent on the power of the engines. Whereas in a conventional aircraft a loss of power on landing would probably not be catastrophic, an aircraft in which the engine is also used to augment the lift would be highly susceptible to falling out of the sky rapidly in the event of an engine failure.

There is also a problem associated with taking off in this kind of aircraft. During landing, reduced power is required for thrust, and so there is plenty to spare for boundary layer blowing. But during take-off, all available power is usually required for thrust to accelerate the aircraft up to take-off speed as quickly as possible. If any power has to be bled off to augment the lift, then there is that much less power available for keeping the take-off run as short as possible.

Boundary layer control by blowing has found its way into other applications as well as lift augmentation. In Chapter 7 we discussed the ways in which circulation could be introduced into the flow around a circular cylinder, so that the cylinder would produce a lift force. We quoted the example of the NOTAR helicopter, illustrated in Figure 7.6, in which arrows show the way in which air is squirted out from the cylinder tangentially to the surface. At the time of writing, research is being conducted into the use of so-called 'circulation control wings', by which it is hoped that the complex mechanical high-lift devices may be replaced by simple blowing slots at the leading and trailing edges of specially designed aerofoils. It is being claimed that such a system could increase the landing coefficient of lift of a Boeing 737 by 150% to 250%, thus reducing approach speed by 35% to 45% and landing distance by 55% to 75%, and that such advances in wing design could allow for substantial wing size reduction in the very large (600 to 800 passenger) aircraft that are currently being proposed and discussed. This is clearly an area to watch with interest.

Although it appears to be diametrically opposed in concept, yet there is another well-established method of achieving boundary layer control, and that is by means, not of blowing, but of sucking. If an aerofoil surface is perforated all over with a mesh of very fine holes, and air is constantly sucked inwards through these by means of maintaining a low pressure inside the aerofoil skin, then the low velocity sluggish air closest to the surface is constantly removed from the boundary layer and replaced by the higher energy air from above. The new boundary layer air has not gone the distance within a boundary layer to make transition, and so remains laminar. Usually a laminar boundary layer would be much more susceptible to boundary layer

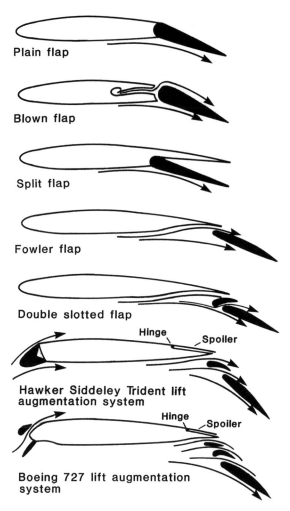

Plain flap

Blown flap

Split flap

Fowler flap

Double slotted flap

Hawker Siddeley Trident lift
augmentation system

Boeing 727 lift augmentation
system

Figure 9.13   Lift Augmentation Systems

separation than a turbulent boundary layer because of its low velocity
close to the surface, but in this case the laminar velocity is still close to
the free stream velocity, since it has not yet had time to be slowed
down by viscosity through closeness to the surface.

This technique has been used in the past for the purpose of stall
delay and lift augmentation, but its effectiveness is limited. A low
pressure cannot go more than one atmosphere below atmospheric
pressure, whereas a high pressure can go as many atmospheres above
atmospheric pressure as you like.

One major application for this technology has been very thoroughly investigated, and that is the possibility of reducing aircraft drag by achieving *laminar flow* over wing and fuselage surfaces of aircraft. Provided the surfaces are kept clean enough, the principle is simply that you gently suck away the boundary layer everywhere on the surface before it has the opportunity to become turbulent. Consequently the skin friction drag is substantially reduced.

With the development of very much more efficient and thus relatively smaller wings in recent years and increase in fuselage sizes, the proportion of an aircraft's total drag that is due to skin friction has grown, especially that due to the fuselage. Consequently the idea of designing a laminar flow transport aircraft appears to be very attractive. However, there have proved to be a number of problems which, even if not insuperable, make the idea less economically attractive than it at first appears. Firstly, there is the need for a chamber or ducting for the sucking air (its pressure must be kept lower than the outside surrounding air pressure at all altitudes) just inside the aircraft surface, and this chamber must envelope the high pressure of the cabin. This effectively leads to the requirement of a double-skinned pressure fuselage and double skinning of the wings, and the inner skin of the fuselage will have to withstand a greater pressure difference than the skin that it replaces on a conventional aircraft. The weight penalty of this would be very substantial. Secondly, power is required to operate the system; although laminar flow may lead to overall efficiencies in terms of power consumption, yet it will certainly necessitate new and complex systems. Thirdly, the little perforation holes have to be very small so as not themselves to disrupt the airflow (like pot-holes in the road), and even after the considerable difficulty of drilling them during manufacture, they have to be kept clean and unblocked. Being virtually microscopic, they may easily get blocked by dust or moisture and not be at all easy to cleanse or even to inspect. Fourthly, and perhaps the ultimate reason why the idea has not caught on, there is the major problem of keeping the aircraft surfaces clean. Even if they have been thoroughly cleaned and polished before take-off (somehow without blocking the perforation holes), it has been found that whilst climbing to cruise altitude the surfaces invariably become contaminated by insects and airborne dirt, which triggers the boundary layer into transition to turbulence. It is difficult to conceive of a system whereby at altitude the aircraft skin could be cleaned again at the start of the cruise phase of the flight.

CAMBER-INCREASING DEVICES

Having looked at some of the ways that boundary layer control has been used for lift augmentation (and other) purposes, let us look now at some of the other devices which are used both singly and in combination with each other. Some of these are illustrated in Figure 9.13.

The first shows a simple plain flap, which we have already discussed. In this diagram the flap is deflected through a fairly small angle, but typically a plain flap can be deflected to round about 80°. The amount by which the lift curve in Figure 9.11 can be pushed up is roughly in direct proportion to the angle of deflection of the flap.

Below this is shown a plain flap with blowing, where the blown air is being injected into the flow around the leading edge of the flap itself, in order to prevent separation there. Not shown is a slotted plain flap, a much more common way of achieving the same effect to a limited extent without the use of auxiliary power. It uses the high pressure of the flow in the concave region under the flap hinge to blow through a gap between wing and flap, the blown air emerging tangentially over the flap to prevent separation over it. As we have mentioned, the idea of circulation control by blowing is re-asserting itself to-day, and the methods proposed involve using a version of the blown plain flap with the ability to deflect to 90° with the flow remaining attached around this corner, emerging downwards normal to the aerofoil chord line.

The split flap was used in the post Second World War era, for example on the Hawker Hunter. Before the use of blown or well designed slotted flaps the flow over the upper surface was prone to separation, so that if large flap deflections were used very little lift was obtained from the upper flap surface. So the idea of the split flap was that the upper surface would continue producing a normal amount of conventional lift (rather than losing out on some of its conventional lift through flap separation), whilst the split flap deflected on the lower surface would create a strong downwash and so increase the lift coefficient. The device clearly produced a large amount of drag, and so for reasons that we shall see below it was well suited to the landing rôle, but was very little help in taking off.

Next down the diagram is the so-called Fowler Flap. This type of flap requires sturdy runners (which are not shown) protruding from the rear of the wing (or alternatively a structure supporting a pivot well below the level of the wing). It is clear from the diagram that the flap works by increasing the area of the wing as well as increasing its camber (by a relatively small amount). Now when looking at the rationale for using lift augmentation earlier in this chapter, we said that the wing plan area S was constant and therefore was not negotiable when augmenting lift; and now we are varying it! We can see now that it is clearly physically possible to vary the wing area, and certainly increasing the wing area will have a very substantial effect of augmenting the lift. However, it is convenient to stick to the convention that S is constant, and so we will now slightly amend our definition of S, and declare that it is the plan area of the aircraft wing (including the fuselage portion) *in its unaugmented state*. The extending of the Fowler flap does not therefore alter the constant quantity S as defined, but temporarily alters the actual wing area to a value which is different from S. Looking now at the lift formula Lift = $C_L \frac{1}{2} \rho V^2 S$, extending the Fowler flap does not alter the value of the term S, and it certainly can't have any effect on the free stream conditions V and ρ. Therefore by default, the effect of the Fowler flap is reflected in an adjustment of the value of the C_L term in the formula, just like all the other lift augmentation devices.

The double slotted flap, the fifth diagram in Figure 9.13, demonstrates the way in which flaps began to mature by incorporating all of the mechanisms that we have already studied. We now have an extending and hinging flap which increases camber as well as area, and which itself has its own little slat and slot. This flap with slat, in turn, has a slot between it and the main aerofoil. The increased pressure in the concave region under the aerofoil creates a flow of air through both of these venturi slots, ensuring that the top surface flow can round the tight turn without separating.

The camber of the wing is further enhanced by the use of a hinged flap at the leading edge. This device has the combined advantage of both increasing camber and pointing the sharp nose downwards into the up-coming air flow, thus reducing the tendency of the flow to separate around the sharp leading edge. There are many versions of the same idea, one particular alternative being shown in the final diagram of the figure. In this one at the leading edge there is both a retractable slat and slot, and also a Kreuger flap, a leading edge flap which hinges downwards and forwards from its hinge on the lower side of the leading edge. This wing, that of the Boeing 727 airliner, exhibits a triple slotted flap at the trailing edge, but even this complicated and sophisticated arrangement is not as convoluted as many of the modern airliners' lift augmentation systems have become.

The last two wings in Figure 9.13 both show spoilers lying flush with the rear of the upper surface. The spoilers are normally rotated quickly up to a nearly vertical position immediately after the aircraft has touched down, whilst the flap systems are being more slowly retracted. The spoilers are provided simply to get rid of all the extra lifting effect that these high-lift wings can produce, and so they are also known as 'lift dumpers'. Although they produce some considerable drag which is certainly useful in slowing down the aircraft on the ground (mainly achieved by the reverse thrust of the engines and the undercarriage wheel brakes), the spoiler's primary purpose is not braking but to ensure that the aircraft will sit firmly down on its undercarriage wheels as soon as it has safely touched down on the runway. This is both to aid ground stability, control and wheel braking, and also to ensure that the aircraft does not balloon up into the air again and perform a series of hops or bounces.

Trailing edge lift augmentation systems do not usually extend along the entire length of the aircraft wing, as the outboard region is usually required for the mounting of ailerons (roll controls). Therefore the very strong lifting effect that they produce drops very suddenly at their ends to a much lower unaugmented value over the outer portion of the wings. In Chapter 12 we will see that the wing-tips of an aircraft produce strong helical (screw-shaped) vortices in the airflow behind the wing-tips, and that the strength of these wing-tip vortices is directly related to the wing lift coefficient. Since there is a commensurately sized drop in C_L at the outer ends of the flaps, additional very strong vortices are shed from this point. Although not visible, these swirling flows (which are most prominent on runways at airfields, since that is where the flap systems are used) create a very serious hazard to following aircraft, especially when there is no cross-wind to move the lingering vortices away from the runway before the next aircraft lands. For this reason substantial spacing (typically of two minutes) has to be allowed between aircraft landing on airport runways. It is actually these trailing vortices that are the limiting factor in the transport handling capacity of an airport. This is very much the down side of using lift augmentation, since high runway utilisation means money in the bank. There could well be an economic argument to support lengthening runways and landing aircraft faster, with less lift coefficient, and consequently closer together, but one wonders what the public response to that would be! You can see aircraft lining up to land in very quick succession, but you can't see the hazardous trailing vortices that are always present today over all busy airports. The person who can devise a way of eliminating the hazard of trailing vortices has his fortune assured!

FLAP SYSTEM DRAG – PRO'S AND CON'S

The one aspect that we have said very little about so far is the substantial amount of drag that is produced by lift augmentation devices. This is largely because, when discussing them, we have almost entirely concentrated on their use during landing an aircraft, but they can also be beneficial when taking off. However, to take-off in as short a distance as is reasonably possible, the aircraft must be able to accelerate to its take-off speed as quickly as possible. This clearly means using the maximum available thrust and imposing the minimum possible drag. In fact, this is the only phase of flight (if the take-off run can be called 'flight') in which the linear acceleration of an aircraft is of major importance.

With plain flaps and with most lift augmentation systems, as the flaps are progressively deployed it is found that, whilst the lift coefficient rises roughly in proportion to the amount of deployment, the drag coefficient increases at first slowly, and then much more rapidly at larger deployments. Therefore for taking off pilots will customarily compromise by selecting a part, typically a third, of full flap deflection, thus ensuring a reasonable boost to C_L whilst adding very little drag penalty.

There is a serious danger in deploying too much (e.g. full) flap before starting the take-off run, since the drag may be so great that the available thrust is insufficient to get the aircraft up to take-off speed within the length of the runway. It is of course too late to realise your error as you approach the end of the runway, going too fast to stop but not fast enough to take off!

But what about the large amount of drag that flaps create when fully deployed for landing? Is this a problem? Fortunately it is not, and in fact drag is a very useful (and sometimes essential) contribution to the control of an aircraft when landing. Road-bound car drivers are used to the fact that, if you just switch everything off, eventually you will come to rest due to the natural friction forces occurring on the car. But it is not quite so simple for the pilot of an aircraft, since if he or she just switches off everything, the aircraft must start descending, and then gravity will tend to make it speed up rather than slow down. Recalling briefly our roller-coaster analogy at the end of Chapter 4, if there were no loss of energy then a descending aircraft would get faster and faster. If the speed is to be kept constant (or to reduce), then some energy must be given up to the surrounding air, which means that some work must be done on this air. To do work involves applying a force through a distance, and the force in this case (acting over the distance travelled during the descent) is the aircraft's drag. Putting this more superficially, to prevent going too fast down a hill, you must put your brakes on. So the drag provided by the flaps, which were primarily installed for their lifting benefit, turns out to be an essential feature – not primarily for slowing down in flight, but for another purpose, as we will now show.

We saw earlier in this chapter that the landing phase of an aircraft's flight is dangerous, largely because the aircraft has to undertake turning manoeuvres near to the ground when its speed is low, and so it is prone to stalling or spinning when it doesn't have the vertical space needed for recovery. The reasons landing speeds are kept low are not primarily aerodynamic, but are to keep the landing run short, to avoid excessive shock loads on the undercarriage and scuffing on tyres and to give the pilot time to cope with handling the aircraft. Aerodynamically it would be much better to go faster, so that the wing could be operated in the middle of its C_L range rather than near the extreme upper limit, and then stalling would not be such a danger. Slow flying aircraft such as small trainers and sailplanes very often actually *increase* their speed from the normal flying speed when landing for this very reason, and it is one of the hardest things to persuade a novice glider pilot that for his or her own safety the speed must be kept higher than usual during the descent!

Slowing down from a high speed to a sensible landing speed can be done without hurry, well before landing, using the natural drag of an aircraft. The aircraft must then not go any slower as it comes in to land, but must maintain a high enough speed for safety. So what is all this about needing the extra drag of undercarriage and flaps for landing? There appears to be some confusion.

The use of high drag during the approach to land is not for reducing the aircraft's speed, but is *to allow the aircraft to follow a steeper descent path without gaining excessive speed*. The more steeply the pilot wishes to descend, the more drag he will need to be able to muster in order to prevent the aircraft gaining speed uncontrollably. A glance at Figure 3.3 will make this clear. This is very much like someone sensible going down a steep hill on a bicycle. The steeper the hill, the more braking is applied, so that the descent speed does not get too high.

There is another very important reason for using air brakes during a descent, and that is to ensure that *speed stability* is maintained. However, this cannot be properly explained until we have covered some more ideas about drag, and so a discussion of this point will be left until towards the end of Chapter 12.

On most aircraft, lowering the retractable undercarriage will typically add virtually the same amount of drag again as the clean aircraft experiences with undercarriage retracted, and so the undercarriage provides a most useful air brake for a descending aircraft. Sometimes more drag is desirable than is available from flaps and undercarriage. The hinged half-cones at the tail of the Buccaneer in Figure 9.12 are deployed air brakes or dive brakes. Gliders and sailplanes are usually fitted with air brakes, draggy protrusions that may be extended out of the wings into the air flow, leaving a gap underneath them so that they do not affect the lift of the wings too much.[7] The pilot can directly adjust his *angle* of descent (whilst maintaining a constant speed) by adjusting the amount of deployment of the spoilers. They are usually operated by a control lever that moves in a complementary way to the throttle of a powered aircraft. Whereas a throttle lever is pushed for-

---

[7] Some gliders use combined spoilers and air brakes, which work somewhat differently.

ward for more thrust and pulled backward for less, an airbrake lever is pulled backwards for more airbrake deployment.

The American U2 reconnaissance aircraft was built to have extremely low drag, in order to be able to stay airborne for very long periods of time. This was largely achieved by having a very high aspect ratio (a drag-reducing feature that is discussed fully in Chapter 12) and partly through its very clean and well streamlined lines. Like most sailplanes, its main undercarriage consisted of a single wheel that retracted neatly into the underside of the fuselage, and even when it was lowered it added very little drag to the aircraft. Whilst being a very efficient aircraft in flight, it had the reputation amongst its pilots of being excessively difficult to land safely. The problem was simply that there was insufficient drag available, so that whenever one tried to descend to a runway the speed would pick up substantially. This in turn would create extra lift (proportional to the square of the speed), and consequently the aircraft would naturally try to pull up into a climb. More nose down control force to avoid this would simply exacerbate the problem!

There are a number of other ways in which lift can be augmented on aircraft and by which the stall can be combated. But these additional ideas relate particularly to swept wings, and so we must first set the scene before solving the problems. In Chapters 10 and 11 we will at last be taking off into the realms of high-speed flight where compressibility and the speed of sound become the order of the day. After looking in Chapter 12 at how the fact that an aircraft is actually three-dimensional rather than two-dimensional must affect our thinking, we will go on in Chapter 13 to look at the pro's and con's of many of the various planforms which are to be found on different aircraft. At the end of that chapter we will be in a position to conclude the current discussion on lift augmentation and stalling.

CHAPTER 10
Supersonic Aerofoils

INTRODUCTION

We reach now an appropriate point at which to break away from the major constraint that we have imposed upon all of our thinking so far, which was the assumption that air is incompressible. Half-way through Chapter 5 we looked carefully at the implications of this assumption and concluded that it enabled us to build up simplified theories (based on the incompressible continuity equation and the incompressible Bernoulli equation) which gave pretty good approximations to the truth provided we did not try to apply them when air speeds became more than round about a third to a half of the speed of sound. But of course the great majority of aircraft flight today does occur at speeds far greater than this, and so we are being dishonest and unrealistic if we cling to the incompressible myth for too long.

Things don't change all of a sudden but gradually as speeds approach the speed of sound. However, beyond the speed of sound itself a major re-structuring of the entire theory of aerodynamics has to be taken on board. To be able to have some awareness of the reason for this, let us deviate for a moment and look at an amusing little mathematical bagatelle.

Think of any number you like, and give it two names: a and b. As Step 1 we will write down the statement of the obvious, that

$$a = b$$

The following few lines of mathematics based on this equation are all almost as trivial, except for Step 4 which involves a little bit of factorising. I promise you that the factorising is done correctly, but you can check it out by multiplying the resulting factors together to convince yourself. The conclusion that we reach at Step 6 is clearly utter nonsense and quite impossible. Somewhere between the initial step $a = b$ and the nonsensical result of Step 6 there has to be something wrong. Can you spot what it is, or where it is?

Here goes.

Step 2: multiply both sides of the equation by a, so that we have

$$a^2 = ab$$

Step 3: take away b^2 from both sides, giving

$$a^2 - b^2 = ab - b^2$$

Step 4: factorise the left-hand side by the 'difference of two squares' method, and factorise the right-hand side by taking out the common factor b. The process of factorising merely changes the appearance and not the value of either expression, and so we can still write an equals sign between the two sides after factorising:

$$(a + b)(a - b) = b(a - b)$$

Step 5: noting that the quantity $(a - b)$ appears as a factor on both sides of the equation, cancel it:

$$a + b = b$$

Step 6: remembering that we started off by asserting that a and b are the same number, replace a by b:

$$b + b = b \text{ or } 2b = b$$

So we have proved the absurdity that, whatever value b has, then its value is also twice as much as itself! By playing around with this silly result, it is not difficult to prove virtually any arithmetical nonsense statement that you like. What has gone wrong? If you haven't spotted the error yet, it is well worth going back and spending a few moments critically examining each step, before you go on to uncover the gremlin as disclosed below.

Steps 2 and 3 both directly apply the principle that you can do any mathematical operation you like to one side of an equation, provided you do exactly the same thing to the other side of the equation, so there is no error there. Step 4 we have already promised is OK. Step 6 is trivial, and there are no hidden catches there. So we must look again at Step 5.

When we say 'cancel' in Step 5, what we really mean is 'divide both sides by $(a - b)$', so that the word 'cancel' is in fact concealing the mathematical operation 'divide'. So, what is wrong with that? The answer to that question lies in the value of $(a - b)$. It is not an unknown value dependent on random values of a and b, because we know that $a = b$, and so $(a - b) = 0$. Therefore 'cancel by $(a - b)$' actually means 'divide by zero'.

There is a fundamental law of arithmetic which says 'Thou shalt not divide by zero'. The above example shows us precisely why this law is needed. If we do divide by zero, even unwittingly, the entire safe and reliable structure of our arithmetic collapses, and the answers we get will be rubbish or totally unreliable.

When one studies the aerodynamics of compressible flows, many formulae consist of fractions with one of the expressions $\sqrt{M^2 - 1}$ or $\sqrt{1 - M^2}$ on the bottom line. This is fine until M, the Mach number, equals 1 which means that the air speed exactly equals the speed of sound. When M equals 1, each of these expressions equals 0, and any formula with one of these expressions on the bottom of a fraction contains the forbidden division by zero, and consequently becomes meaningless and useless. Furthermore, if M is just a little bit greater than 1, then the first expression $\sqrt{M^2-1}$ is the square root of a very small positive number, which is another very small positive number, but if M is just a bit below 1 then the same expression $\sqrt{M^2-1}$ is the square root of a negative number, which only exists in the realms of imaginary numbers and is not a real number at all. (The same change in reverse happens to the other expression.)

Thus we have a little glimpse of the way in which both our subsonic mathematical model of aerodynamics and the supersonic model become totally invalid at the speed of sound itself, and many of the rules and principles of aerodynamics actually reverse themselves in a surprising way at the watershed point where $M = 1$.

WHY THE SPEED OF SOUND?

What has the speed of sound got to do with aeroplane flight? Why should there be any connection at all between the speed at which a sound travels through the air, and the speed at which an aircraft is travelling through the air? What is the nature of sound, and what is it about the nature of sound that impinges on flight in some curious way? These are good questions for us to start off with, since the answers may not be immediately obvious.

Do you remember the 'Slinky', the long straggly spring toy that could walk down the stairs? If a 'Slinky' were laid out across a table or a smooth floor as in Figure 10.1 and one end of it were given a sharp brief push towards the other end, then a *compression wave* would visibly travel along the spring from one end to the other, as Figure 10.1 illustrates as best it can in still pictures. This illustrates very simply and effectively the way in which sound travels in the air. The air is itself springy – we say compressible – like the spring, and it is the molecules that get closer together and then further apart (or more precisely their mean separation that varies) as the sound wave travels through the air. If the air were really incompressible, as we have been assuming up to now, that would be analogous to gluing each coil of the spring to the next one all the way along, thus making it incompressible. No wave could travel along the spring, and synonymously no sound could travel through the air. Thus compressibility is a necessary condition for sound to travel.

You will observe, incidentally, that there is no obvious way, other than sending this wave, in which any form of information or knowledge about activity at one end of the spring could be transmitted through the spring from one end to the other. Likewise, the only way

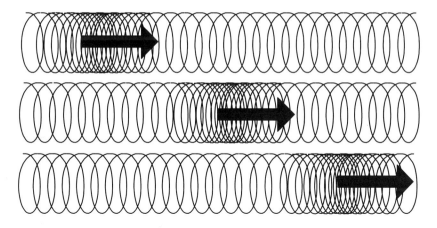

Figure 10.1   A Compression Wave

in which information of activity in the air can be transmitted through the air is via pressure waves, or sound waves. (Light and other forms of electromagnetic waves do not transmit information about the behaviour of the air, since they do not require the presence of air for their transmission.)

So there is a clear direct link between sound and compressibility of air – but this still does not answer the question as to how sound and compressibility relate to aircraft flight. The clue is in the new idea that we have introduced, that of transmitting information.

Figure 10.2 shows the behaviour of a few streamlines around an object (in this case an aerofoil) in a subsonic airflow. Let us follow the progress of a particle flowing along the streamline labelled SS, as it enters the scene of the figure from the left. Before it enters a region close to the aerofoil, the particle is in an undisturbed uniform airflow, and is moving along the straight line shown by the dotted line extending across the figure. A good number of chord lengths upstream of the aerofoil all the particles somehow become aware that there is an obstruction ahead of them, around which they are all going to have to adopt modified paths if a nasty collision is to be avoided. Acting on this insight, the particles do indeed modify their routes in plenty of time, so that a smooth, collision-free progress can be maintained

Figure 10.2   Deflection of Subsonic Airflow Upstream of Object in Airflow

around the aerofoil, with no unseemly jostling between the particles.

How does our particle 'know' that there is something to be avoided ahead of it? Certainly it cannot 'see' in the optical sense. As we have seen, there is only one way in which information about activity in the air can be transmitted through the air, and that is by pressure, or sound, waves. Although pressure and sound waves are the same thing, often as in this case pressure waves are such weak sound waves that they cannot be heard by the human ear. It is by pressure waves that the pressure inside a car tyre becomes the same at all points within it, although the increased pressure during inflation is actually only applied by the pump at the valve nozzle. The pressure does not instantly equalise at all points within the tyre, but the new pressure is transmitted at the speed of sound (i.e. pressure wave propagation) from the nozzle to all other points. Therefore there is a small delay between the pressure being increased at the nozzle and the pressure reaching the same value at the far side of the tyre – but the delay *is* small, since the speed of sound is pretty fast and the wave hasn't far to go.

So the information about the possibility of impending collision if no avoiding action were taken is transmitted upstream from the aerofoil at the speed of sound by pressure waves to the approaching air particles, so that they have plenty of time to take smooth and gentle avoiding action. This is fine provided the particle is approaching the aerofoil more slowly than the pressure messages are coming out to meet it. But what happens if the free stream flow, including our particle, has a greater speed towards the aerofoil than the speed of the pressure waves coming out to meet it? In this case, the stream of pressure messages being transmitted in all directions from the aerofoil is being swept downstream by the airflow faster than the messages can travel upstream, and so no information travels upstream at all. Consequently the particle and its companions are unaware of the need to take avoiding action, and continue in a straight line. Those particles directly in line with the aerofoil will suffer a severe collision with it (just as if they had been advancing blind), and subsequently their neighbours will get embroiled, not directly in the collision themselves but with the particles ricocheting off the aerofoil. The tranquillity of the subsonic flow is thus destroyed.

This is the answer to our question, 'why is aircraft flight concerned with the speed of sound?' The aircraft is in for a rough ride if it flies into the air faster than it can send pressure messages out ahead of it to warn the air that it is coming. The messenger is always too late, and his arrival is always overtaken by events.

MACH LINES, ZONES OF INFLUENCE AND ZONES OF SILENCE

Having discussed the transmission of information by pressure waves, we can now tighten up a little on our thinking, whilst at the same time introducing some important new concepts and terms. Although pressure transmissions from an object in air spread out radially in three directions, we will use a powerful two-dimensional analogy to think about what is happening, that of dropping small pebbles into water, and observing the progress of the ripples produced.

If a pebble is dropped into still water, it produces an instantaneous very small disturbance, resulting in a surface wave (a ripple) which grows from the source as an ever-increasing circle. The ripple speed (which we denote by a), is analogous to the speed of sound in air. If a succession of pebbles is dropped into still water at one-second intervals, a ripple pattern like Figure 10.3(a) will be created.

If now the procedure is repeated, this time not into still water but perhaps from a bridge into a stream flowing at a speed V which is less than the speed of the propagation of ripples, the pattern of Figure 10.3(b) is generated, as each circular ripple moves bodily downstream whilst it grows in size. Information about the pebbles entering the water, in the form of ripples, still travels upstream (although slower than downstream) and in time the entire stream will be affected by the ripples.

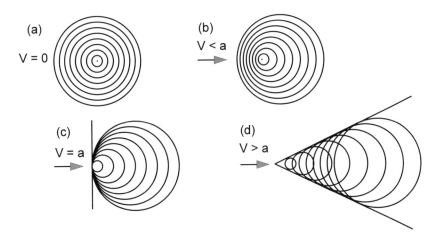

Figure 10.3   The Propagation of Ripples or Pressure Waves

An interesting side issue emerges at this point. If you were a duck floating downstream at speed *V* with the current, close to the centre-line of the circles in Figure 10.3(b) (not *on* the centre-line, or you will get hit on the head by a pebble!), then as you approach the point where the pebbles are entering the water you will bob up and down quite rapidly as you meet the ripples coming out to meet you – they are close together. Once you have floated past the pebble entry point, the ripples are considerably more spaced out, and you will bob up and down at a much more leisurely frequency. This lower frequency is the signal that the danger of being hit on the head is passed.

Exactly the same phenomenon is observed if you are standing on the side of the road when an ambulance passes you at speed, sounding its siren. As it approaches you, the sound is high pitched, but as soon as the ambulance has passed you and is going away from you, the sound of the siren is considerably lower in pitch. Of course, the fre-quency transmitted by the siren does not change, but the speed and direction (i.e. the velocity) of the source relative to the listener affects the frequency at which the sound is experienced by the listener. This effect is called the Doppler effect. The closer the speed of the source comes to the speed of propagation of the waves, the greater is the dif-ference between the frequency before and after source and receiver pass each other. The only difference between the duck and the ambu-lance situation is that the stream, and hence the duck (the receiver of the wave), is moving relative to the stationary source of the ripples, whereas the ambulance, the source of the sound, is moving relative to the stationary listener standing on the pavement. As with aerodynam-ics and wind-tunnel testing, it is the *relative* velocities that matter.

Let us go back to dropping pebbles into the stream. If the speed of flow of the stream is now increased to exactly the same as the ripple propagation speed, then Figure 10.3(c) will result. The centre of each ripple moves downstream at exactly the same speed as the ripple is growing outwards from its centre, and so the point on the ripple trying to flow directly upstream from the pebble dropping point never moves away from there. Consequently all the ripple circles touch each other at this point. If a ripple carried on growing bigger and bigger without weakening at all, the shape of the circle would (after an infinite amount of time) end up as the straight line in the figure, which is what happens to a circle when its radius becomes infinite.

None of the ripples will ever cross over the straight line from right to left in Figure 10.3(c). In the three-dimensional supersonic airflow equivalent situation, the ripple circles become spherical pressure-wave fronts, and this straight line becomes a plane normal to the flow. Even so, its representation in two-dimensional drawings is a line (as in Figure 10.3(c)) and it is called a *Mach line*.

Thus a Mach line is a boundary between two regions of the flow. On one side of it is a region in which is confined all of the disturbance occurring in the stream or airflow, whereas no disturbance or information about it ever reaches the other side of the Mach line at all. The disturbed or informed region is known as the *zone of action* or *zone of influence*, and the other side is known as the *zone of silence*. If our Doppler Duck drifts downstream in this situation, assuming she is blind, she will be totally unaware of the fact that someone is dropping pebbles into the stream until she has drifted past the danger point. If the ambulance came along the road towards you at the speed of sound, with siren blaring, you would hear nothing at all until it passed you.

We will now allow the stream speed to increase further, so that it is greater than the ripple propagation speed, as in Figure 10.3(d). Each circle together with its centre now moves downstream further in a second than the amount by which its own radius increases in that second, and consequently the circles overlap each other in the orderly manner shown. The two common tangents to the circles are straight lines which form a wedge-shaped region, and these lines can be easily seen in the water stream if the supply of pebbles is replaced by a sharp pencil point just touching the undisturbed surface of the water, so that the disturbance is created continuously rather than at one-second intervals.

Once again these lines are the Mach lines. In the corresponding three-dimensional airflow situation this region becomes a cone, which is known as the *Mach cone*. The region inside the Mach lines containing the circles (or inside the Mach cone containing spheres) is the zone of influence, and the entire region outside the Mach cone, both upstream and downstream of the dropping point now, is the zone of silence. Unless Doppler Duck is in direct line of fire of the pebbles, she will this time have drifted right past the danger point, and downstream of it by some distance, before she is even aware of the fact that she had been in any danger.

It was perceived wisdom during the Second World War that, if you saw someone aiming a gun in your direction at some distance away and you heard the 'bang' of the gun, you could breathe again, as the shot that had been fired at you had already safely passed you by. Bullets usually travel considerably faster than the speed of sound, so that the sound of the gun firing would reach you some time after the bullet had either hit you or missed you.

Now Figure 10.3(d) represents all cases in which the stream speed is greater than the disturbance propagation speed. However, the greater the stream speed, the more spaced out the circles will become, and the sharper the angle between the two Mach lines will become. In order to

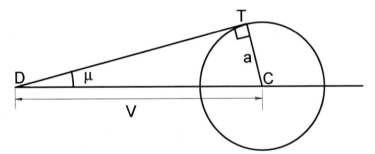

Figure 10.4   Relationship Between Mach Number and Mach Angle

find out how the angle of the Mach line is related to the speed of flow, we will look at Figure 10.4, which shows one particular circle (centre C) that was started at the disturbance point (D) exactly one second ago, so that its centre has moved a distance V and its radius has grown to a, as shown. The stream line through the point of disturbance and the centre of the circle, and one Mach line tangential to the circle at T, are also shown. The angle $T\hat{D}C$ is defined as the *Mach angle*, and is denoted by the Greek letter μ. Now the triangle is right-angled at T and V is the hypotenuse, so that for those who are familiar with trigonometry,

$$\sin \mu = \frac{a}{V}$$

Now the Mach number is defined as the speed of the airflow divided by the speed of sound, and so $M = V/a$ or $1/M = a/V$. Combining this with the previous equation gives us the following relationship between a Mach number and a Mach angle:

$$\frac{1}{M} = \sin \mu$$

This means that, if we can see and measure the angle of the Mach lines produced by a small disturbance in a flow, then we can use this to find the Mach number of the flow, or vice versa. As an example, if the speed of an airflow is twice the speed of sound, then $M = 2$, $V = 2a$, sin $\mu = \frac{1}{2}$ and the Mach angle is 30°. Clearly from Figure 10.3(c) if the Mach number is 1 then the Mach angle is 90°, and so the Mach lines have to do a large amount of sweeping back as the flow speed increases from Mach 1 to Mach 2. There is much less room for further sharpening up (or reduction in μ below 30°) as M increases to values greater than 2, and so the rate of sharpening up decreases.

THE SPEED OF SOUND

Before moving on, let us look briefly at the nature of the speed of sound itself, since it is clearly a quantity to which we are going to be making very frequent reference. Sound travels in any medium, be it solid, liquid or gas, but of course it cannot travel in space or in a vacuum, which is a total lack of medium.

The speed at which sound travels in different media depends on a measure of the compressibility of the medium called the bulk modulus, with which we do not need to concern ourselves, except to note that what we have said implies that all substances are compressible. Although a gas is clearly compressible, we tend to think that solids and liquids are incompressible, and for many purposes such an assumption is very useful and fully valid. If you propel a punt along the river by pushing against the bottom of the river with a quanting pole, then the pressure that you apply to the pole with your hands is not instantaneously transmitted to the river bed at the end of the pole, but only reaches there after travelling down the pole at the speed at which pressure waves travel in the wood. A push or a pull is not a process with an instantaneous response at the other end of the thing being pushed or pulled, but is the initiation of a pressure wave through that object.

But we can confine our attention to the speed of sound through the one gaseous medium, air. Even here it is not a constant value, but it depends on the temperature of the air. Temperature is a measure of molecular activity, and there exists a temperature at which all molecular activity would totally cease (if we could make something that cold). This temperature is called absolute zero, since no temperature below this could possibly exist – indeed, the very word temperature could not be defined if no molecular activity were occurring. Its value is about −273 degrees Celsius, and by adding 273 to any temperature measured in degrees Celsius we convert the temperature to a scale called the Kelvin absolute temperature scale. Now the speed of sound in air is found to be directly proportional to the square root of the absolute temperature of the air, which we can write down as

$$a \propto \sqrt{T}$$

where T is the absolute temperature.

A typical sea level temperature of 15°C converts to an absolute temperature of 288K (which is the conventional way to write 288 degrees on the Kelvin scale), and at that temperature the speed of sound is 340 metres-per-second or 773 miles-per-hour. If the air were to be cooled down to a quarter of this absolute temperature, i.e. 72K, which is −201°C (pretty cold, but not difficult to achieve in a laboratory,) then the square root of T would be halved, and consequently the speed of sound would be half what it is at 15°C, or 386 miles-per-hour. Thus in air at this low temperature an aircraft could be flying super-sonically at less than 400 miles-per-hour. The advantages of cryogenic wind-tunnels, referred to in Chapter 8, are thus not only that high Reynolds numbers can be achieved but also that high Mach numbers can be reached at much lower speeds than usual. Taking this principle to a rather absurd extreme, if the air temperature were reduced to 2K, we find that the speed of sound is only about 64 miles-per-hour, so that most motor cars would be capable of travelling supersonically in air at that temperature.

This same principle applies also in the opposite direction, in air that is heated above its normal temperature. This proves very fortuitous in the exhaust gas of an aircraft's jet engine. It is in the nature of aircraft propulsion that the exhaust gases from the engine have to be expelled faster backwards than the aircraft is travelling forwards. A large pro-portion of all flight, particularly long-range commercial flying, is for economic reasons carried out at speeds a little lower than the speed of sound, and we will look closely at the justification for this in the next chapter. Since the jet engine exhaust must come out faster, it is clear that there is a high likelihood that the exhaust gases will need to be expelled supersonically, adding considerably to the energy losses and design difficulties of the engine. However, fortunately this does not normally occur, since the exhaust gas from the jet engine is at a very high temperature compared with the surrounding air temperature. The consequence of this is that the speed of sound within this gas is much greater than in the surrounding air, so that even if the gas's speed is much higher than the speed of sound in the surrounding air it is still lower than its local speed of sound, and so it is still subsonic.

SHOCK WAVES

You may at this stage have already thought that we had started to look at shock waves, because these oblique lines coming from a point of disturbance look very much like the pictures you may have seen of shock waves. However, Mach lines are emphatically *not* the same thing as shock waves, although they are closely related to them. We will come back a little later to clarify the distinction between Mach lines and shock waves, but first of all we must tackle the subject of shock waves themselves.

Virtually everybody associates the phrase shock wave with super-sonic aircraft flight, with 'breaking the sound barrier' and perhaps with thunder and earthquakes. Everybody knows that shock waves are fairly violent natural phenomena of some sort, but to most people that is about all. So when I started teaching principles of flight to Royal Air Force Engineer Officers, I knew that first of all I must

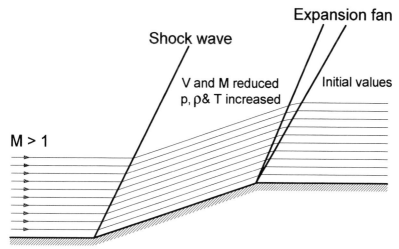

Figure 10.5   Relationship Between Mach Number and Mach Angle

tackle the fundamental question 'what is a shock wave?' I had just completed a two-year full-time course studying aerodynamics in depth, and was well versed in handling and manipulating the theory of shock waves, so this question should have presented no problem. However, when I faced myself with the direct question 'what is a shock wave?', I realised that I really had no idea of the answer!

So I did the natural thing and turned to a highly regarded authoritative book on the subject[1] and looked in the 'index' for 'shock wave – definition'. Having turned to the relevant page and hunted through the bland print, I came across the brief passing phrase: 'A shock wave, which is a discontinuity in the flow, . . ' I know that, I mused, but what *is* it? Gradually I realised that in fact I had the definition of a shock wave in front of me. It is not what happens *inside* a shock wave that is important (some molecular shenanigans occurring within a layer of air only about one thousandth of a millimetre thick), but it is the *effect* of this layer on the air flowing through it that is important. In fact in ideal flow a shock wave is regarded as an instantaneous discontinuity, and the error of a thousandth of a millimetre or so is not going to upset that way of thinking very much.

When we were looking at Figure 10.2, we came to the conclusion that if the aerofoil were in a supersonic flow there would be a fairly violent event occurring in the air at the front of the aerofoil itself. Because of the lack of forward-propagated pressure wave information in supersonic flow, the air is forced to react suddenly and violently to disruptions that it encounters. A shock wave is simply the place at

[1]Liepman and Roshko: *Elements of Gas Dynamics*, published by Wiley.

which, and the mechanism by which, such a reaction occurs. After the shock wave, the flow properties are substantially changed from those of the flow before it.

The scenario of Figure 10.2 would be very complicated to analyse in detail, and so it will be useful for us to introduce a much simpler model by means of which we can examine what is happening. Let us consider a uniform supersonic flow travelling from left to right parallel to a flat plate, as in the left-hand region of Figure 10.5. We will assume no viscosity, and so there will be no boundary layer to take into account in the present discussion. The flow meets a wedge, i.e. another flat plate at an angle to the first, which forces the flow to turn inwards (or concavely) on itself. It is convenient to picture the flow in thin parallel bands, within which the air consists of an array of well spaced particles.

Let us look first of all at the bottom band. Since the flow is supersonic, the particles can receive no advance warning of the presence of the wedge, and so they will continue undisturbed in a straight line until they strike it. At this point, everything that happens is just what one would predict simply by applying common sense, or by empathising with an air particle. The particles might be expected to bounce off the wedge upwards, but in fact the layers of air above the lowest layer totally prevent this possibility. The air cannot hang around at the corner, since more air keeps coming up behind it, and so it has no choice but to turn abruptly and follow the direction of the wedge wall. As it does so, it is quite shaken up or 'shocked', and as might be expected certain changes occur:

a. The flow slows down.
b. The particles get squeezed together or compressed. They thus occupy a smaller volume, and so their density is increased.
c. As a result of this compression, the band becomes narrower after the deflection.
d. The collision results in increased molecular activity, which shows itself by the pressure and temperature of the air both increasing.
e. The temperature rise implies an increase in the speed of sound a in this local air. This together with the reduction in the speed V results in a reduction of the Mach number V/a. However, the Mach number is still greater than one and so the flow is still supersonic.

Thus very suddenly at the wedge corner, the speed and Mach number of the flow decrease, whilst the relevant fluid properties (temperature, pressure and density) all increase. The change is virtually instantaneous, and the air in its new direction and with its new flow properties carries on parallel to the wedge wall without further ado or alteration, but occupying a narrower band than before.

Let us look now at the next band up. It cannot reach the wedge surface because of the band below, and it is unaware of the disturbance until it encounters the deflected first band, i.e. slightly downstream of the point where the wedge surface meets the first surface. Then it is forced to behave in every respect in exactly the same way as the first band behaved at the corner. The same is true for all the higher bands in the airflow, reaching upwards indefinitely.

All the turning points of the stream lines between layers of air will be seen to form a straight line at an oblique angle to the undisturbed flow. If the bands are considered to be vanishingly narrow, then this straight line is a *shock wave*, and is the line across which the fluid and flow properties have changed. There will be no further change downstream of the shock unless a further disturbance is encountered.

This shock wave is called an *oblique shock wave*, because it is at an angle other than 90° to the original direction. If the wedge angle is gradually and progressively increased, the intensity of the impact with the corner or the air layer below increases, and the shock wave angle also increases. During this process, the Mach number of the flow behind the shock wave decreases, and when a certain wedge angle is exceeded the flow behind the shock wave changes from supersonic to subsonic.

Very soon after this, a critical wedge angle is reached at which the shock wave is normal to the first surface, and as we have seen the flow behind the shock has become subsonic. Information can now be transmitted around the entire region behind the shock wave, including

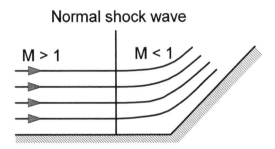

Figure 10.6   Stand-off Normal Shock Wave

upstream, and so the streamlines will revert to their subsonic, smoothly curving style, as illustrated in Figure 10.6. At the same time, the shock wave, which has now settled to being normal to the original flow direction, backs off a little way upstream from the corner, and becomes what is called a stand-off shock wave.

It is generally true (except near the critical wedge angle referred to above) that an oblique shock wave has supersonic flow on both sides of it. But what is *always* true, and an important principle to grasp, is that:

A normal shock wave always has supersonic flow ahead of it and subsonic flow behind it.

At the start of this section we asserted emphatically that Mach lines are not shock waves. However, they are essentially the same phenomenon. The difference is that a Mach line is caused by an infinitely small disturbance in the flow, so weak that no changes at all in flow velocity or fluid properties occur across it. In other words, a Mach line is an infinitely weak shock wave. This is why when we earlier replaced the pebbles being dropped into the stream by a pencil, we said that it must be a pencil *point*, *just* touching the water surface, so that the disturbance would be as weak as possible yet sufficient to show a trace of the Mach line. An inclined plate inserted into the water deflecting the flow, on the other hand, would have generated a 'shock wave', which would have been at a different angle to the flow from that of a Mach line.

Just now we considered what would happen to the shock wave in Figure 10.5 if the angle of the wedge were increased. If on the other hand the angle of the wedge were progressively reduced, then the shock wave angle would also get less and less, and the shock would lie back closer to the downstream wedge surface. If this process of reducing the wedge angle were continued all the way until the wedge angle became zero and the wedge was exactly in line with the upstream flat plate, then the angle of the shock wave would reduce until it finally settled at exactly the Mach angle, whilst its strength would become less and less until the deflection became zero, at which point in perfect conditions the shock wave would disappear from view. It is at this stage that the shock wave has become a Mach line, and so, in perfect conditions, a Mach line would be totally invisible. However, if there is any small kink (such as a very fine hinge line) at the foot of the now flattened wedge, then this will be sufficient to make the Mach line visible, whilst producing no appreciable disturbance in the flow. In practice, the very smallest of blemishes on the surfaces of objects in supersonic flow are sufficient to render the Mach line visible (using appropriate viewing equipment).

EXPANSION FANS

We have looked carefully at the effect of deflecting the flow from its free stream direction in Figure 10.5. So let us now consider what happens if we allow the flow to resume its original direction, by adding a third flat surface parallel to the first as on the right-hand side of the same figure. A shock wave was created by the earlier concave corner, but we now have a convex corner. This also produces (or perhaps permits) a change in direction, but this time the flow speeds up and the pressure and temperature and density all fall, to values which are so close to the original values that we can assume they are the same. Thus the effect of the convex corner is to undo in all respects the effect of the concave corner.

There is a difference in the manner in which these reverse changes occur, which again agrees with common sense if we empathise as before with our particle of air in the airflow. On reaching the concave corner, it is suddenly *free*, but not *forced*, to expand, to shake itself out of its strait-jacket, and to resume its progress as it had been before the initial disturbance. Since there is no sudden constraint to do this, the transition occurs smoothly and over a small region of the flow rather than at an abrupt line like a shock wave. This region is called an expansion fan, or more correctly a Prandtl-Meyer expansion or a Prandtl-Meyer turn. Conveniently, however, the expansion region is of a fairly small angle, and so to a first approximation it may be thought of as a sudden discontinuity, and is often represented by a single line rather than a fan.

Although the name of Meyer has been swallowed up into obscurity within aviation history, it would be unbecoming to present a book on the principles of aircraft flight without referring briefly to Ludwig Prandtl. A German physicist born in Bavaria in 1875, he was Director of the Institute of Applied Mechanics at the prestigious University of Göttingen in Germany from 1904 until his death in 1953. While there he built his laboratory into the world's greatest aerodynamic research centre of the 1904-1930 period. He has been recognised as the 'father of modern aerodynamics', and is largely responsible for giving us both the concepts and the mathematical theory for the majority of the material in this book, perhaps his most notable contribution being the theory of boundary layers. A gracious, studious and friendly man, he was also an accomplished pianist. As a lecturer he was considered tedious because he could hardly make a statement without qualifying it, but despite this he attracted many excellent students who later distinguished themselves in the field of fluid mechanics. A man whose accomplishments will never be forgotten, his life and achievements deserve further reading, and are well summarised in John D. Anderson Junior's book *Fundamentals of Aerodynamics*.

Returning briefly to the Prandtl-Meyer turn, there is one further important thing that should be noticed about it. It may well come as a surprise to you to see the airflow turning neatly round the convex corner at the levelling off of the wedge in Figure 10.5, rather than separating at the sharp corner and streaming off in a straight line continuing the direction of the wedge. After all, we've spent some considerable time looking at boundary layer separation and stalling, and sharp corners are just what it takes to make an airflow separate. What is going on?

When introducing Figure 10.5 we made the assumption that the flow was inviscid, so that we would not need to worry ourselves with the boundary layer whilst looking at the overall flow, just as we did when looking at ideal incompressible flow. In incompressible flow this assumption let us down very badly as soon as we came to the rear parts of objects in an airflow, since we found that the flow was prone to separate. But we can be very grateful that, as we move into supersonic flow situations, we have actually left the problem of flow separation completely behind us, and the real flow really will behave as indicated in Figure 10.5. How can this be?

The answer lies in the concluding remarks of the introduction to this chapter, that many of the rules and principles of aerodynamics actually reverse themselves in a surprising way at the watershed point where $M = 1$. Most significantly here, it is the pressure that behaves differently. We have seen that through the shock wave the pressure increases, and that through the expansion the pressure reduces back to its original value. This means that the pressure gradient across the shoulder where separation might be expected is *favourable* (from high to low) rather than adverse, as occurred at such points in the case of subsonic flows. A favourable pressure gradient will never cause boundary layer separation, since there is a ready supply of pressure energy making good the energy that is given up to the surface through skin friction. Consequently sharp convex corners are no problem at all when it comes to designing supersonic aerofoils or other objects. Furthermore, this principle can be extended to the leading edge. In subsonic flow we found it necessary to have well-rounded leading edges to prevent leading edge stalling. But in supersonic flow there is no such problem, since there is only a favourable pressure gradient around the top of the leading edge, and the flow will be smoothly carried around this corner through a Prandtl-Meyer turn. Therefore, if it is found to be desirable for other reasons, there is no harm in using sharp (even very sharp) leading edges on supersonic aerofoils and bodies.

THE FLAT PLATE AEROFOIL

It follows that all the struggling with aerofoil concepts and forms that characterised the early pioneering days of aviation become completely irrelevant and unnecessary when trying to conceive of the best form for a supersonic aerofoil. Let us therefore start by examining the very simplest possible device that looks as if it ought to give good lift without undue drag – a flat plate. This is shown in Figure 10.7, set at an angle of attack α to the supersonic free stream flow.

The airflow which passes under the lower surface has to negotiate a concave turn at the leading edge, just as at the leading point of the wedge flow in Figure 10.5 except that in this case the turn is downwards instead of upwards. This generates a downwards oblique shock wave, and the pressure behind the shock wave (which is what we are interested in) is higher than the free stream pressure, as indicated by the symbol p^+ under the aerofoil. At the rear of the lower surface, the flow turns through a convex turn, reverting to the free stream conditions of pressure and Mach number through a Prandtl-Meyer expansion fan.

Over the upper surface there is a convex turn and an expansion around the leading edge, which gives rise to a fall in pressure to a value lower than the free stream pressure, indicated by p^- above the aerofoil. Then the convex turn at the trailing edge compresses the flow through a shock wave back to free stream direction and conditions again.

Thus we have an extremely simple pressure distribution around the

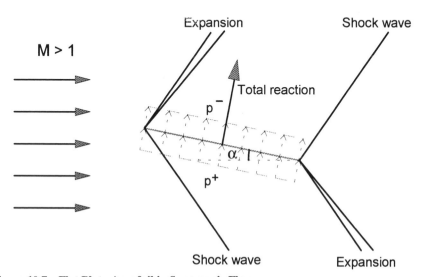

Figure 10.7 Flat Plate Aerofoil in Supersonic Flow

aerofoil, uniform over both top and bottom surfaces, which we have indicated by the dotted arrows and the dashed envelope-line. On the top surface the pressure is below atmospheric so that there is a suction in the upwards direction (perpendicular to the aerofoil), and on the bottom the pressure is above atmospheric so that there is a pushing force, again upwards perpendicular to the aerofoil. It is a simple step to multiply the pressures by the areas to give the forces, and add these together to give the total reaction, which is shown in the figure.

Although by no means trivial to derive, there is a very convenient and simple 'back-of-the-envelope' method of working out approximately the coefficients of pressure on each flat face of a supersonic aerofoil, depending on just the free stream Mach number M and the angle δ (in radians) at which the face is inclined to the free stream direction. It is called Ackeret's First Order method, and states that, provided δ is small so that the shock waves and expansions are weak (like Mach lines),

$$C_p = \pm \frac{2\delta}{\sqrt{M^2 - 1}}$$

In the case of the flat plate, δ equals α. Whether there should be a plus or minus sign is determined by looking at the nature of the turns that the flow has made to arrive at this face, just as we have done above for

the flat plate. Remembering that $C_p = \dfrac{p - p_\infty}{\frac{1}{2}\rho_\infty V_\infty^2}$ and knowing the free

stream conditions, it is thus possible to work out the actual pressures on each surface. Multiplying these pressures by the areas of the surfaces, the force normal to each surface can be calculated, and the resultant of the pressure forces on the different faces will give the total reaction, from which lift and drag can be found by resolving the vector. It is thus very much easier to predict the forces on a supersonic aerofoil in supersonic flow than those on any aerofoil in subsonic flow.

WAVE DRAG DUE TO LIFT

Turning back to the flat plate aerofoil again, we have now established that the total reaction is upwards, acting perpendicular to the aerofoil chord line. Since the chord line is inclined at α to the flow, this means that the total reaction is inclined at an angle α backwards from the vertical. If α is a small angle, then the lift component (in this case vertical since normal to the airflow which is horizontal) will be approximately equal to the total reaction. But there will also be a small component of the total reaction in the rearwards direction, which is a drag force.

So a supersonic aerofoil, even approaching it by ideal flow theory ignoring viscosity, has a drag force. This force is called *wave drag*, and is a consequence of operating supersonically and thus generating shock waves. d'Alembert's Paradox of no drag in ideal flow still holds for lower speed compressible flow provided the flow speeds everywhere are subsonic. However, it does not apply as soon as some or all of the flow becomes supersonic and shock waves occur. Wave drag is a new form of drag experienced by a two-dimensional body, in addition to boundary layer generated profile drag, and when wave drag occurs it is typically very much greater than profile drag.

The wave drag of the flat plate aerofoil depends directly on its angle of attack, and is actually called wave drag due to lift. The only way to reduce the wave drag is to reduce α, but the chief consequence of this will be to reduce lift. It so happens that, as α is reduced, the ratio of lift to drag continues to rise to as high a value as you like until it approaches infinity when you have got no α and no lift or drag remaining. So the flat plate aerofoil is theoretically the most efficient possible supersonic aerofoil shape.

THE DOUBLE WEDGE AEROFOIL

But there is a rather serious problem, which we may have overlooked by getting too carried away by theory. To make a wing of the flat plate aerofoil type, it must have some thickness in order to allow it to be given cantilever strength to withstand flying loads. Without thickness, it effectively has the strength of a flat sheet of paper. If we just make the flat plate thick with rounded or squared off leading and trailing edges, then immediately we have a leading edge which is going to create an immense amount of wave drag. Instead of having a nicely attached oblique shock wave beneath the sharp leading edge, we will have a region of a normal shock wave in front of the leading edge with subsonic flow, a stagnation point and a very large nose pressure behind it, thus losing the aerodynamic advantage of the flat plate aerofoil.

So we must look again for an aerofoil shape that has a sharp leading (and trailing, but this time less important) edge, whilst also providing depth for structural strength. A simple and very common solution is the so-called double wedge aerofoil, in the form of a doubly symmetrical rhombus or diamond as shown in Figure 10.8. In this case, although the aerofoil will produce lift if set at a non-zero angle of attack, yet in order to illustrate the important features clearly, we have set the aerofoil at zero angle of attack so that the flow over the top and bottom surfaces is exactly symmetrical. The thickness of the aerofoil is greatly exaggerated in the figure, and in practice a wing of this cross-section looks much more like a flat plate than the double wedge shown here.

The top and bottom flow at the leading edge is deflected concavely,

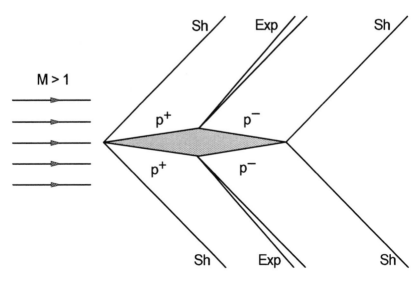

Figure 10.8 Double Wedge Supersonic Aerofoil

resulting in shock waves and thus an increase in pressure to p^+. At the shoulder the flow does not just expand to the free stream direction, but by the same amount again so that its pressure falls right through p_∞ to p^-. Then both flows experience a compressive turn at the trailing edge, producing shock waves and the pressure reverting to p_∞. Since all of the four surfaces are at the same angle as each other to the free stream flow, Ackeret's formula gives the same numerical value for C_p on each surface, and the signs are taken from the sign of the pressure in each region as discussed above.

Looking at the pressure forces on the front two faces, their magnitudes are equal and both act inwards on the aerofoil. Their vertical components cancel out, but they both provide a smaller component from left to right, i.e. in the drag direction, which compound each other. There is suction on the rear two faces, and again the vertical components cancel out but each provides a horizontal component, once again in the drag direction. Effectively the aerofoil is being pushed back by its front two faces and pulled back by its rear two faces. Consequently, although with zero angle of attack there is no lift being produced, there is a drag force, which is contributed to by the pressure forces on all of the faces.

With the flat plate we had wave drag due to lift. In the present case there is no lift produced, but we still have wave drag, this time due to *thickness*. If the double wedge aerofoil is now inclined to the airflow, it will also produce some additional wave drag due to its lift. Any object in supersonic flow, then, whether producing lift or not, is going to experience wave drag due to its thickness, and if it is also producing lift then that will account for an additional amount of wave drag.

It is very important to minimise aircraft wave drag due to thickness – as is illustrated by the Concorde supersonic airliner. On entering the cabin, one cannot but be aware of the fact that the fuselage is very much narrower than any subsonic airliner fuselage, and the space for seating is much more restricted. This is a direct result of the need to keep the frontal area of the aircraft as small as possible, in order to keep the wave drag due to thickness low.

LOW SPEED/HIGH SPEED DESIGN CONSIDERATIONS

We have seen that the leading edge of a supersonic wing has to be very sharp if the wing is to be aerodynamically efficient and to have low wave drag. But we also know that at subsonic speeds sharp leading edges are very bad news. At high subsonic speeds in straight flight, i.e. when high lift coefficient values are not required, sharp leading edges may just about be acceptable at subsonic speeds, but as soon as even relatively small angles of attack are applied there is the problem of the leading edge stall.

A similar consideration applies to aerofoils such as the double wedge form, which have flat aerodynamic surfaces and sharp turns such as the shoulders between front and rear faces. Although very satisfactory for supersonic-only flight (and hence frequently used on missiles which never need to perform subsonically other than during a brief acceleration phase), they are totally unsuitable for an aircraft that also has to fly subsonically, because the flow will always be separated over the rear half of the wing on both faces. An alternative shape sometimes used is that of the bi-convex aerofoil, where the top and bottom surfaces are both arcs of circles, like a two-dimensional bi-convex lens. The leading and trailing edges are sharp, but there are no other corners.

An additional feature of supersonic aircraft is the requirement to keep the frontal area as small as possible in order to minimise wave drag due to thickness. Not only does this apply to the fuselage as in the case of Concorde, but also to the wings, which therefore tend to be kept very short. We will see in Chapter 12 that there is no aerodynamic advantage (as there is in subsonic aircraft) to having long wings, and there are also structural as well as aerodynamic advantages in keeping the wings short, but this of course tends to imply a small wing area and S term in our lift formula.

Flying an aircraft which is optimised for its supersonic performance slowly enough for landing is a serious problem. The difficulties are particularly exemplified by the Lockheed F-104 Starfighter, whose

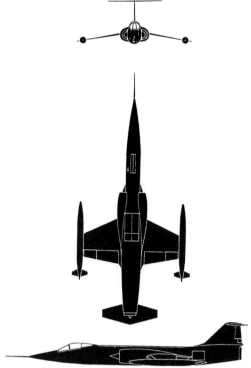

Figure 10.9   Lockheed F-104 Starfighter

profiles are shown in Figure 10.9. The top view shows the very small frontal area for the minimisation of wave drag due to thickness, achieved in particular by the very thin wings and small wingspan. The very thin wings necessitate very sharp leading edges, ideal for the supersonic performance (up to Mach 2.2), but even with the most elaborate lift augmentation systems that there is room for in the tiny wings and with arrester parachutes and other deceleration aids, the aircraft has always had a reputation of being particularly demanding to land, with a landing speed in the region of 200 miles-per-hour.

This obviously will not do as a design philosophy for the sophisticated supersonic aircraft of today, and so a better solution had to be sought. There is an answer, however, which is tied up with the zones of influence and zones of silence that we thought about earlier. If the leading edge of a supersonic wing is normal to the free stream direction (or not far off it, as in the case of the Starfighter,) then the first thing the approaching supersonic airflow knows about the presence of the aircraft is when it hits the wing or the shock wave produced by the wing. For this reason the leading edge has to be sharp, so that this sudden impact is kept as drag-free and as clean as possible. If, however, the air could be warned

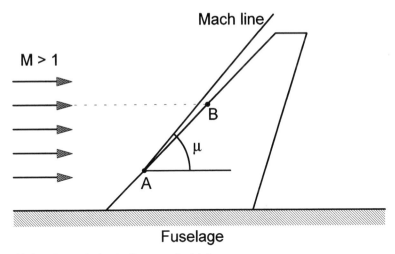

Figure 10.10   Swept Wing in Supersonic Airflow

in advance by pressure wave information that it was about to meet an object, then as in subsonic flow the air would be able to take curving avoiding action, and so the leading edge could after all be curved rather than sharp, even though the free stream airflow is supersonic.

Surprisingly, this can be very simply achieved, and the method of doing so is to sweep the leading edge of the wing (either backward or forward, but usually backwards for structural reasons[2]). Figure 10.10 is a simplified drawing of a swept back wing of a supersonic aircraft. We will look particularly at two points (*A* and *B*) on the leading edge, but try to bear in mind that these are not special points but representative of all of the points along the leading edge. The only stipulation is that *A* is inboard of *B*.

The point *A* is on the leading edge of an aerofoil, which will be dividing the flow upwards and downwards out of the plane of the paper, and consequently oblique shock waves will be shed upwards and downwards out of the paper by point *A* together with all of the other points on the leading edge. But those shock waves out of the paper are not our concern in the present context. Instead, we must note that, although there is no deflection of the air in the plane of the paper, yet every point *A*, being a point on an object in a supersonic airflow, does still produce a Mach line in the plane of the paper, just like the pointed tip of the pencil in the flowing stream; both situations

[2]No room to explain this here, but it will be easily understood if you put your arm out of a moving car window and point it about 45° forward with the palm of your hand extended flat. Then raise or lower your hand a little. It will be difficult to hold it still. Forward swept wings will be discussed more fully at the end of Chapter 13.

are two-dimensional. This Mach line is shown in the figure, and its related Mach angle is shown as μ.

Now the angle at which the wing is swept back is such that point B of the leading edge, being outboard of A, is behind the Mach line from A, and is consequently inside the zone of influence of A. Let us think back to what this would mean in the case of the ripples from the pebbles being dropped into the flowing stream. Our old blind friend Doppler Duck floats into the scene along the streamline indicated with a dotted line, and there is a barrage of pebbles being dropped in from a bridge all the way along the leading edge line. The stream's current is 'supersonic' and the duck will have passed point A before getting any warning. Yet just before she reaches her own danger point B she will cross the Mach line and will thereafter bob up and down on the ripples, getting a warning (albeit very brief) in time to take avoiding action (if she happens to be carrying her tin hat with her) before passing under the danger point at B.

Translating this to the supersonic wing scenario, this means that, provided that the wing leading edge is swept back enough to take it inside the Mach cone for the maximum design Mach number, then the airflow approaching *every point* of the leading edge will have got inside the Mach cones generated by all of the points inboard of that point before it gets to the leading edge, and so it will get some advance pressure wave warning – enough to take subsonic-type evasive action. The swept leading edge therefore sees its approaching airflow as subsonic and not supersonic at all, and so it has no need after all to be sharp. It can instead be rounded (although it will still have a pretty small radius of curvature, because of the thin-ness of the wing), thus providing an extremely useful concession to the aerodynamic demands of slow speed flight for landing and take-off.

Concorde is an excellent example of this principle being invoked, although the line of the leading edge has become somewhat corrupted by other supersonic and subsonic aerodynamic requirements. The low speed lift of Concorde during landing and take-off is in fact provided by an entirely unconventional means which we will refer to again at the end of Chapter 13.

For our present discussion, a simpler example for us to investigate is that of the BAC Lightning aircraft illustrated in Figure 10.11. Designed for a rôle very similar to that of the Starfighter, its maximum flight Mach number is declared as 2.27. The leading edges of wings and tailplane are swept back from the unswept position by an angle of $60°$, and so they will perform as if they were in subsonic flow up to Mach 2, for which μ is $30°$, but at the absolute maximum flight Mach number of 2.27 the Mach lines will lie behind the leading edge, so that the benefit will be lost.

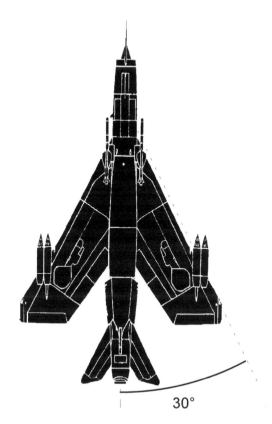

30°

Figure 10.11   BAC Lightning, Demonstrating Supersonic Leading Edge Sweep

SEEING SHOCK WAVES

On a number of occasions through this chapter we have referred loosely to 'seeing' shock waves or expansion fans or Mach lines, just as we can see the ripples on a stream. In fact, since air is itself invisible, shock waves and Mach lines and expansion fans cannot usually be seen with the naked eye unless they occur in conditions where there is some additional visible medium such as water vapour present in the air.

It is, however, possible to use special optical systems (at least in wind-tunnels in the laboratory) which render these aerodynamic features visible and project them onto a screen or the film in a camera, and by use of different colours to distinguish between compressions (shock waves) and expansions very dramatic photographs of shock waves may be produced.

The most common method for achieving these effects is called the Schlieren system as shown in Figure 10.12. Parallel rays of light (represented by the two solid lines starting at A and B) are sent through glass walls of the wind-tunnel test section D and across the region where the shocks and expansions are occurring. After emerging, the rays are focused to a point at F by means of a large convergent lens[3] at E. On diverging again beyond this focal point, they are then passed through another lens G which focuses the light onto a screen, or through a camera lens onto a film. With the wind-tunnel air not flowing, the image on the screen H or film will be just clear featureless light.

All the rays of light in the parallel bundle of rays between A and B will be concentrated into a very narrow waist at the point F. At this point, a knife-edge with its blade normal to the axis of the light beam is raised into the bundle from below, just far enough to cut off about half of the thickness of this narrow waist of light rays. As a result, only about half of the original light carries on past F, and so the image at H is about half of its natural brightness. However, this image is not affected in any other way.

Now if a ray of light passes through a region of air in which the density of the air is changing, as we have already seen occurs in both shock waves and expansions, then this has the effect of bending the ray of light. It is exactly the same phenomenon that gives rise to mirages in the desert, or more familiar to most of us the appearance of

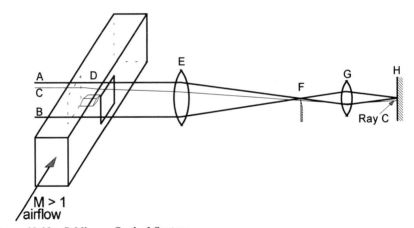

Figure 10.12 Schlieren Optical System

---

[3]In practice a concave mirror is usually used, as it is lighter and cheaper (though by no means cheap) and easier to produce than the very large lens that would be required. It also conveniently brings the image back to near the tunnel test section. Optically, however, a lens would serve the same purpose, and it makes the explanation simpler.

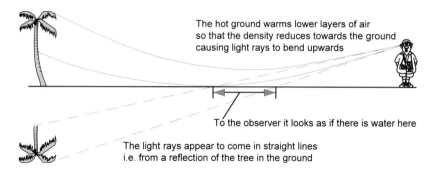

The hot ground warms lower layers of air
so that the density reduces towards the ground
causing light rays to bend upwards

To the observer it looks as if there is water here

The light rays appear to come in straight lines
i.e. from a reflection of the tree in the ground

Figure 10.13   A Mirage

water on the road ahead on a very hot dry day. Figure 10.13 shows
how this happens.

Now comes the clever bit. Returning to Figure 10.12, let us assume
that the supersonic airflow is turned on, so that the model in the test
section is creating some shock waves and expansion fans, but that the
rays A and B happen not to pass through these shocks or expansions.
Nothing changes for these rays, nor for all the other rays which happen not to pass through a shock or expansion. But consider now a ray
(labelled C in the figure) which does pass through a shock or expansion. It is therefore passing through a region of changing air density
and gets bent, and just like the rays from the top of the palm tree were
bent when they passed through varying density air near to the hot
ground. We have illustrated the ray C as being bent downwards in the
test section D (and have exaggerated), but depending on whether it
goes through a shock or expansion it would bend in opposite directions. The actual direction of bending depends on a careful examination of the physics at the point in question, and need not concern us.
The point is that shocks and expansions make the ray bend in opposite directions.

When ray C emerges from the test section, it is no longer travelling
parallel to A and B but very slightly downwards. After passing
through the lens E it is still going downwards relative to the other
rays, and so when it reaches F it will be lower than the other rays.
Consequently, more than half of ray C will be cut out by the knife-
edge, and so it will emerge from point F as a weaker or fainter ray
than the unbent rays. When the light of ray C is focused on the screen
at H, it will therefore show a darker image than any of the unbent
rays.

We have considered ray C to be bent downwards through the test
section, and consequently to be lower at F and hence to emerge
weaker. If another ray were bent upwards in the test section (by the

opposite type of aerodynamic phenomenon) then it would be higher than normal at F, less than half of it would be cut out by the knife edge, and so it would project a brighter image on the screen.

Thus any rays of light which pass through shocks or expansions will show up as dark or light regions on the screen, whereas regions of constant pressure will show up as being uniformly illuminated. We thus have a picture of the shocks and expansions occurring around the model, which is the nearest we can get to actually seeing them. We can use such images for measuring angles, and then using the theory based on what we have already been looking at we can work out many features of the flow situation.

In the next chapter we will be looking at flow around aerofoils at about the speed of sound itself, and at the start of this chapter we prepared ourselves for the fact that both subsonic and supersonic theories break down badly at the speed of sound. This is a situation in which the evidence of Schlieren photography really comes into its own, and can reveal all sorts of curious features, as we will shortly discover.

CHAPTER 11
Aerofoils in Transonic Flow

INTRODUCTION

After looking at the straightforward and almost clinical nature of supersonic flow around aerofoils, we are now in for a rather bumpy ride. As we have seen, we cannot depend on mathematics to model what happens at or close to the speed of sound itself, since we are either at or perilously close to the forbidden 'division by zero' syndrome, which causes an irrecoverable breakdown in mathematical theory.

If an aircraft starting from rest is to fly above the speed of sound, there is no conceivable way that it can get there without passing through the speed of sound itself. Likewise, if the aircraft is to land and stop, it must at some point decelerate through the speed of sound again. Therefore, whether mathematics is of any help or not, the aircraft designer must investigate and learn to understand air flows at around this speed. Such investigations became the next essential step in the progressive development of manned flight (projectiles from guns having for a long time travelled supersonically), from as early as the late 1930s and through to the 1950s, at which time no appropriate wind tunnels or supersonic aircraft existed. As discussed briefly at the start of Chapter 8, the problem was tackled through very adventurous and demanding test flying of some of the fastest subsonic aircraft of the day, followed by specially designed and built research aircraft. Appropriate flight data and voice recording equipment did not exist, and so pilots had to divide their time between controlling their aircraft under extreme and critical conditions in unknown and dangerous manoeuvres, and recording every minute detail of their experience with a pencil on a notepad strapped to the right upper leg. It is a most fascinating story of individual courage and determination and of corporate tenacity and conviction, nowhere better related than in his book *Testing Early Jets*, by the highly distinguished and accomplished test pilot Roland Beamont, published by Airlife.

Transonic flight is the term applied to flight not only exactly at the speed of sound, but over a range of flight speeds from quite a considerable amount below that speed up to a little bit above. Since the speed of flow around an object in an airflow varies (as we have seen) according to the path that the air has to take to negotiate the object, the flow at some points around the object will reach the speed of sound earlier than at others. The transonic regime is simply the range of flight Mach numbers over which there exists a mixture of supersonic flow and subsonic flow around the object, excluding the boundary layer. (There will always be a layer of subsonic air at the bottom of the boundary layer, since the no-slip condition still applies at the surface, and if the airspeed down through the boundary layer has got to drop to zero at the surface, it cannot avoid going subsonic on the way.)

In the early days transonic flight was associated only with the so-called 'sound barrier', that inhospitable boundary that had to be crossed in order to reach the 'promised land' of supersonic flight beyond it. Today however that is no longer the case. It is found that the most efficient mode of flight for nearly all but the shortest routes or journeys (both cost-wise and in terms of time-saving and operational requirements) is actually to fly well into the transonic regime, with a mixture of subsonic and supersonic flow occurring over the wings. The related problems have been thoroughly investigated and overcome, and the design of wings and aerofoils has become substantially changed in order to accommodate supersonic flow over parts of them, taking advantage of the high speeds available rather than avoiding them. Nowadays, if you fly in any jet airliner, it is probable that during most of the flight there will be a substantial region of supersonic airflow over the wings and accompanying shock waves, and occasionally in certain atmospheric conditions it becomes possible actually to see these shock waves with the naked eye.

THE PROBLEM

So what was it that suddenly made life so very traumatic and unnerving when one flew close to the speed of sound? What was it that gave rise to the great myth of an unpenetrable 'sound barrier', and that claimed the lives of intrepid test pilots? Let us start to find out by investigating the flow around a subsonic cambered aerofoil as the speed of the free stream airflow increases towards, through and beyond the speed of sound. We will deliberately maintain a constant zero angle of attack of the aerofoil, at which a small lift coefficient will arise solely from camber. Thus we are comparing situations that would be dynamically similar if it wasn't for the effect of varying Mach number. (If this sentence puzzles you, check back to the text of Chapter 8 in the section headed 'The Modelling Problem' around the formula $C_F = f(Re,M)$ (page 203). We may safely ignore variations in Reynolds number in the present discussion, since the effects of these pale into insignificance in comparison with the Mach number effects.)

Figure 11.1 presents a series of diagrams that illustrate the details of what is going on as the free stream flow around the aerofoil is gradually increased from well below the speed of sound, through the transonic regime, up to a substantial supersonic Mach number when the flow

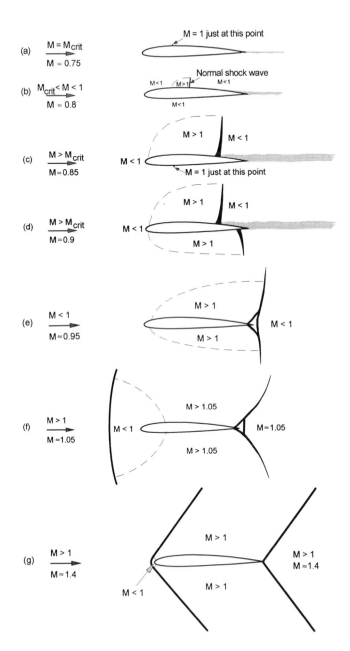

Figure 11.1 Development of Flow Over a Subsonic Aerofoil as M Increases Through M = 1

everywhere has reached supersonic speed. A lot of complicated things happen during this progression, and ideally a video would be a much better way to present it. However, being restricted to the pages of a book we must make the most of a sequence of 'snapshots'.

Let us start at the beginning, with Figure 11.1(a). The free stream airflow has been gradually increasing up to the value shown here, and the flow around the aerofoil has been behaving perfectly normally in the manner that we have come to expect, with some speeding up of the flow over both top and bottom surfaces, the speeding up being greater over the top surface because of the aerofoil's camber. As this process develops, there will come an instant when the point of greatest air-speed on the aerofoil surface outside the boundary layer, typically on the top surface near the point of maximum thickness, reaches the speed of sound, so that locally $M = 1$. It is at this instant that the 'snapshot' of Figure 11.1(a) is taken, and the free stream Mach number is defined as the *critical Mach number*, designated M_{CRIT}. The critical Mach number is the free stream Mach number at which the transonic range begins.

The Mach number at which sonic speed flow first appears depends on the shape of the aerofoil, and in particular on the thickness. The range of values of this critical Mach number may range from as low as about 0.65 for very thick (low-speed, high-lift) wings to about 0.78 for the very thinnest wings. From these figures it is clear that the speeding up effect that occurs over aerofoils is a lot more substantial than we might have instinctively guessed. Even over the thinnest of wings the air is speeded up by more than a quarter of its free stream value, and on the very thickest aerofoil sections the air flow speed is increased by more than half. The cruising Mach numbers of jet airliners usually fall into a similar Mach number range, although they actually cruise at above their critical Mach number, by the use of supercritical aerofoils as we shall see later. In Figure 11.1 we have chosen to depict (approximately) an aerofoil whose critical Mach number is 0.75, so that typical Mach numbers may be given for other significant stages in the development for comparison.

Still looking at Figure 11.1(a), we notice that a thin wake is depicted. This wake may be just the combination of the two turbulent boundary layers merging after leaving the trailing edge, as discussed in Chapter 6 and shown in Figure 6.6. Alternatively, one or both of these boundary layers may have separated just before reaching the trailing edge, but the difference is not important. In either case there will be a thin wake of turbulent air, which has very little effect on the sub-critical Mach number performance of the aerofoil. We are drawing attention to its existence in view of the fact that the behaviour of this wake plays a very significant part in what happens from Figure 11.1(b) onwards.

We now turn our attention to Figure 11.1(b), in which the free stream Mach number has reached a value a little higher than M_{CRIT} and is still rising towards $M = 1$. The point at which the speed of sound was first reached on the upper surface has now increased to a small (but growing) region of supersonic air flow. The upper and left boundary of this region is depicted with a dashed line; nothing significant happens to the airflow here as its speed smoothly passes from subsonic to supersonic. However, as we have seen in the previous chapter, there is always a normal shock wave and a violent and abrupt change in properties where air flow slows down from a supersonic to a subsonic speed, and this is seen at the rear of the supersonic region. At first the shock wave is quite weak and quite short, terminating at the supersonic region's top boundary, but as the free stream Mach number increases further this supersonic region grows, as does the shock wave, which also moves back towards the trailing edge, as a glance ahead at Figure 11.1(c) will show.

What effect does the development of this supersonic region have on the performance of the aerofoil? In fact, the region in which $M > 1$ has no adverse effect whatsoever, and can be very beneficial in producing low pressure, contributing to the wing's lift. It is the shock wave at the rear of this region that is the bugbear. We recall that pressure rises suddenly through a shock wave, creating a local but intense adverse pressure gradient. Finding itself towards the rear of an aerofoil and thus in a region of natural adverse pressure gradient anyway, this shock wave can only aggravate the boundary layer's natural tendency to separate before reaching the trailing edge. Thus in Figure 11.1(b), although the shock is still small, the pressure jump across it has had the effect of retarding and thickening the boundary layer, causing the boundary layer to separate before reaching the trailing edge. The previously innocuous wake has thus become thicker, and the form drag has risen.

The progression through Figures 11.1(a), (b) and (c) is smooth and continuous, and so we allow our attention now to move to part (c). The free stream Mach number is still subsonic, but the supersonic region on the upper surface has grown to cover the majority of the upper surface, and the shock wave has become very much stronger. The most crucial effect of this is that the large pressure rise across the shock wave proves too much for the boundary layer to cope with, resulting in total boundary layer separation at the foot of the shock wave, and a very thick, turbulent, wake of separated flow behind it. This is no longer just a wake of two turbulent boundary layers moving downstream at the free stream speed (as in Figure 6.6). Rather, it is a fully developed stall, characterised by large scale turbulence, reverse flow eddies and no pressure recovery, in every way identical to the conventional (high angle of attack) stall as discussed fully between

Figures 6.7 and 6.8 of Chapter 6, but on this occasion not caused by a high angle of attack but by a shock wave. The phenomenon is called a *shock stall*, and its effect is so dramatic and severe that we will need to refer to it frequently in the following few pages.

Before looking at the effect of the shock stall, let us see what is happening on the aerofoil's lower surface in Figures 11.1(c) and (d). We recall that the aerofoil is cambered, and this means that, compared with the top surface, the lower surface is relatively flat. Less speeding up occurs there than on the upper surface, but just as before at some subsonic free stream Mach number the speed somewhere on the lower surface will reach the speed of sound. Because of the flatness, as soon as $M = 1$ is reached at one point this point very rapidly grows into a substantial supersonic region as shown in Figure (d), and the normal shock wave which develops at its rear very quickly moves towards the trailing edge, actually overtaking the shock on the upper surface. So although shock stalling occurs on the lower surface at this stage, the shock is so near to the trailing edge that we can mainly ignore its effect in comparison with that of the upper surface, although it may have produced a rather violent 'wobble' during its appearance and rapid progress to the trailing edge.

Before moving on to what happens next, a few comments are in order to explain the rather odd appearance of the shock waves in Figure 11.1 (c) and (d), when compared with the neat straight lines of theoretically infinite thin-ness that we had come to expect from our work in Chapter 10. In the transonic flow around an aerofoil designed specifically for subsonic conditions as we have here, the development of shock waves is decidedly messy compared with the idealised supersonic model situation that we had earlier, and shock waves do indeed appear (in two dimensions) as thick, bent, tree-trunk-like manifestations. The bentness is explained by the curvature of the surface and the fact that the velocities are varying across the plane of the figure. A little later, when the free stream flow exceeds Mach 1, the bentness will also be because the shocks are at least in part oblique shocks.

From a look at the boundary layer behaviour in this region we can shed some light on the perceived thickness of the shocks. We have shown the feet of the shocks in Figure 11.1 to be solid but splayed out, yet in fact these feet very often splay out so much that they become distinctly bifurcated as shown in Figure 11.2. This figure is effectively an enlargement of the region around the trailing edge of Figure 11.1(c), but for a more typical shock wave form. It is called a *lambda foot shock wave*, because of its resemblance to the lower case Greek letter λ.

The upper dashed line in Figure 11.2 represents all the points in the aerofoil boundary layer at which the Mach number is one. Thus

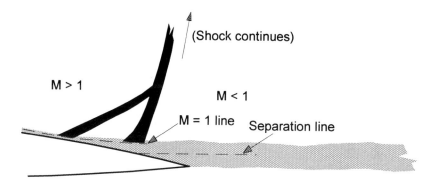

Figure 11.2   A Lambda Foot Shock Wave

upstream of the shock where the flow Mach number is greater than one this dashed line is slightly below the outer edge of the boundary layer, which is shown by the grey region. This dashed line of course disappears at the second branch of the shock, since all the flow downstream of that shock is subsonic. Clearly the shock wave branches do not go right down to the surface, since the flow is all subsonic there, but have their base near to the top of the boundary layer.

Imagine for the moment that the first, the highly oblique, branch of the lambda foot shock wave in Figure 11.2 is not there at all, but that only the second, the more normal, branch exists. The flow, including the streamlines just inside and outside the boundary layer, are slowed down by the shock wave, and so the boundary layer becomes thickened. Now we have previously seen that information cannot get upstream ahead of a shock wave, since the flow velocity ahead of it is always supersonic. However, the flow in the lower region of the boundary layer is always subsonic, and so pressure waves can certainly travel upstream down there, warning the boundary layer ahead of the shock of what is happening. The boundary layer thickening effect of the normal shock is thus carried upstream a little distance, causing the boundary layer itself to become wedge-shaped ahead of the normal shock. The supersonic stream flow in this region therefore has to negotiate a wedge shape in the flow, consisting of the boundary layer itself, just as we discussed following Figure 10.5 of Chapter 10, and so it generates an oblique shock wave. Being oblique, this shock wave impinges on the normal shock wave, and at this point the two shock waves coalesce to form one.

The effect of the strong normal shock wave is, as we have already seen, to force the boundary layer to separate, and the aerofoil to stall. The lower dashed line in Figure 11.2 is the line of zero streamwise velocity or the dividing line between the now separated boundary layer above it and the large scale turbulent eddies beneath it. After a short distance the distinction between these regions will disappear, as does the lower dashed line, and thereafter there is just a thick turbulent wake behind the stalled aerofoil, shown by the grey band.

Let us return to our study of the sequence of diagrams in Figure 11.1 and see what happens next, now that our free stream velocity is getting very close to the speed of sound. Essentially from about Mach 0.9 to Mach 1 a consolidation of the previous events takes place, as shown in Figure 11.1(e). The lower shock wave very quickly became stabilised near to the trailing edge, and now the upper shock wave will continue its progression towards this same point. As it does so, the thickness of the turbulent wake will become progressively less and less, until the effect of the shock stall disappears altogether. As the two lambda foot shocks reach the trailing edge, their normal (rear) limbs will spill over the trailing edge of the aerofoil, and the two will merge with each other to form one normal shock behind the trailing edge.

We may now ask, what happens when the free stream Mach number is at exactly Mach one? The answer, strangely enough, is 'nothing'! At least, nothing that can be seen around the aerofoil, but something rather strange does occur *ahead of* it. We recall that at the leading edge of an aerofoil (or any other object) there is a stagnation point where the flow velocity is zero, and that this is the case even if we assume ideal flow conditions and ignore the boundary layer. Now, once the free stream becomes slightly supersonic, it has to slow down somewhere through $M = 1$ to a subsonic speed before instantaneously coming to rest at the stagnation point. In this subsonic region information can travel a long way ahead of the aerofoil as we have seen, and so the change at first happens far upstream. Now slowing down from supersonic to subsonic speed can only happen at a normal shock wave, and so such a shock wave appears literally 'out of thin air' across the bows of the aerofoil a long way upstream. When it starts it is weak and far away, but as the free stream Mach number grows a little above Mach one it comes closer to the aerofoil and strengthens up. Away from the centre-line (the stagnation streamline) it is slightly oblique, as the region behind it merges with the upper and lower surface supersonic regions so that it has supersonic flow both sides of it. As a result of these developments, the flow pattern is now as shown in Figure 11.1(f). Notice also that the Mach number downstream of the entire system is now supersonic, (i.e. the free stream Mach number,) so that in consequence the two trailing edge shock waves become increasingly oblique, and take on the elegant swallow-tail form.

Although the flow is now almost everywhere supersonic around the aerofoil, there is still a substantial region of subsonic flow around the leading edge, which is associated with the stagnation point there. As the free stream Mach number increases further, the bow shock moves closer to the aerofoil and its curved limbs develop into the straight oblique shock wave limbs appropriate for the new supersonic flow conditions on both sides of them. If the leading edge were sharp, (absolutely sharp,) then the normal wave across the bows would disappear and the two oblique limbs of the bow shock wave would attach themselves to the aerofoil as we saw with sharp supersonic aerofoils in the previous chapter. But this will not quite happen around our subsonic aerofoil, as there must still be a stagnation point and a small related region of subsonic air flow. The situation is depicted in Figure 11.1(g). Strictly, therefore, a subsonic aerofoil or a body with a blunt nose can never actually break out from the transonic flow regime, since it will always retain a vestige of subsonic flow around the front stagnation point; but in practice this can be ignored.

At the trailing edge of the aerofoil during this final phase of transonic flow, the normal shock linking the two oblique shocks from the trailing edge moves downstream away from the aerofoil, remaining normal to the flow and attached to the two oblique shocks, so that the isosceles triangle that it forms gets larger and larger, as the supersonic region inside it grows to encompass the entire downstream flow field. Eventually, just as the bow wave appeared from 'thin air' upstream of the aerofoil, so now the normal wave at the rear will disappear into 'thin air' behind the aerofoil, leaving two clean oblique shock waves attached to the trailing edge, as predicted by the supersonic theory of Chapter 10. The transonic phase is now over, and the aerofoil is now performing supersonically.

SO WHAT?

So, what does this careful study of the behaviour of the flow and formation of shock waves tell us? We still don't appear to have tackled the issue with which we opened the last section, that of discovering what it was that made the so-called 'sound barrier' so troublesome and dangerous. No, we haven't quite answered that question yet, but we have thoroughly prepared the ground-work. We have earlier studied aircraft stalling characteristics, we have examined the effect of shock waves on air pressure, and now we have examined how these two ideas come together around an ordinary subsonic aerofoil in the transonic flow regime. The final step is just that of bringing these concepts together.

The flight problems that we are now considering were first experienced unintentionally from the late 1930s onwards by such aircraft as the Hurricane, the Spitfire, the Typhoon and the Messerschmitt Me109, some of the first single-engined monoplane fighters with retractable undercarriages. Because of their low drag they would frequently reach very high subsonic speeds in a dive in combat, and certain unanticipated and dramatic events occurred. It was quickly appreciated, long before the phrase 'sound barrier' became common parlance, that the events being experienced resulted from the compressibility of the air, and so they have always been referred to as 'compressibility problems'.

The compressibility effects were indeed occurring at high speeds for the aircraft of the time, but the aircraft air-speed indicators were certainly not indicating anything like the speed of sound when the compressibility effects began to occur. We have seen in the first part of this chapter that shock waves start to form at a critical free stream Mach number, considerably lower than Mach 1. Although this may be less than 0.7 for thick wings, yet the design efforts put into reducing the subsonic drag and high subsonic speed performance of the Second World War fighter aircraft had enabled them to have critical Mach numbers of above 0.8, and that of the Spitfire was said to be about 0.9. Surely that should have placed these slippery aircraft well out of harm's way?

But that was not the case, for a number of reasons. For a start, the chances are that the aircraft will be flying very much higher than sea-level, so that the air temperature will be substantially lower. Up to an altitude of about 36,000 feet, a level which is called the tropopause, the temperature falls from its sea-level starting value of about 15°C (288K) by about 2°C (2K) for every 1,000 feet of altitude gained. At the tropopause the *temperature lapse rate*, as this regular falling of temperature is called, fairly suddenly stops, and the temperature above this stays roughly constant at about −56°C (217K) up through all the rest of the atmosphere (at least as far as aircraft are concerned). Recalling from Chapter 10 that the speed of sound is proportional to the square root of the absolute temperature, we can work out the speed of sound in the region of the atmosphere above the tropopause (known as the stratosphere), and it is found to be about 660 mph. Thus an air-speed of 430 mph is at this height over 0.65 of the speed of sound, so that the Mach number is in the region of possible critical Mach number values.

Now we have only referred to the critical Mach number for an aerofoil in a low C_L orientation, and this is appropriate for an aircraft in a straight high-speed dive or fast straight level flight. However, in the Second World War days of air-to-air combat when compressibility effects first became apparent, high-speed manoeuvres were the order of the day, during which the aerofoil would be at a much greater angle of attack than when flying straight. The circulation around the aerofoil, and thus the speeding up over its upper surface, was thus increased, and so the critical Mach number was reduced from its value at a low lift coefficient. In these circumstances, compressibility effects may occur before an air-speed of 400 mph is reached.

But there is one over-riding consideration that we have conveniently put on one side so far, and have only briefly mentioned once, in Chapter 4 in the last paragraph of the section on static and dynamic pressure. This is the distinction between true air-speed, the quantity that we refer to when we talk about the free stream speed over an object or the speed of an aircraft through the air, and indicated air-speed, which is the value that the pilot actually reads from his air-speed indicator, the cockpit instrument which is driven by a pitot-static probe in the undisturbed airflow ahead of the aircraft. We recall that the pressure difference measured by a pitot-static probe gives directly the dynamic pressure $\frac{1}{2}\rho V^2$, so that if the air density ρ were constant the air-speed indicator could be calibrated to give the pilot the aircraft's air-speed directly. In fact ρ is not constant but decreases as altitude increases, not just up to the tropopause (like temperature) but continuously throughout the entire atmosphere until it reaches zero in outer space. Consequently the measurement of $\frac{1}{2}\rho V^2$, depending on two changing variables, is not very useful for calibrating the air-speed indicator. The solution adopted is to use a fixed value for ρ, and the value chosen is that of the internationally agreed standard sea-level air density, and it is denoted by ρ_o. The speed V which the formula now gives is the only variable quantity, and it is denoted by V_e and called the *equivalent air-speed*, sometimes referred to as the EAS. For our purposes, we can take it that the equivalent air-speed and the indicated air-speed (called the IAS, the direct reading of the air-speed indicator or ASI) are exactly the same as each other, although in practice a couple of corrections have to be made to the IAS to give the EAS. (These are relatively small compared with the conversion between indicated air-speed and true air-speed.)

Having calibrated the air-speed indicator at the fixed air density ρ_o, it can now be considered as measuring $\frac{1}{2}\rho_o V_e^2$ rather than $\frac{1}{2}\rho V^2$ As a result, regardless of altitude, the instrument gives the value of V_e, which is the speed which the aircraft *would be flying at* if it were at sea-level density at a speed giving the same pitot-static pressure difference. Both expressions $\frac{1}{2}\rho V^2$ and $\frac{1}{2}\rho_o V_e^2$ are equal to the same pressure difference, that between the total pressure and the static pressure as measured by the pitot-static probe, and so the two expressions are equal to each other. Based on the resulting equation $\frac{1}{2}\rho V^2 = \frac{1}{2}\rho_o V_e^2$, if the pilot needs to convert from IAS to TAS (for example, for navigation purposes), then he may calculate his true airspeed from the formula

$$V = V_e \sqrt{\frac{\rho_0}{\rho}}$$

Since ρ is always less than ρ_0 (except at or below sea-level), the square root in this formula is always greater than 1, and so the true airspeed is always greater than the indicated air-speed. Looking at this the other way round, an air-speed indicator always (except at or below sea-level) reads a lower value than the actual speed of the aircraft flying through the air, and the difference becomes greater and greater as altitude increases, until if the aircraft were a space rocket and left the atmosphere altogether at a very large true air-speed, its indicated air-speed once there was no more atmospheric pressure to measure would fall right off to zero.

At an altitude of 40,000 feet, a little above the tropopause (which has no specific significance in the case of indicated air-speed) the air density is a quarter of its value at sea-level, and so the indicated air-speed is half of the true air-speed. Thus the pilot of an aircraft diving through an altitude of 40,000 feet with an air-speed indicator reading of 200 mph would actually be flying at a speed of 400 mph. Whereas it is the indicated airspeed that is of most value to the pilot, telling him about the aerodynamic loads on the aircraft (since all aerodynamic forces are proportional to the dynamic pressure $\frac{1}{2}\rho V^2$), it is the true airspeed which is needed, in conjunction with the speed of sound, to calculate the Mach number. However, aircraft designed to operate at speeds approaching or beyond the speed of sound are provided with a Machmeter, so that the pilot does not have to perform complicated calculations to find the aircraft's Mach number.

As we have seen, the aircraft which first gave rise to compressibility effects and which were used for the early transonic flight tests had fairly high critical Mach numbers, and tests were usually done in straight diving flight with low lift coefficients, and so the test-flight speeds were higher than the lowest possible compressibility speeds as discussed above. What better way of finding out about the dramatic experiences of these high-speed diving flights, than to hear first hand from the then production test pilot of Hawker's Aircraft at Langley, Wing Commander Roland Beamont[1]:

> 'On 16 October 1943 I was detailed for the next flight in the Typhoon 'Straingauge' series of tests during which in previous weeks I had reached a number of odd conditions ... On this particular flight I was to begin to look at ... the last unexplored corner of the flight envelope at

[1]From *Testing Early Jets* by Roland Beamont, published by Airlife; page 2.

the highest combination of indicated airspeed and altitude which could be reached. Flight test engineer Charlie Dunn briefed me that from a maximum power "level" at 30,000ft, a push-over into a near vertical dive should enable us to reach about 450 mph indicated at 20,000 feet [i.e. 616 mph true air-speed, or $M = 0.87$] This, he said, would do for a start.

It was a day of variable layered cloud as I sat in EK 152 behind the clattering, roaring Sabre engine with the "saloon car" doors leaking vee-shaped draughts which utterly defeated the efforts of the hot-air system to keep the pilot warm. At 28,000ft there was no clear space in sight for the required dive but I levelled at 31,000ft on top of a cirrus deck and pushed up the power to maximum boost and the phenomenal Sabre RPM limit of 3,750rpm. As speed built up a break occurred in the clouds to port and, at the bottom of a quite well defined cloud shaft, a bend in the Thames near Eton was visible. The hole looked just about big enough.

Setting the instrumentation switches and noting the initial flight conditions on the test pad I rolled down to port, bringing the RPM back slightly as a margin against loss of propeller constant speed control. Rolling out into a near vertical dive, I trimmed the elevators [tail surfaces for controlling the aircraft in pitch] with a slight residual push force as a safety margin and this time against the anticipated nose-down trim effects of compressibility. At 27,000ft the general noise and fuss was becoming impressive with buffet vibration building up through the controls, seat and cockpit sides – even the "motor car" windows were vibrating visibly at their natural frequency, and it was while observing this with interest that the situation developed suddenly. I was conscious of the controls stiffening up quite rapidly, of the port wing trying to drop and of the aircraft becoming nose-heavy to the accompaniment of violent buffeting and a general feeling of insecurity; and when beginning to bear back on the stick to hold the dive angle from getting too steep and holding off starboard aileron [wing-tip surface for controlling the aircraft in roll] to maintain wings level, it was markedly apparent that these actions were becoming less effective. A full two-handed pull failed to reduce the dive angle at all and we were now going downhill and rolling to port with maximum noise, buffet and general commotion, and with no conventional control of the situation at all. Here was this thing called 'compressibility' ... Throttling right back, I continued to ride the shuddering and largely uncontrolled Typhoon down through 20,000ft until passing about 15,000ft. There, as the Mach number dropped at the still nearly constant indicated airspeed, [assuming the IAS to have been 500mph in standard atmospheric conditions, the TAS would have been 630mph, and the Mach number 0.87,] the shock waves were supposed to subside allowing control effectiveness to recover. This indeed occurred, and with subsiding buffet aileron effectiveness recovered first, enabling the wings to be levelled, then the nose began to rise under my still heavy pull-force until at last it was possible to ease off and recover to a level attitude, still with the throttle closed, the ASI dropping back from 500mph and, impressively, the altimeter steadying at only 8,500ft.

This was the classic pattern of compressibility incident which was encountered subsequently, with minor variations according to type, on all the final generation of piston-engined fighters and the first generation of jets.'

Exciting stuff indeed; and that is just an extract from one of many gripping accounts from those pioneer days. Our purpose now is to try to come to grips with just exactly what was going on. To do so, we will turn our attention now to looking one at a time at the special features of transonic flight, many but not all of which are referred to in the above passage.

TRANSONIC FLIGHT FEATURES
Drag Increase

Despite the considerable problems of control and buffeting that dogged the early excursions into transonic flight, it was undoubtedly the very high drag associated with transonic flight that gave rise to the perplexing idea that there might be an impenetrable 'sound barrier', and that it was physically impossible for anything to fly in the air faster than the speed of sound. As we have seen, theory (in the form of the so-called Prandtl-Glauert relationships) states that the effects of compressibility may be allowed for in evaluating a number of quantities e.g. C_p, C_L) by dividing the value arrived at using incompressible theory by $\sqrt{M^2-1}$ (for $M>1$) or by $\sqrt{1-M^2}$ (when $M<1$). When M is very close to 1 (either above or below) this would imply division by a very small amount, giving rise to a very large answer. The natural tendency for some people was to think that the drag would rise to infinity at the speed of sound, so that it would require an infinite amount of thrust to exceed it. This thinking was enhanced by the fact that, considerably before the speed of sound is reached, both the piston engines and the propellers that were being used to power aircraft suffer a very serious decline in their performance, and at the time the alternative of the jet engine had not been sufficiently developed to take over.

Cool-headed aerodynamicists and engineers, on the other hand, knew for three very good reasons that these arguments pointing to the existence of an impenetrable sound barrier were entirely spurious.

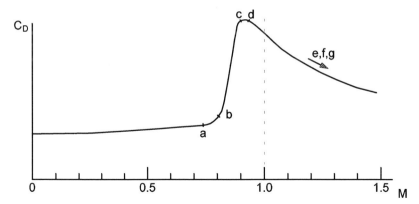

Figure 11.3 Variation of Drag Coefficient with Mach Number for an Aerofoil

First of all, the Prandtl-Glauert formulae are based on potential flow theory. When one is considering subsonic drag of a two-dimensional object, d'Alembert's Paradox quite unequivocally tells us that we must totally discount such theory, since it only gives us the nonsensical zero result. Consequently there is no use in looking to mathematical theory to predict drag at Mach one. Secondly, even if we did, division by zero does *not* necessarily give rise to an infinite result; rather, it produces unreliable consequences and a total break-down of the dependability of conventional mathematics, as we saw at the start of Chapter 10. But better than mere theoretical arguments is the fact that bullets from guns had long since broken through the sound barrier and travelled supersonically, so that such a thing was clearly not impossible.

So how, more precisely, does the drag of an aerofoil behave at around the speed of sound? To answer this question, it will be useful to look at the sketch graph in Figure 11.3 showing the typical way in which the coefficient of drag of an aerofoil varies with Mach number in this region. There are many things happening over a very small range of Mach numbers, and the effects overlap and may vary considerably from case to case. However, for the sake of illustration the letters a, b, c and d have been entered at the graph points approximately matching the corresponding lettered parts of Figure 11.1.

Let us follow the progress of the drag coefficient graph as Mach number is increased from zero over our aerofoil, remembering that the aerofoil is maintained at a constant angle of attack and thus a constant coefficient of lift. (This is not a typical flight situation, since the lift is not constant.) Before point *a* is reached, it can be seen that the drag coefficient is approximately constant, although increasing slightly due to subsonic compressibility effects. After the critical Mach number has been passed at *a*, the drag begins, gently at first and then more rapidly, to rise due to the onset of the normal shock wave.

This drag rise due to the existence of a shock wave arises largely from an important feature of shock waves that we have not yet talked about and so we must step back a couple of paces to gain a proper perspective. We have said that the static pressure (i.e. the pressure that would be read by a static tapping in the surface, without slowing the air flow down) is higher behind a shock wave than it is in front of the shock wave. But the energy represented by this static pressure is, at least as shown in the incompressible Bernoulli formula from Chapter 4, only one of the two parts of the total energy represented by the total pressure p_o, the other part being the kinetic energy represented by the dynamic pressure or $\frac{1}{2}\rho V^2$. In incompressible flow no other energy types become involved in the changes occurring, and the total energy is regarded as being composed of varying proportions of these two constituents. Now, however, the flow is compressible, which means that changes in density enter the picture, and consequently we also have changes in temperature occurring. We have already seen this effect, since when air passes through a shock wave changes occur not only to its static pressure and density but also to its temperature. Since temperature, and thus heat energy, also now enters into the before-and-after energy balance, the two-component incompressible Bernoulli equation has to be expanded into a three-component compressible version. Instead of saying that $p + \frac{1}{2}\rho V^2$ is constant we must add a new term and say that $p + \frac{1}{2}\rho V^2 +$ [heat energy per unit volume] is constant (recalling that the pressure terms are both energy per unit volume). The volume of a given amount (i.e. mass) of gas no longer remains constant, and so it is now more convenient to work in terms of energy per-unit-mass rather than energy per-unit-volume. This is achieved simply by dividing all the parts of this new equation by the density ρ, giving

$$\frac{p}{\rho} + \frac{1}{2}V^2 + e = \text{constant}$$

where e is the heat energy per unit mass, more usually referred to as the internal energy per unit mass[2]. Now the first two terms of this equation are exactly the same as the two pressure terms of the Bernoulli incompressible equation after dividing by the density, and so together they are the total pressure divided by density, p_o/ρ. Thus we can see from the above equation that, if the temperature and hence the internal energy rises, then the total pressure will fall. The total pressure is no longer constant as it was in incompressible flow. Instead a new quantity consisting of total pressure per-unit-mass plus

[2]Quantities which are defined per-unit-mass are frequently referred to as 'specific' quantities: e.g. e may be referred to as specific internal energy. This terminology is not adopted in this book.

internal energy per-unit-mass is now our reference quantity which remains constant through flow changes. In passing, although we will not use the word again in this book, this new quantity, the constant of the above equation, is called the *total enthalpy* per-unit-mass, and the two terms on the left excluding the dynamic pressure term together constitute the *enthalpy* per-unit-mass. Enthalpy in compressible flow is analogous to static pressure in incompressible flow.

We are now in a better position to understand why the formation of the shock wave on the top of the aerofoil causes an increase in drag. Behind a normal shock, although the static pressure of the air is increased, the total pressure of the air is actually reduced, and this means that, even if the pressure were to recover completely to a stagnation point at the trailing edge, it would not have recovered so much total pressure, and hence static pressure (dynamic pressure being zero at a stagnation point) as it had before the shock. Thus the leading edge stagnation region pressure is no longer balanced by the trailing edge stagnation region pressure, and the imbalance creates a drag. This wave drag is as before (in Chapter 10) an ideal, inviscid flow drag, since we have not had to mention viscosity or the boundary layer to explain it.

While we are on this point, it will be valuable to deviate just a little further, since by doing so we can provide a painless and digestible explanation of another technical term which frightens most people away, and that is *entropy*. Entropy is a concept which originated not in the aerodynamics of aircraft flight but in the aerodynamics (or gasdynamics) of gas turbine engines. Air is the working medium of such engines, and as with flight aerodynamics it is the pressure of the air which is its useful feature, in this case for creating pushing forces to drive turbine blades around. When used on aircraft, this air has to be 'hoovered' up from the atmosphere ahead, and it is important that as much as possible of the total pressure of the atmospheric air is preserved in tact during this process, since it is only the air's energy in the form of total pressure which is useful. All the rest, the internal energy, is unusable in the process of providing motive power, and so to the propulsion engineer is pure waste. This wasted energy, which is not destroyed but which is no longer in a usable form, is associated with the concept of entropy. Any change occurring to air (such as passing through a shock wave) which causes a redistribution of its energy from total pressure to internal energy is accompanied by an increase in entropy, and thus entropy may be thought of as a measure of the unusability of the air's energy. An increase in entropy implies a downgrading of the quality of air (for mechanical purposes), and so it is normally undesirable. Normal shock waves, in which the flow is brought abruptly down to subsonic speeds, are particularly bad at preserving total pressure and create lots of entropy, and so normal shocks are avoided as far as possible on the intakes of supersonic aircraft engines, and instead the air is slowed down by a series of oblique shock waves created by wedges or cones.

Returning to our thoughts about the drag of the transonic aerofoil, we see that after point *b* in Figure 11.3 the drag goes up extremely rapidly. It is at this point that the shock stall is taking place. Exactly as in the case of a high angle of attack stall, there is no pressure recovery at all, even towards the reduced total pressure, once the boundary layer has separated at the normal shock. It is the severity of this graph's slope and the extent of the rise in C_D during the shock stall which serves as our first indicator of the very alarming and dramatic effects that accompany the shock stall.

By point *c* (Figure 11.1(c)) the shock stall has become fully established, and from *c* to *d* the drag remains at around its peak value. The supersonic region on the lower surface grows so rapidly from its starting point to covering the entire surface, over such a small Mach number range, that the lower surface shock does not have time to create an effective shock stall before the shock moves right on out to the trailing edge.

As the Mach number progresses through the speed of sound, the supersonic region grows further and the offending shock wave moves towards the trailing edge. Whilst the shock stall does not stop during this period, the surface area behind it over which there is no pressure recovery is reducing in size, and so also is the resulting drag force.

During the subsequent progression there is a steady falling off of drag coefficient due to the departure of the shock stall effects off the trailing edge. However, although the drag coefficient eventually drops to a value that is not very much higher than the pre-transonic value, we must remember that this is not a graph of drag *force*. The drag force depends also on the square of the speed, and so even with a not excessive ultimate drag coefficient, supersonic drag values will always be very high.

Longitudinal Trim Changes

Aircraft drag, in the piston engine and propeller era, was thought to be potentially the limiting feature in approaching supersonic flight. But it was not drag that was predominantly occupying Roland Beamont's mind during test-flights such as that which he describes above. Although engine and propeller alone could not in level flight produce the required speeds for transonic effects to be investigated, by putting the aircraft into a steep dive and invoking the assistance of gravity such speeds were not too difficult to attain. It was not drag, but the reported, and now the experienced, loss of control which was the test pilot's chief and most immediate concern. Such loss of control manifested itself in a number of diverse and very curious ways, but without doubt the most dramatic, the most feared, and the most predictable, was the tendency of the aircraft to pitch irresistibly nose down into an ever steeper dive towards the Earth below, just at the moment when the pilot would have most liked to pull out of the dive and take refuge from the compressibility effects.

We saw in Chapter 2 that for an aircraft to change direction (either vertically or horizontally) it requires a large force, a centripetal force, acting on the aircraft as a whole directed towards the centre of the circular path that the aircraft is intended to fly along. The hinged control surfaces on the rear of wing-tips, tailplane and fin cannot supply these forces, but are provided in order to orientate the aircraft in such a way that the required centripetal force in the appropriate direction is produced by the wings. In view of this, if we wish to investigate the tendency of a diving aircraft to pitch down and refuse to pull out of the dive, we must look not only at the pitching (i.e. rotating) effects of both wing and tailplane on the aircraft and how they are affected by the shock waves, but also at how the wing lift force behaves, since this is ultimately what will or will not enable the aircraft to pull out of the dive. Since in practice so much will be happening all at once and since many of the signals will be conflicting with other signals and rapidly changing, it will in fact be virtually impossible for the test pilot to discriminate accurately between these two aspects of the problem.

Since it is the easier of the two parts of the problem to examine, let us look first of all at how the lift coefficient of an aerofoil varies with Mach number up to and through the transonic regime. We will follow this by referring to Figure 11.4, which is structured in a similar format to that of Figure 11.3, again for an aerofoil set at a fixed angle of attack.

Let us first of all take a glance at the fully subsonic phase, which we know something about already, in order to get our bearings. In a sim-

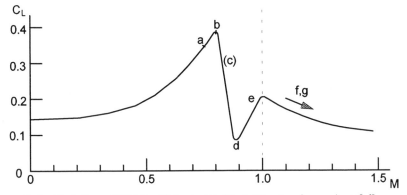

Figure 11.4 Variation of Lift Coefficient with Mach Number for an Aerofoil

ple discussion of low-speed flow we usually make the tacit assumption that C_L is independent of Mach number, as with Reynolds number, and that at a given angle of attack it is constant. We can see now, however, that even keeping Mach numbers strictly subsonic everywhere, the coefficient of lift increases to more than twice its zero Mach number value. Since we are now dealing with lift rather than drag, we can indeed apply the Prandtl-Glauert formula to subsonic and to supersonic values of C_L, and by doing so (except close to $M = 1$) curves similar to those shown (and found in practice) are produced. This illustrates very clearly that compressibility effects are by no means restricted to situations where the Mach number exceeds unity, and that only very loose approximations can be obtained by assuming incompressibility at any Mach number more than about $\frac{1}{3}$.

This steady rise of C_L continues increasingly rapidly right through to stage b, at which the maximum value of approximately twice the low-speed C_L value occurs. At this point, the upper surface of the wing has developed a small but substantial region of supersonic flow, with consequently very low static pressure, but the shock is still just beginning to appear and has not yet become strong enough to cause boundary layer separation. This phase of steadily increasing lift coefficient occurs whilst our test pilot is accelerating in a straight dive towards his goal of reaching transonic Mach numbers. Whilst doing so, there will be a stronger and stronger tendency for the aircraft to pull out of its dive and level off because of the increasing lift force resulting from both the increasing C_L value and the increasing speed. In order to remain in the dive, the pilot will require to apply steadily increasing forward pressure on the control column to lower the elevators, raise the tailplane, and thus reduce the angle of attack so as to keep a constant lift force. So the pilot is actually having to work quite hard, at this stage, at getting his aeroplane up to the required speed, which it is reluctant to do. Fortunately, as we have already seen, the drag coefficient is scarcely increasing at all at this phase, so that the pilot can still successfully accelerate.

But suddenly, at a point much more clearly defined on the C_L graph than in the shock wave progression diagrams, the lift coefficient (and hence the lift) falls off very steeply to a value even less than the original low-speed value. There are two very significant and completely independent causes of this very sudden drop. First of all, perhaps the most obvious is the shock on the top surface becoming strong enough to cause a substantial pressure increase behind it, and this pressure, acting downwards on the upper surface, has a negative influence on the aerofoil lift. The stalled flow and the thick turbulent wake themselves are not major contributors to the loss of lift, any more than during a high angle of attack stall does an aerofoil suddenly loses all of its lift. It doesn't; the lift curve just falls away from its maximum, but usually remains high.

So it seems that something more drastic must be happening, and to find out what it is we must look at the lower surface. Between point c (whose position cannot be reliably predicted) and point d, which corresponds to a Mach number range of only about 0.05, the flow over the entire lower surface has rapidly changed from all subsonic to all supersonic. Consequently there has been a substantial drop in pressure over the entire lower surface, and this is the main feature responsible for the steep plunge in the C_L curve.

The effect on the pilot can be quite alarming. Having been deliberately pushing the stick forward in order to prevent the aircraft automatically pulling out of its dive, suddenly most of this lift disappears, and so there is now a major excess of force in the 'downwards' direction relative to the flight path. Suddenly the pilot is being forced into a push-over, a drastic steepening of his dive, which only a moment earlier he was fighting to achieve. In the words of Roland Beamont from the above passage, '…it was while observing [the 'motor car' windows vibrating visibly at their natural frequency] with interest that the situation developed suddenly. I was conscious of … the aircraft becoming nose-heavy … When beginning to bear back on the stick to hold the dive angle from getting too steep … it was markedly apparent that these actions were becoming progressively less effective. A full two-handed pull failed to reduce the dive angle, and we were going downhill … with no conventional control of the situation at all.'

In that particular flight it would seem that Beamont did not break through into the next transonic phase. Had he done so, amongst other effects, the lift coefficient would have recovered again fairly suddenly to a limited extent, but not to its earlier maximum value or enough to solve his problem, as shown between d and e of Figure 11.4. To find the reason for this further sudden change we must turn our attention back to the upper surface, where the supersonic region is still growing and the shock is still progressing towards the trailing edge. This means that the negative lift contribution of the region behind this shock is now being swept out of the system, and the high pressure is being replaced with low pressure as the supersonic flow replaces the turbulent subsonic flow. Once e is reached, the flow almost everywhere around the aerofoil is supersonic, and so supersonic Prandtl-Glauert conditions take over.

So we have seen how the lift coefficient changes quickly and drastically, and what effect this has on the progress of the aircraft. But still surely the pilot ought to have been able to pull his control column back, giving up-elevator, downward load on the tailplane, and thus tip the nose 'up' (relative to the flight path) and gain increased angle of attack? What

effect this would have had on the wing flow (which we have only examined at a constant small angle of attack) is a somewhat academic question, since other things happened which rendered this action impossible.

In order to increase angle of attack, the aircraft must receive a nose-
up pitching moment, and this can come from two sources. It can come
from a download (or negative lift) on the tailplane under the control
of the pilot, which is highly effective because of the tailplane's long
moment arm behind the aircraft's centre of gravity; or alternatively it
can come from the wing itself, if for some reason its lift is not distributed fore-and-aft in the way the wing was designed for. In this latter
case, the moment arm is very much smaller than that of the tailplane
since the wing centre must be placed near to the aircraft centre of
gravity. But since the wing is much larger than the tailplane, such
moment effects cannot be ignored.

Let us confine our attention firstly to the wing. Having looked at
how C_D and C_L vary with Mach number for an aerofoil, a consistent
approach will be to represent the pitching moment as an aerodynamic
coefficient, and to trace its progress as the Mach number increases
over the same aerofoil at constant small angle of attack. Near the end
of Chapter 5 (under the heading 'Simplifying Aerodynamic
Coefficients') we looked at four straightforward steps of a procedure
to develop any aerodynamic coefficient. Let us use that method in the
present case.

The first instruction is simply to draw a line, to remind ourselves
that we are developing a fraction. The top and bottom will both have
to be in the same units, so that the result will be dimensionless.

The second step is to put M on top, to stand for the moment that we
wish to measure and discuss. M is a doubly convenient letter to use,
firstly because it stands for moment, and secondly because it is the
middle one of a triple of letters L, M, N which fairly naturally trip off
the English tongue. This triple of letters we will meet again (over and
over again) in *Flightwise: Aircraft Stability and Control*, since they are
used to represent the three moments on an aircraft about three perpendicular axes of the aircraft. Suffice it to say that, conveniently, M is
indeed the one member of the triple that is conventionally used for
pitching moment. We will define a positive value of M as a moment
which is trying to tip the nose of the aircraft up, and a negative value
as nose down.

A moment is somewhat different in kind from the quantities (forces
and pressure) that we have used up to now for aerodynamic coefficients. A moment is the turning effect of a force, and this effect is calculated by multiplying a force by the distance between the line of that
force and the line that the object is rotating about, if indeed it is rotating. But suppose that the object is not in fact rotating at all, which is

exactly the situation we require for our aircraft in pitch (and, incidentally, in roll and in yaw) when flying in any straight line[3]. In this case we cannot say what point it is rotating about, since it is not rotating. From what point, then, do we measure the distance to the line of the force, the moment arm? The answer in fact is that this is entirely arbitrary, so long as we are consistent within any one particular analysis. However, in order to ensure such consistency, it is absolutely essential that the point that was used for the measurement, the moment centre, is clearly specified.

Aerodynamicists are usually quite good at remembering this, but in fact they nearly always use the same point of reference when talking about aerofoils. It is the quarter-chord point, or the point on the chord line a quarter of the chord length aft of the leading edge. This point in fact has very important physical significance as maybe discovered in Volume Two when dealing with longitudinal static stability, and it is the theoretical position of what is called the aerodynamic centre of the aerofoil. Unfortunately we would have to deviate too far from the matter in hand to explain this term here, but all we need to know for our present purpose is that it is a convenient fixed reference point on an aerofoil, and that if a writer or illustrator has forgotten to specify what point moments are being taken about when dealing with an aerofoil, it can be fairly safely assumed that it will be about the quarter chord point.

The third step in developing our Coefficient of Pitching Moment, as we shall call it, is to put $\frac{1}{2}\rho V^2$ on the bottom of the fraction. This we always do, as it directly relates the quantity being measured to the free stream flow conditions producing the aerodynamic effect under consideration.

Finally we examine what else must be multiplied into the bottom line, in order to make it have the same dimensions as the top line. The top line, being a moment, is force times length. To produce force (as with C_L and C_D) we must multiply the pressure $\frac{1}{2}\rho V^2$ by an area, and for consistency we will use the usual area S, the wing plan area. But to achieve a moment we must multiply the force by a length, and so we still need another factor on the bottom line which is a length. Since we are talking about an aerofoil, we use the reference length which most naturally comes to mind, that of the aerofoil chord, which we designate c. If we are talking about an aircraft rather than a two-dimensional aerofoil, this will have to be adapted to $\bar{c}$, the mean chord, or quite frequently $\bar{\bar{c}}$, the aerodynamic mean chord, which we will not define here.

We can now combine all of these steps and write down the expres-

---

[3]For the purists amongst you, we could include here rotations at constant rotational speed, since it is rotational accelerations, and not rotational speeds, that are caused by moments. But in the present context, for our purposes here, a simplified discussion will suffice.

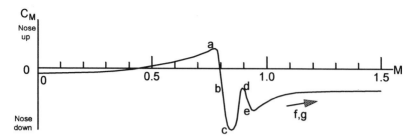

Figure 11.5   Variation of Pitching Moment Coefficient with Mach Number for an Aerofoil

sion for the coefficient of pitching moment, in which we will define M as being taken about the quarter chord point of the aerofoil, with nose up being the positive sense:

$$C_M = \frac{M}{(\frac{1}{2}\rho V^2)Sc}$$

In keeping with our previous approach, let us study the graph in Figure 11.5 illustrating how, typically, the pitching moment coefficient of an aerofoil at constant angle of attack behaves as the free stream Mach number is increased towards, through and beyond the speed of sound. This is going to be a substantially more difficult graph to follow than the others, since there are now two possible contributing causes to any effect, force and distance from the quarter-chord point. You should be very cautious of everything you read on the subject of pitching moments, since errors of interpretation are very easily made, and without your wits about you you may be easily misled.

Our consideration of the effects separately must not be thought to imply that they are neatly compartmentalised and separately identifiable. Rather, it is an attempt to put some classification structure onto what is in practice a very confused and untidy set of events. There *are* identifiable causes, but they are blurred together, and the actual positions of the letters *a-e* must be regarded as very approximate.

An initial overview of Figure 11.5 shows that at low subsonic speed C_M has a small negative (nose down) value, whereas at fully established supersonic Mach numbers its value is settling down to a considerably larger nose-down value. The initial nose-down value is a natural feature of any cambered aerofoil. The overall change to a finally greater nose-down pitching moment, on the other hand, occurs because in incompressible flow the centre of pressure of the aerofoil (the point where the total aerodynamic reaction acts on the wing, which has a disconcerting habit of drifting forwards and backwards as the angle of attack is varied) is normally well ahead of the middle point of the aerofoil. However, in fully established supersonic flow, a glance at the pressure distributions around the supersonic aerofoils in Chapter 10 will quickly persuade you that the centre of pressure is at the midpoint of the chord, so that the overall lift force has shifted substantially backwards.

This sizeable shift of the centre of pressure has to be seriously taken into account when designing a supersonic aircraft. If the tailplane is designed and set appropriately for balancing out the small nose-down pitching moment at incompressible speeds, then at supersonic speeds when the centre of pressure has moved a long way backwards a substantially greater download will be required by the tailplane, which will bring with it a considerable amount of additional extra drag, the last thing wanted when designing for supersonic flight. The solution adopted on the Concorde supersonic airliner is to shift the centre of gravity of the entire aircraft aft as the aircraft is accelerating through the speed of sound, and to move the centre of gravity forward again as it slows down through Mach one in preparation for landing. Rather than moving all of the passengers and baggage backwards and forwards in flight, the centre of gravity shift is achieved by means of mechanically pumping a large volume of fuel between forward wing tanks and tail fin tanks. The elaborate system required for this perpetual fuel transference is just one of the many complex necessities built into Concorde to enable it to do its job successfully. Clearly further aircraft control problems may be encountered if the total amount of fuel on board is allowed to fall below a sufficient minimum to enable this re-trimming process to take place whilst decelerating before landing. But we deviate, and must return to our thinking about transonic problems.

The steady subsonic rise in C_M before reaching point a is again accounted for by the Prandtl-Glauert compressible flow theory. When the region of supersonic flow first appears and then grows on the upper surface, it starts and remains centred at about mid-chord position, well behind the quarter-chord point. Consequently the strong suction produced in this region causes a rapidly strengthening nose-down pitching moment as the region grows, which accounts for the steep down-turn of the C_M curve in Figure 11.5 after a and through b to c.

Once the shock stall becomes established at c, the positive downwards pressure in the separated wake region behind the normal shock, being well aft, tries to compensate for the previous effect by pitching the aerofoil nose-up. Also the low pressure supersonic region is now forming on the lower surface centred aft of the quarter-chord point, and this also provides a nose-up pitching moment. Together, these two causes account for the up-turn in the C_M curve between c and d.

Finally the upper surface shock wave moves aft to the trailing edge, so that the nose-up effect of the high pressure behind the shock disappears off the back, resulting in a further down-turn in the C_M curve. Hereafter (from point *e* onwards) the development follows the predicted supersonic pattern.

We have now looked at the effects of compressibility on both the lift and the pitching moment produced by the aircraft's wing. Contrary to popular belief, it is the variation in lift which is the chief contributory cause to the pilot's problem as we have discussed. Although the pitching moment fluctuations of the wing discussed just now are indeed substantial, the application of a flap during low-speed flight also causes a change in pitching moment, and it can quickly be trimmed out by the pilot using the conventional pitch controls, so that pitching moment fluctuations are not of themselves critical. So we must still tackle the truly critical question, which is, why could the pilot not pull out of the compressibility dive in the ordinary way? To answer this question, we will now turn our attention away from the compressibility effects on the main wings of the aircraft, and consider what is happening at the various control surfaces.

Control Heaviness and Loss of Effectiveness

Before being specific about any particular control surface and the possible problems associated with that control, let us consider for a moment the principle underlying the general control surface concept, so that we can then investigate how a control surface's function is likely to be affected by compressibility.

Conventional aerodynamic control surfaces, be they ailerons on the wing-tips, elevators on the tailplane or a rudder on the fin, all consist of the trailing portion of the aerofoil (perhaps about the last third of the chord) being hinged to the front part, like a plain flap. The purpose is to enable the lift of the flying surface (wing, tailplane or fin) to be increased by hinging down the flap and hence increasing the camber. When the aerofoil's camber is increased in this way, the circulation around the entire flying surface is modified by adjusting the pointing direction of the trailing edge and hence affecting the Kutta condition. Consequently the pressure distribution around the entire flying surface is modified, and not just that in the neighbourhood of the relatively small hinged control surface itself. By this means much more extra lift can be generated than it would be reasonable to expect the control surface itself to provide or to bear. This principle was well understood by St James, who in his Epistle in the New Testament uses the power of the ship's rudder (which is identical in principle) as an analogy of the power of the tongue to do good or harm. In James Chapter 3 and Verse 4 of the Authorised Version we read:

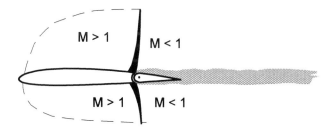

Figure 11.6   Subsonic Flying Surface in Supersonic Flow, with Control Surface

> 'Behold also the ships, which though they be so great, and are driven of fierce winds, yet are they turned about with a very small helm, whithersoever the governor listeth.'

Now the reason that this is possible is that, as we saw in Chapter 10, information in the form of pressure waves travelling at the speed of sound can travel upstream of the rudder through the water in the case of the ship or upstream of the control surface through the air in the case of the flying surface. If, however, any of the air through which this information has to travel upstream has reached the speed of sound, then no information can travel forwards into or through this region, and the region is a zone of silence.

Let us consider a situation between the stages represented by Figures 11.1(c) and (d), and assume that now the rear part of the aerofoil has been replaced by a hingeable control surface, whose hinge line (at this instant) coincides with the feet of the two shocks. This is shown in Figure 11.6. In fact this is merely a transitory stage in the process, but after looking at it we can briefly switch out attention to the before and after.

The control surface is shown undeflected. If it were to be deflected (either up or down) this would change the pressure distribution around it, but because of the supersonic regions upstream of the hinge (bounded by the shock waves) it is totally impossible for the pressure information generated by the control surface to travel upstream at all. Consequently, whatever deflection is applied to the control surface can only affect the pressure distribution on the surface itself, and can have no effect on the main portion of the flying surface upstream of it.

Just before this, in the situation of Figure 11.1(c), information from the control surface could still be transmitted upstream on the lower surface, so that the pressure distribution down there could be modified appropriately, but since by far the greatest part of an aerofoil's lift is produced by the upper surface, this is of very limited helpfulness.

At the identified stage following, that of Figure 11.1(d), the lower surface including that of the control surface is totally immersed in supersonic air flow. Now the control surface itself is operating as a supersonic aerofoil rather than a subsonic one, and the flow over it will deflect concavely or convexly at the hinge line (depending on the direction of control surface deflection) producing an oblique shock or expansion and a consequent substantial pressure increase or decrease respectively on the control surface itself; but once again there is no effect upstream. Not very long later (Figure 11.1(e)) the upper surface shock wave has itself reached the trailing edge, thus immersing the upper surface of the control surface also in totally supersonic flow, so that a shock or expansion will emanate from the hinge line up there as well.

There are thus two mechanisms by which the control surface supplies and experiences forces during the transonic phase: that when the control surface itself is in a subsonic flow, and that when it is in a supersonic flow. But in both cases, if the airflow ahead of the control surface is supersonic, then all the required force must be applied by the control surface itself, rather than by the flying surface to which it is attached. Remembering that the area of the control surface may be typically no more than a third of the entire flying surface area, then even with all other things being equal, a force (and therefore also the pilot's stick force) of the order of three times the normal control force will be needed to produce the required control effect.

But this is only if all other things are equal, which they are not. We have already looked carefully at the strong effect that the loss of lift will have on steepening the dive, and moreover the perturbations in the pitching moment of the wing itself are certainly not going to help, being predominantly nose-down, and so the required force will probably be very much more than three times normal. This accounts for the fact that even pulling on the control column with all the pilot's strength, as often reported, was not sufficient to sort out the problem.

But there is yet another factor to take into consideration, and it is that, before fully supersonic flow develops around it, the control surface is itself operating inside the thick and highly turbulent subsonic eddying wake of the shock stall. This may have a number of undesirable effects on the control surface such as buffeting, but it certainly means that, while in this wake, the control surface's effectiveness will be drastically curtailed compared with what it would be in a clean air flow. It may even flop around a bit inside this wake with no resisting force, which could account for the experience reported by German test pilot Heinrich Beauvais[4]:

---

[4]Ibid, page 7.

'I had the impression of very high stick forces, which I only applied after due consideration. I believe that I can now [in 1981] remember, however, that some pilots had stated that in the compressibility dive the stick could be moved without force.'

We have considered the wing by itself, and now the tailplane by itself. However, some of the most serious control problems encountered, compounding all of those that we have already discussed, arise from the fact that the tailplane is behind the wing. A shock stall occurring on the wing will create a thick turbulent wake which may strike and immerse the tailplane, rendering the tailplane totally ineffective, and also buffeting it very drastically. The buffeting produced by this turbulent wake did not affect only the tailplane, but also the wing creating it, and (close to the wing roots) the aircraft's fuselage. It was largely the shock stall turbulent wake that accounted for the many and varied reports of rattling and shaking and vibrating that pervade all test-flight accounts of the era.

Roll Control Problems

We have so far applied the control surface principles to answering only the questions about the pitch control problems experienced. However, we must not overlook the fact that roll control, using ailerons, also produced problems, as reported by Roland Beamont. Where he speaks of 'the port wing trying to drop', probably it might almost as easily have been the starboard wing which tried to drop. We have seen how rapidly and drastically the variations in lift coefficient can occur, and it would only take a slight imbalance of airflow speed or direction between the wing-tips for one of the wing-tips to have lost lift before the other. For example, the propeller of the Typhoon rotated anticlockwise as viewed by the pilot, so that the swirling slipstream would produce marginally more angle of attack on the starboard wing-tip than on the port one. More angle of attack means more circulation, which in turn means relatively less air-speed (in the free stream direction) on the lower surface. If this were in fact the case, then it is likely that the other wing, the port wing, would have reached supersonic speed on the lower surface first. And it is this feature that we have seen causes the lift coefficient to drop drastically.

It is not surprising, from our general discussion above of transonic control problems, that pilots found that they could not resist such out-of-balance rolling moments. But there is one widely experienced effect that was not reported by Beamont in the passage earlier, probably because he was too pre-occupied with trying to sort out the pitch problem to be over-concerned with roll control. The problem is called control reversal, and is perhaps the most celebrated, and certainly the most bizarre, of the many transonic problems that have been experienced.

Have you ever been to a garden fête and been faced with the challenge of riding a certain bicycle a distance of about five yards? At twenty pence a go, and the promise of a £10 prize if you succeed in accomplishing this trivial feat, you have a go, only to discover that when you turn the handle-bars to the right the front wheel turns to the left, and vice-versa. Undaunted, you have a number of attempts at riding the bicycle, but find that it is quite impossible to stay balanced for any distance at all. The £10 prize money is very safe!

Pilots are used to pushing the control stick or turning the control yoke in the direction in which they want the aircraft to roll when commencing a banked turn, and so if the aircraft were one day to perform in exactly the opposite way it would be as unnerving as the cyclist's attempt to ride the rigged bicycle. But that is exactly what happens when transonic control reversal occurs. First of all, for the reasons already discussed, the pilot discovers that the control forces required to have any effect at all on the ailerons, and hence to cause the aircraft to roll, become very large. Then, if the pilot persists in applying all of his might to try to deflect the ailerons and control the aircraft, what he actually succeeds in doing is making the aircraft roll the opposite way!

So what is going on here? Control reversal generally only happens with ailerons, and not with elevators, because ailerons are at the ends of long, flexible flying surfaces, the wings. By comparison, tailplanes are short, stubby and stiff. Now let us suppose that the pilot of an aircraft in transonic flight wishes to roll to his right in order to do a right-hand banked turn. He finds that he needs to apply a very large right stick (or clockwise yoke) force, which he does, so that the left (port) wing aileron is forced to deflect downwards in the teeth of a locally supersonic airflow, and the aileron has to take all of the additional load that ought to be taken by the outer wing. By Newton's Third Law of Action and Reaction, this aerodynamic force must be resisted by the wing itself, and the force is transmitted through the aileron hinge. The hinge is behind the centre of the wing chord, and is being pushed hard upwards by the aileron. Consequently the wing-tip is subjected to a twisting moment which tends to twist the trailing edge upwards and the leading edge downwards. This has the effect of reducing the angle of attack of this region of the wing, which in turn causes the lift coefficient and hence the lift to be reduced. So an action which was intended to increase the lifting effect of the wing-tip region has actually caused a C_L reduction. This will tend to cause the left wing to move downwards rather than upwards, so that the pilot's right stick push has resulted in a roll to the left, which is extremely disconcerting.

LIVING WITH COMPRESSIBILITY

We have considered a large number of effects and problems that occur as aircraft approach the speed of sound. The purpose of the perilous test-flights was not mere dare-devilry but was done in the interests of scientific experimentation, in order to learn to understand the problems so that solutions to them could be found. For the rest of this chapter we will consider some of the outcomes of that research, looking at some of the design features employed in high-speed aircraft.

Overcoming the Sound Barrier

As we have said, the earliest consideration was for aircraft to be able to break through the so-called 'sound barrier' in order to fly in the relatively peaceful supersonic regime beyond, and at that time the fundamental problem was high drag and lack of sufficient thrust. How could an aeroplane be designed to have less drag, especially at the crucial Mach number (about Mach one) where the drag coefficient was found to peak?

One of the most famous and effective answers to this question lay in what was called the *area rule*, which could potentially reduce the drag coefficient peak by about a half. The best way to understand how this rule achieves the required result is, surprisingly, to examine a rather fanciful, ingenious and impracticable theoretical supersonic idea, called the *Busemann biplane*. A supersonic biplane certainly sounds like a weird idea, but this biplane gives us a new insight into the ways of shock waves and expansions, guiding us towards using them for our own ends.

First of all, look at the isolated supersonic aerofoil of Figure 11.7(a), which has its top and bottom faces parallel to the supersonic free stream. The air flow over the top surface is unaffected by the aerofoil. On the lower surface, the pressure rises to p^+ through the nose shock, falls back to p_∞ at the first expansion, falls again to p^- at the second expansion and back to p_∞ at the shock from the trailing edge. The pressing and sucking pressure forces on the front and rear lower surfaces respectively both have rearward components, and so there is wave drag due to thickness (but no lift).

In Figure 11.7(b) a mirror image aerofoil is brought up underneath the first, creating the Busemann biplane, which here is set at zero angle of attack and hence produces no lift. The spacing between the aerofoils is arranged such that the shock from the leading edge of the upper aerofoil impinges on the front shoulder of the lower aerofoil, and *vice versa*. Now shocks can be reflected at solid surfaces, which is what one might expect to occur at this shoulder. However, we would also expect to see an expansion springing from this same shoulder on account of the convex deflection of the air around the lower aerofoil

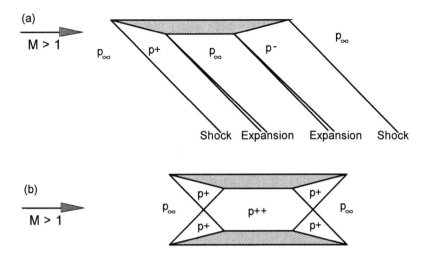

Figure 11.7   The Busemann Biplane

at this point. As we can from see from Figure 11.7(a), the shock arriving at the shoulder is of exactly the same strength as the expansion that would have emanated from that shoulder, since both have equal but opposite effects. The physical result of this meeting of opposites is a total mutual annihilation of both: the expansion exactly cancels out the reflected shock, and so the arriving shock stops at this shoulder. Exactly the same thing happens at the front shoulder of the upper aerofoil, where the expansion that should have been created exactly cancels with the shock from the lower aerofoil leading edge. Between the two aerofoils the two shocks are shown to pass through each other without any mutual interference or bending, and this is approximately what occurs in practice.

If we now examine the flow through the Busemann biplane, we see that the pressure rises through the front shocks to p^+ on the front inclined faces, and then the flow goes through a second shock, which further increases the pressure to a higher value denoted p^{++} in the middle. At the rear end the lines are expansions rather than shocks, and for simplicity these have been approximated to straight lines rather than fans. At these expansions the process is reversed, reducing the pressure from p^{++} to p^+ and then back down to p_∞.

The resulting pressure distribution gives us equal positive pressures on all of the inclined faces, which are all equally inclined to the horizontal. The vertical components of each pair of faces, the front faces, the central horizontal ones and the rear ones, all exactly cancel each other out, so that there is no resultant lift force as we would expect.

The surprising feature is that the horizontal components of the pressure forces on the rear two faces now act *forwards*, exactly cancelling out with the rearward components of the pressure forces on the front two faces, and so there is no drag force. Thus Busemann had created a supersonic aerofoil system, having thickness, but having *zero wave drag due to thickness!*

We have here met an example in which the mutual interference between shocks and expansions on an object (the pair of aerofoils) is used beneficially to reduce – in this idealised case to eliminate – the drag of the object. Can such an idea be used to reduce the high drag peak of an object at around the speed of sound, when any shocks present will be normal rather than oblique? In fact it can, and the approach is known as the *area rule*. To get our minds working around the system we will have to be prepared to think in three dimensions rather than just in two.

Think of an as yet amorphous object, roughly torpedo-shaped, which we wish to propel in the direction of its longitudinal axis through air at the speed of sound, so that the speed everywhere around it is a little bit higher than Mach one. The object must clearly have a finite volume, and so we cannot reasonably hope to make the drag zero. But if the object has any places along its length at which its thickness *suddenly* grows in, let us say, the sideways direction, then a normal shock will be generated at this point. Although the thickening is only in the sideways direction, the shock will actually spread out in the entire vertical plane normal to the stream direction, i.e. upwards and downwards as well as sideways. If it were possible, at the same point, to design the shape so that its thickness actually increased less rapidly in the vertical direction, then this would have the effect of shedding an expansion at the same point, which would also spread round the entire body in a vertical plane. Now if by careful design this expansion is of the same strength as the shock, then the expansion and the shock will totally cancel each other out, so that the air can flow past this plane without interference, and the shock drag here will be ameliorated.

When designing an aeroplane, the basic torpedo-like shape of the fuselage must have a number of items protruding, such as the cockpit canopy, the wings and the tailplane, which at certain points would tend to make the cross-sectional area of the aircraft as a whole increase suddenly, and would thus produce normal shock waves. All we must do is to make sure that there is a corresponding reduction in the rate of growth of the cross sectional area at these points, and this can be achieved by modifying the smoothly changing shape of the fuselage itself. The overall aim is to make sure that the cross sectional area of the aircraft increases and then reduces very smoothly, all the way from nose-cone to the tip of the tail, with no sudden changes.

Perhaps the best known example of this design philosophy being put into effect is in the case of the Buccaneer, which was illustrated in Figure 9.12. Here the so-called 'coke bottle' shape of the fuselage is noticeably waisted at the point where the thickness of the wings adds to the cross-sectional area, and is given a bulge between the wings and the tail in order to compensate for the lack of extra cross sectional area in this region.

Today less attention is given to designing combat aircraft with the area rule in mind. In the case of supersonic aircraft, getting through the drag peak is no longrer such a problem with the abundance of thrust that is now available from powerful jet engines. Theoretically it might be possible to apply the area rule for a supersonic aircraft, following a similar approach to that used in the Busemann biplane. To do this the cross sectional area would have to be measured in planes inclined at the Mach angle to the fuselage axis. But the problem is that at best it could only be optimised into the design for one particular Mach number and Mach angle, and it would be likely that the efforts might actually have a detrimental effect at other flight Mach numbers.

Later in this chapter, in the section headed 'Supercritical Aerofoils', we will see that all today's long-range transport aircraft cruise in the transonic regime, so that the range of Mach numbers in the flow around the aircraft straddles the value of $M = 1$. In such situations normal shocks do occur, and so the creation of expansions to cancel these out are beneficial to reducing wave drag. For this reason some area ruling can be found in the tail regions of such aircraft as the Boeing 757 and 767.

Raising the Critical Mach Number

All of our thoughts so far have concentrated on flying through the transonic region in order to get to the other side of Mach one. But as we have seen, although the drag coefficient falls away above Mach one, the total drag is still substantially greater than at subsonic speeds. When designing commercial airliners, the designer's eye must always be on the financial 'bottom line', and so all aspects relating to design and operation must be taken into account and carefully measured up alongside each other. This is a very complex matter, but the essential conclusion is that, for all but the shortest of routes, the most economical way of operating an airliner is found to be at fast subsonic speeds. How fast is fast? The answer to this is that, beyond a certain speed, the cost of the fuel required to produce the thrust to overcome the additional drag increases more rapidly than the savings due to short journey times and high aircraft utilisation.

We can get an idea of what this speed, or rather Mach number, is by looking at the graph of C_D against Mach number in Figure 11.3. Up to point *a* there is no appreciable increase in C_D, but thereafter the drag coefficient rises very quickly. Thus for many years designers of long-range transport aircraft went for cruise speeds just below the critical Mach number (point *a*), whilst at the same time perfecting a couple of tricks to push the point *a* as far to the right as possible, or in other words to delay the onset of supersonic flow and the accompanying troublesome shock waves until as high a Mach number as possible. Shock waves had proved themselves to be bad news, the stuff of adventurous jet-jockeys, and it was maintained that commercial passenger aircraft should avoid them at all costs.

The first of these tricks is really very obvious. Shocks occur because the air is speeded up over the aerofoil, and speeding up is greatest over the thickest aerofoils. Therefore, to fly fast without shock waves, you simply use the thinnest possible aerofoil sections.

Back in Chapter 9 we gave considerable attention to the pro's and con's of using very thin aerofoil sections, and overall came to the conclusion that they were generally bad news, both for structural reasons and because of the low values of maximum C_L available and the danger of leading edge stalling. Despite these disadvantages, economic pressures forced the use of the thinnest possible wings compatible with safety and structural integrity, and this created the additional problem of providing very limited volume for the stowage of undercarriages, storage of fuel and space for the elaborate mechanical systems needed for operating the controls and the sophisticated lift augmentation devices that such thin wings necessitated.

The second M_{CRIT}-raising trick was a surprise and far less obvious. It was to sweep the wings. Earlier we saw that swept wings could be used to great advantage in supersonic aircraft, enabling them to use subsonic leading edges. But how can the same device be useful for avoiding supersonic flow and shock waves at transonic speeds?

In Figure 11.8 is illustrated a portion of a wing swept from a line normal to the fuselage by an angle Λ, the upper case Greek letter Lambda, which is conventionally used for this purpose because it looks like swept wings. This sweep may be forwards or backwards, but for structural reasons it is usually backwards. The free stream flow relative to the wing (whose Mach number is shown by the vector arrow M) can be split into two components, one normal to and one parallel to the leading edge of the wing. The component parallel to the wing (whose Mach number is $M \sin\Lambda$) is not affected in any way by the by the aerofoil thickness, and so does not get speeded up at all and is not relevant to our present concern. (It does, unfortunately, have other effects since it produces a boundary layer towards the wing-tip; but we will look at that in Chapter 13.) It is only the component normal to the leading edge, having magnitude $M \cos\Lambda$, which goes across the

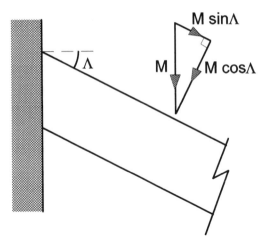

Figure 11.8   Delay of Shock Onset Using Wing Sweep

aerofoil, and so only this component contributes to the wing lift and is speeded up over the aerofoil section. Thus, provided that the Mach number of this normal component is less than the critical Mach number of the aerofoil section it passes over, there will be no shock waves on the aerofoil surface. If Λ is set at 30°, and if M_{CRIT} for the aerofoil section is 0.75, then the free stream Mach number M can be up to 0.87 before any shock waves will form, because 0.87 × cos30° is only 0.75. The greater the sweep angle, the greater is the benefit that can be realised in this way.

In Chapter 12 we will be looking at the advantages to be had from designing wings as long and as slender as possible, i.e. with a high aspect ratio. Unfortunately the three requirements of sweep, thinness and high aspect ratio are all directly adverse to good structural design, and compromises always have to be struck.

Supercritical Aerofoils
Eventually the designers of transport aircraft realised that they were on a hiding for nothing by trying to avoid the effects of transonic flow altogether, as they had clearly reached the limit in how far they could take the aerodynamically required sweep, thin wings and high aspect ratio in the face of mounting structural and safety difficulties. Therefore, following the maxim 'If you can't beat 'em, join 'em', they started to investigate the question as to whether they could design a new type of aerofoil that would not only live happily with the existence of supersonic flow and of shock waves on it, but would actually derive benefits from the supersonic flow. Instead of being limited to operating to the left of point *a* on Figure 11.3, they would thus be able

to operate up to some higher Mach number corresponding to a point around *b*, up to which the drag had still only increased moderately. The (somewhat arbitrary) Mach number beyond which the drag begins to surge unacceptably became known as the *drag divergence Mach number*, abbreviated M_{div}. The result of this fresh approach was the development of a completely new breed of aerofoils, known as supercritical aerofoils.

Having accepted the idea of a shock wave on the upper surface, a number of fundamental changes in approach can be adopted, as shown in Figure 11.9. Firstly, there is no longer any need to keep the upper surface speed subsonic, and so it is allowed to go supersonic from a very early chord-wise position. There is thus no longer any over-riding need to keep the aerofoil thin. This in turn allows for the use of a much more rounded leading edge, which creates substantially more suction over the forward part of the aerofoil, and thus more lift, as well as obviating the sharp leading edge problems at high angle of attack. Cleverly, this also allows for a substantial element of what we might call 'negative drag', since a good portion of the sucking force over the rounded leading edge is in the forward direction.

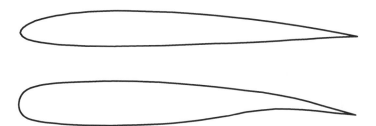

Figure 11.9   Comparison between a Conventional Aerofoil and a Supercritical Aerofoil

Once the upper surface flow has become supersonic, the suction there and hence lift is good. It is therefore desirable to retain the supersonic flow over as much of the upper surface as possible, to delay the inevitable shock wave to as far back as possible, and when it occurs to ensure that it is only weak. This was at first achieved by having a relatively flat upper surface, although on more advanced types there has been a move back towards it being more curved. Care is required in designing the aft part of the upper surface, to ensure that the shock is weak, and that the boundary layer does not separate.

Having taken care of the upper surface, a fresh look was taken at the aerofoil lower surface, and the most noticeable 'new' thing about the appearance of a supercritical aerofoil section is its shape in this region. Having the additional thickness to play with, it is possible to create a concave rear portion, where the pressure of the subsonic air-flow will increase. This provides a substantial boost to the wing's lift in the rear portion where the upper surface lift is falling off, thus making the whole chord length of the aerofoil work for its living. This shape implies that the trailing edge is almost cusped, i.e. that the angle between the upper and lower surface directions at the trailing edge is close to zero. Aerodynamically this is a good thing, but it causes a potential structural weakness. This is avoided by thickening and squaring off the trailing edge slightly.

The advantages to be reaped from adopting this new aerofoil design philosophy were immense. Aerodynamically, the shape was much more efficient at producing lift spread over the entire wing area, whereas using a conventional aerofoil the lifting effort was concentrated very strongly at the forward part of the wing, with the rear half making very little contribution indeed. This meant that the wing loading, which is the averaged-out lift per-unit-area, could be very substantially increased, so that for the same overall weight of aircraft, wings of considerably smaller plan area could now be used.

The other great boon that it presented to the designer was the release from the strait-jacket of very thin wings. At last the designer had some sensible space to play with inside the wings, making the design of retractable undercarriages and lift augmentation devices and controls considerably easier. But probably the greatest benefit derived from the extra depth of wing now permitted was the scope that it offered for increased structural efficiency, so that higher aspect ratio wings could be built. Although we have frequently alluded to the advantages of long slender wings, we have not yet discussed properly how it is that they make for lower drag, and so we will defer further discussion of this subject until the next chapter.

A new design thrust such as the development of supercritical aero-foils involves the use of optimisation, by which the supercritical aero-foil is designed to be as efficient as possible at normal operating (i.e. cruise) conditions, even at the expense of some loss of aerodynamic efficiency in some other phases of flight. Thus its adoption has not always been a total triumph. The Harrier GR5 jump-jet differed from its Harrier predecessors in that it was the first to have a supercritical wing. Not being an airliner, it was not always going to be operating at optimum conditions, and so a great deal of the advantage was lost. Furthermore, the aerodynamic performance of the aircraft was found in a number of ways actually to be inferior to that of its predecessor. Perhaps the moral is, 'horses for courses'!

Slightly tongue-in-cheek, I have always thought that the very name 'supercritical wing' was most unfortunate. Fine when one, like ourselves, understands what it is all about, but what about your average airline passenger, who is far from 'flightwise'? Is his or her confidence in the already fear-inducing process of flying going to be boosted by being told that the wings of the aeroplane are 'supercritical'? The word critical appears to imply 'on the very edge of what is safe practice', so that supercritical sounds as if the designer has lost his senses and has designed the wing just a little beyond the limits of safety! A case, perhaps, where ignorance is bliss. Certainly most passengers are unaware that major parts of their so-called subsonic airliner are in fact flying supersonically nearly all the time, although people occasionally report seeing shock waves on top of the wings when looking out of the window in certain atmospheric conditions.

Overcoming Control Problems

Finally in this chapter we will take a look at some of the ways in which the transonic problems of controlling an aircraft have been solved, whether it be for airliners flying for most of their operating lives in the transonic region or fighters getting through that region as quickly as possible.

Looking first at the crucial issue of controlling the aircraft in pitch, our attention moves to the design of tailplane and elevators. Despite our not giving it pride of place in the fore-going discussion, one of the major problems of flying the pre-transonic aircraft into the shock stall was that the stalled wing wake totally engulfed the tailplane, so that the elevators had little chance of being effective even if they hadn't had problems of their own in a clean air flow. The solution to this problem was to build new transonic aircraft with their tails well out of the line of the wing wake. On low-winged transport aircraft this has usually meant mounting the tailplane some way up the fin rather than at its root. In the case of the Buccaneer the tailplane was placed at the top of the fin. On high-winged aircraft such as the French Dassault Mirage and the English Electric Lightning the tailplanes are mounted well below the wing.

Having decided on the best positioning of the tailplane to avoid externally imposed problems, attention can turn to the design of the control surfaces themselves. The chief problem was that only the rear part of the flying surface, the hinged control surface, took any of the load because information could not be transmitted upstream. The solution to this in the tailplane was found to be to do away with aft-hinged control surfaces altogether and to substitute all-moving, or slab, tailplanes, in which the entire tailplane surface is hinged at its midpoint. Operating loads were high, too high for pilots to be able to control with manual controls, and so powered controls also became the norm.

Let us turn next to the problem of roll control. A number of different solutions have been successfully adopted in different situations. Some combat aircraft (such as the British Aerospace Tornado) have made double use of their all-moving tailplanes by making the two sides of these operable independently of each other. They are given the name of 'tailerons', and provide the function of ailerons when operated in opposite directions and of elevators when moved together. The main problem with tailerons is that they only operate at a very short moment arm from the fuselage, (usually less than a quarter of the tailplane span) and so have to produce very large differential forces. Furthermore, their effort has to be shared with the elevator function, and so they may come into conflict if maximum authority is required of both systems at once. There is also the structural consideration of the large twisting moment that has to be resisted by the fuselage – the wings now have to be turned *by* the tail via the fuselage, against substantial aerodynamic and inertia resistance, instead of the wings turning the fuselage and tail.

Because of this last consideration, tailerons would not be appropriate for airliners in view of the high aspect ratio wings and the large mass and inertia of the wings which normally hold a lot of fuel and may also carry the engines. Powered hinged ailerons are therefore the preferred means of roll control if possible, but being at the rear of a highly swept wing of high aspect ratio there is a serious problem of twisting of the wing-tip region, a phenomenon known as aeroelasticity, which makes the ailerons especially prone to control reversal. Stiffening up the wing is not ideal since it adds weight. However, the moment arm of ailerons at the wing-tips is more than adequate, and the solution often adopted is to have a second pair of so-called 'inboard' ailerons only half way out along the wings instead of at their tips.

Of course this does not overcome the problem of the poor responsiveness of hinged controls when behind a supersonic region. The solution often adopted to this problem is to supplement the wing-tip ailerons with spoilers, devices that simply protrude into the upper surface airflow when demanded, and destroy some of the lift there so that that wing falls relative to the other. Although widely employed and very effective, the use of such an aerodynamically destructive device tends to go against the grain for an aerodynamicist whose goal is usually the quest for greater aerodynamic efficiency.

CHAPTER 12
Introduction to Three-Dimensional Effects

INTRODUCTION

So far we have concentrated chiefly on two-dimensional airflow, by which we have implied that the aerofoil or cylinder being considered extends indefinitely into and out of the paper on which it is drawn, and so the airflow streamlines depicted have been typical of any cross-section of the aerofoil or cylinder. This condition is unattainable in practice on aircraft wings since all wings must have wing-tips. The inevitableness of this fact makes it necessary to consider in some detail how the forces of lift and drag of a real, finite wing differ from their counterparts in two-dimensions as discussed so far.

A cursory glance at a range of plan views of aircraft will show that there is a tremendous range of design approaches to the planform shape of wings. There are straight-edged and curved wings, wings of rectangular and of tapered planforms, swept back (and even swept forward) wings, long slender wings (i.e. having a high aspect ratio) and short, stocky wings (of low aspect ratio). The differences are substantial, and are far more than mere design refinements.

The choice of planform and aspect ratio has a substantial effect on the overall aerodynamic and structural behaviour of the wing. We have already seen (at the end of Chapter 10 and in Chapter 11) how sweep-back can be used to reduce drag. Later (particularly in Chapters 13 and 14) we will examine in some detail the effects of planform on lift, and in *Flightwise: Aircraft Stability and Control* we will see that planform also plays a significant part in that context.

For the present we will be concerned with the effect of aspect ratio alone on an aircraft's drag, and for simplicity will assume that the planform is straight and rectangular. We will see near the end of the chapter that supersonic wings are virtually unaffected by wing-tips, and so we can safely restrict our investigation to subsonic wings at first.

We have already met form drag and skin friction and have seen how they both depend entirely on the existence of the boundary layer, in the absence of which d'Alembert's Paradox of no drag occurred. We have also met wave drag, which we saw to be a purely inviscid pressure drag resulting from the compressibility of the air. The existence of wing-tips gives rise to an additional form of drag, which is variously named induced drag, vortex drag or lift-dependent drag, the reasons for which will shortly become apparent. Induced drag is closely associated with aspect ratio, probably the most important of all planform considerations. We will look at the effects of aspect ratio on aircraft performance, and the principles underlying its choice.

It is important to appreciate that the phenomenon of induced drag is not viscosity or boundary layer related, but is a purely inviscid flow phenomenon, and consequently may be analysed completely by means of potential flow methods. If this appears to be in contradiction with d'Alembert's Paradox, remember that his paradox was a correct conclusion emerging from a study of *incompressible two-dimensional* flow. As with the addition of compressibility, so the addition of an extra dimension makes it no longer valid.

HORSESHOE VORTEX SYSTEM

We saw in Chapter 7 that the lifting effect of a two-dimensional wing may be represented by a free vortex, and this may be illustrated diagrammatically by a straight line representing the axis of the vortex, replacing the aircraft's wings. On a real aircraft with wing-tips, the line would end at these tips.

However, in practice, ignoring the eventual dissipation that occurs as a result of the fluid's viscosity, nature does not permit the termination of a free vortex in any circumstances except at a boundary of the host fluid. A vortex can't just stop with a free end in mid-air. Two natural examples illustrate this well: that of a tornado (a 'whirlwind' or 'twister'), which terminates at the ground but extends upwards to infinity; and that of a smoke ring (a 'toroidal vortex'), where the vortex axis is a closed loop and hence endless.

So what happens to the wing-lifting vortices at the inevitable wing-tips? Figure 12.1 illustrates how the pressure difference between upper

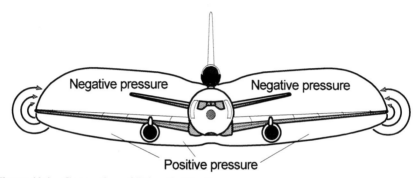

Figure 12.1   Generation of Wing-tip Vortices

and lower wing surfaces spills up and around the wing-tips continuously, thus providing a rotational flow. This combined with the streamwise airflow results in a helical (corkscrew-shaped) flow behind the wing-tip, known as a wing-tip or trailing vortex. Thus at a wing-tip one vortex (the bound, or lifting vortex) ends and another (the trailing vortex) begins. Nature is satisfied by considering the trailing vortex to be a continuation (round a corner) of the lifting vortex. If the trailing and bound vortices are thought of as bundles of smaller vortices, each of which must obey the 'no termination' principle, it follows that each trailing vortex must contain the same number of small vortices, and thus be of the same strength (circulation), as the bound or lifting vortex.

The resulting three-sided pattern of vortex lines is known as a horseshoe vortex (strange horse!), and is illustrated in Figure 12.2. This horseshoe vortex provides a very simple yet powerful model, on the basis of which our study of induced drag will be based. (In fact, it is a

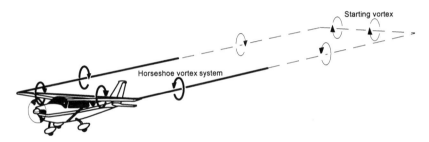

Figure 12.2   Horseshoe Vortex and Starting Vortex System

drastic simplification, and it will be modified in Chapter 13 when we consider other wing planforms.)

It appears from the horseshoe vortex model that the vortex termination problem has not been solved but merely shifted downstream to some point behind the aircraft. In fact, as we discussed in Chapter 7 and at Figure 7.10, when the wing first starts from rest to move through the air (i.e. on the threshold of the runway), we saw that a vortex of opposite sense[1] is shed from the wing trailing edge. But whereas in Chapter 7 the system was two-dimensional and the two vortices were separate from each other, here the shed vortex with the bound vortex and the two trailing vortices together complete a closed loop, or a very long thin toroidal vortex in the form of a rectangle whose length is the distance travelled through the air and whose width

[1]The word 'sense' refers here to direction of rotation (clockwise or anti-clockwise). If the word 'direction' had been used, it might have been thought to refer to a direction along the vortex axis line.

is the aircraft's wingspan. This is shown by dashed lines (very much curtailed) in Figure 12.2.

Wake Vortices

In practice, of course, the earlier history of this vortex loop is eventually lost by dissipation as a result of the viscosity of air. But in the meantime the wing-tip vortices are much more than a mere manifestation of the aerodynamicist's theory – they may be very substantial in both size and extent, and often present a serious hidden hazard to other aircraft flying into or through them. In aviation circles this flow is called *wake turbulence*, although the use of the word turbulence in this context is unfortunate. Turbulence implies the presence of eratically disturbed and randomly moving air, such as exists in a turbulent boundary layer, or on a larger scale in atmospheric wind passing over a region of buildings and other obstructions. The air flow in a trailing vortex wake is highly ordered flow, which as we have seen lends itself well to mathematical analysis, and as such can in no way be described as turbulent (until it has become dissipated beyond recognition). However, ordered or turbulent, these vortices are no less of a phenomenon to be reckoned with.

If you are able to come up with a method of eliminating wing-tip vortices, your fortune will undoubtedly be assured, since thanks to your invention it will be possible approximately to double the capacity of all of the world's largest and busiest airports at a stroke. It is the presence of wing-tip vortices that dictates the maximum utilisation and hence the capacity of the runway of any airport. If an aircraft flys into one of the invisible wing-tip vortices of another aircraft, there will be a strong tendency for that aircraft to roll over rapidly and uncontrollably, with potentially disastrous consequences. It is found in practice that the most serious problems arise when aircraft of very different sizes wish to follow each other landing on the same runway, and also the magnitude of the problem is found to depend, for any given size, on the actual design of the aircraft shedding the vortices. Furthermore, safe separation times also depend on the strength of wind across the runway, since a strong crosswind will quickly shift the hazard out of the way, whilst if there is no crosswind the vortices will linger over the runway until they peter out through dissipation. Consequently a fairly complex schedule of separation times (typically two minutes) is laid down to try to obtain minimum safe separations between different aircraft on landing. Unfortunately, however, shed vortices are not at all easy to measure for strength, and furthermore are invisible, and so the rules are inevitably somewhat *ad hoc*.

When landing, aircraft use very large values of lift coefficient in order to keep landing speeds low, as we saw in Chapter 9. A large lift coefficient implies a lot of circulation around the wings, and consequently large, strong trailing vortices from the wing-tips. Lift augmentation devices do not normally extend over the entire span, but usually over approximately the inner two thirds of the wing span (to leave room for ailerons), and so there is a substantial drop in the wing lift coefficient at this point. Consequently very strong vortices are often shed from the ends of the flaps as well as from the wing-tips, although some distance downstream these will coalesce into one.

If the vortices shed by today's largest passenger aircraft could be seen, the magnitude of the problem would be more readily grasped, but perhaps many of the flying public would be put off flying altogether! The problem is going to be a very major concern of designers of the proposed future generation of very large passenger aircraft (of up to about 1,000 passengers) that are currently being considered, since if these bring with them the need for greater runway separations one of the chief advantages of their larger size will immediately be cancelled out.

Another scenario in which wing-tip vortices are a problem to be reckoned with is that of air-to-air refuelling. Not only is the task of aligning the smaller aircraft's refuelling probe accurately on a drogue behind one wing of the tanker made very difficult by the presence of the wing-tip vortex, but also, as we will see in the following section, the pilot will have to take account of a substantial *downwash* behind the tanker, forcing him to fly 'up-hill'.

DOWNWASH

Imagine yourself to be shrunk to any point inside the horseshoe vortex system (the solid vortex lines) in Figure 12.2: let us say, for example, the point where the first '*H*' of 'horseshoe' is located. Now consider each of the three limbs of this vortex system, and decide which direction the air flow at your point would be going as a result of just that vortex on its own. The vortex flow around the bound vortex from wing-tip to wing-tip is such that its direction is rearwards over the top of the wing (speeding up the flow to produce low pressure) and forwards under the wing, and consequently at every point behind the wing, including the point *H*, the resulting flow due to this vortex is downwards. The point *H* is quite near to the trailing vortex springing from the more distant wing-tip, and so its velocity influence, being inversely proportional to the radius as we have seen, is quite large. Also, from a look at Figure 12.1 it is clear that the flow direction at *H* due to this vortex is downwards. Finally, the flow at *H* due to the trailing vortex from the nearer wing-tip has a much smaller speed since its distance from the vortex line is much greater, but once again the direction is downwards.

Thus the rotating flows around all three limbs of the horseshoe vortex are such that they all contribute a downward velocity, or downwash, at H and similarly at every other point inside the horseshoe. The velocity contribution of each of the three vortices at any point in the downwash region is inversely proportional to the distance of that point from that vortex, and so there is quite a complicated distribution of downwash magnitudes within the region, but a consistent downward direction. For our present discussion, we will simplify the situation by assuming a mean value to apply everywhere.

This downwash is what we would expect from a lifting wing, in accordance with Newton's Third Law (the one about 'action and reaction'). An upward force on the wing must imply a downward force and hence deflection on the airflow causing it. The surprising fact is that there was apparently no overall downwash in the two-dimensional case. This is accounted for by the fact that the quantity of air affected by unit span of a two-dimensional wing is infinite (above and below), and so the consequent overall deflection is infinitesimal. This coincides with the fact that Newton failed (as discussed at the start of Chapter 7) to derive a satisfactory method of analysing wing lift on the basis simply of his rate of change of momentum principle. In the two-dimensional case the upwash ahead of the wing due to the upward velocity of the bound wing vortex exactly balances and cancels the downwash behind it, resulting in zero overall downwash. It is only the contribution of the trailing vortices from the wing-tips which ensures an overall positive downwash behind a finite wing. Thus the phenomenon of

downwash is inseparably linked with the existence of wing-tip vortices.

Before proceeding to establish the connection between downwash and drag, we should briefly consider at this point the 'standard' explanation of induced drag frequently offered in introductory books, and tacitly accepted by many as adequate. Proponents of this explanation firstly show, as above, that real and substantial wing-tip vortices do in fact exist in practice. They then argue that work has to be done on the air to 'stir' it into these vortices, just as work is done through a teaspoon stirring a cup of tea, and that the energy thus provided to the air must be supplied by energy extracted from the aircraft. The extraction of energy from the aircraft 'obviously' implies a resistance to the aircraft's motion – hence induced drag! There is nothing whatsoever wrong, in the sense of inaccurate, with this explanation, except that it is not an *explanation* of the drag force at all! As discussed in Chapter 3, aerodynamic forces are produced only by means of pressure distributions and shear force distributions, and in the present case we are taking it on trust that the latter may be neglected. Any explanation of induced drag must therefore take account of the total reaction of the pressure distribution around the wing, which depends on the velocity distribution. The importation of energy into the discussion – a more complex quantity than force, being equal to work, which is force times distance moved by the force – would at best offer the possibility of a more convoluted and devious explanation of induced drag. In fact, the introduction of the word energy apparently takes the matter sufficiently far to satisfy many readers, on the principle that it sounds like good common sense, and that they may now legitimately 'switch off', as they would otherwise be entering into realms which are best left to the experts! For us, a proper explanation will be more honest, more intellectually satisfying, more useful in terms of further development, and, conveniently, much more simple, than any possible explanation based on energy transfer. We therefore resume our analysis at the point where we left off in the previous paragraph.

The downwash behind a wing has a substantial effect on both the lift and the drag of the wing, and it is the latter which is our interest here. (The effect on lift becomes particularly significant when we look at aircraft gust response, which we will do in Chapter 14.) In order to examine the effect on drag, let us look at Figure 12.3, where the aerofoil shape represents the mean section of the wing of an aircraft in level flight. The angles in the figure are substantially exaggerated for clarity, but the upstream free stream direction has been clearly shown as horizontal to remind us that the aircraft is in level flight despite the

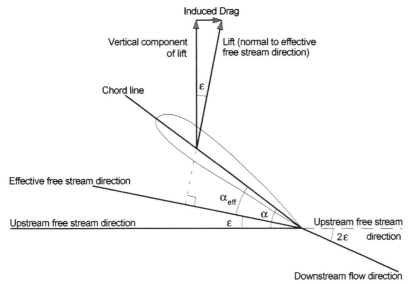

Figure 12.3 Induced Drag

unlikely looking angle of attack. The flow far downstream (to the right) is considered to be straight and deflected (because of the downwash already discussed) from the upstream free stream direction by an angle arbitrarily designated as 2ε. (ε is the lower-case Greek letter epsilon, pronounced ep'-sillon or ep-sy'-lon.) 2ε is the overall downwash angle. The inclusion of the factor 2 simply implies that we are defining ε itself as *half* of the overall downwash angle, for the following reason. The flow around the wing is not straight, but it is convenient to think of this local flow as having an effective free stream direction which is the mean of (i.e. half-way in between) the far upstream and far downstream flow directions. The downwash angle locally to the wing is thus ε, since this is the mean of 0 and 2ε. Consequently the effective angle of attack α_{eff} is less than the free stream angle of attack α by an amount ε:

$$\alpha_{eff} = \alpha - \varepsilon$$

INDUCED DRAG

As we have seen, the downwash causes the local effective flow direction to be inclined downwards at an angle ε relative to the free stream flow direction. Recalling that lift is defined as the force component at right angles to the direction of the flow causing it, the lift force in this case will not be vertical but will be inclined backwards from the vertical, also by an angle ε. It is as though the aircraft were always flying 'up hill' even though it isn't gaining height. As shown in Figure 12.3, the rearward component of the lift force is given the name of *induced drag*, or alternatively *lift dependent drag* or *vortex drag*.

Notice that induced drag is a purely inviscid drag, something that d'Alembert's Paradox had led us not to expect under any circumstances. But that was for two-dimensional flow, and we now have three-dimensional flow with the additional effect of downwash behind the lifting vortex line. There is still no drag force parallel to the local free stream direction, because there is assumed to be no viscosity. Rather, induced drag is a component of the ideal flow lift.

As an analogy of what is going on here, consider a car parked facing up a hill so that, like the aircraft, it is not gaining height. The reaction of the road on the car is normal to the road surface, and thus has a rearwards component. This will tend to make the car roll back down the hill, and if the brakes were released that is what would happen.

The situation is also very similar to that of a motor-boat travelling along on the water at a moderate speed, generating a bow wave onto which it is trying to climb, and which is tilting the boat backwards. As

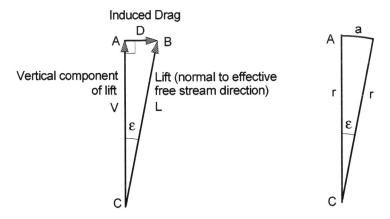

Figure 12.4   Quantifying Induced Drag

with the stationary car facing up a hill, there is a tendency for the boat to slide back down the slope of the hill or wave. In the case of the boat, if there is enough power available from the motor to pull the boat up this slope, then it can ride up onto the top of the wave, tip its prow downwards and ride along just ahead of the crest, just like a surf board rider. The reaction from the water is now inclined forwards, and so its horizontal component is now in the forward direction, providing an additional 'thrust' rather than a 'drag'.

Let us briefly consider the magnitude of the induced drag. Those familiar with the terminology of trigonometry will note from Figure 12.3 that the induced drag equals the lift times the sine of ε. If that satisfies you, you may safely skip to the next paragraph whilst we briefly explain this trigonometrical statement. Figure 12.4 (left) is a direct copy of the relevant part of Figure 12.3, with the addition of the letters L, D and V to designate the resultant and the two component forces respectively, and with the further addition of the letters A, B and C to designate the three corners of the triangle, which has a right angle at A. Because of this right angle, the ratio of the sides AB to BC is defined as the sine of the angle ε. This is also the force ratio D/L. Thus we can write

$$\frac{D}{L} = \sin \varepsilon \quad \text{or} \quad D = L \sin \varepsilon$$

Now mathematicians usually talk about angles in *radians* rather than degrees. A radian is an angle measurement which is derived as the ratio of two lengths, so that it is conveniently absolute and dimensionless, whereas the size of a degree has been initially arbitrarily chosen[2]. From the right-hand diagram of Figure 12.4, ε is defined (in radians) simply as the ratio of a/r, where r is the radius of a circle through A with its centre at C, and a is the length of arc of this circle, starting at the point A and ending at the line of the lift force L. Looking at the two figures side by side, it is clear that, provided the angle ε is small (which it normally is in the present context), there is very little difference between the length of CB (representing L) and the radius of the circular arc, and also a is scarcely any different from AB. Consequently, for small values of ε, the ratio of AB/BC is approximately equal to the ratio a/r. Now AB/BC is the definition of $\sin\varepsilon$, and a/r is the definition of ε in radians. We therefore conclude that, for a small angle ε, $\sin\varepsilon$ is approximately equal to ε itself (in radians). The formula in the previous paragraph can therefore be re-written as follows:

$$\frac{D}{L} \approx \varepsilon \quad \text{or} \quad D \approx L\varepsilon$$

where $\approx$ means 'is approximately equal to'. Since we are talking about a geometrical system and not variations in flight conditions such as speed or height, it will be convenient for us to continue our discussion in terms of force coefficients rather than actual forces. This presents no problem, since we merely divide all our forces by a uniform $\frac{1}{2}\rho V^2$ for the local flight conditions and a uniform S for the aircraft's wing area. In all ratios this operation will cancel out on top and bottom. Using C_{Di} for the induced drag coefficient, our equation can now be written as

$$C_{Di} \approx C_L\varepsilon$$

Thus for small angles the induced drag coefficient is simply related to the lift coefficient (which approximately equals the coefficient of the vertical component of lift which we could call C_V) and to the downwash angle. It is possible to show, furthermore, that the downwash angle is itself proportional to C_V. Thus the induced drag coefficient C_{Di} is finally proportional to the square of the vertical lift component coefficient. Consequently, remembering that it is what we have in the present context called C_V that is really the aircraft overall lift coefficient for flight purposes, we conclude that

> **induced drag is low at low aircraft C_L values (which are associated with high speed level flight), but increases rapidly as C_L is increased, either in a manoeuvre or as speed is reduced.**

[2]The division of a full rotation into 360 degrees probably arose in the first place because it is approximately the angle that the Earth rotates around the Sun in one day, since there are about 365 (which is not far off 360) days in a year. Furthermore, 360 is a very convenient number, since it can be exactly divided by very many smaller numbers.

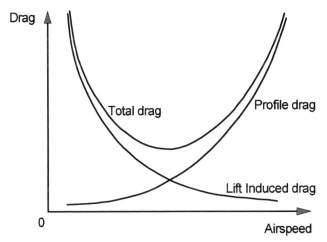

Figure 12.5   Drag Versus Speed in Level Flight

Thus in level flight, in comparison with profile drag (i.e. form drag plus skin friction) which increases with the square of aircraft speed, induced drag is seen to reduce with increasing speed. The total drag is the sum of the two, as shown in Figure 12.5. From this figure it is clear that there exists for an aircraft at a particular flight condition (speed and height) a minimum drag speed for steady straight and level flight, with which there is associated a minimum engine thrust for this condition (since thrust equals drag). Much information is available relating to aircraft performance from this figure.

ASPECT RATIO

Just as it is important to minimise profile drag, so it is equally important to design an aircraft for as low an induced drag value as is compatible with other demands. There is no induced drag in the case of a two-dimensional or infinitely long wing, and so we would like the wing to be as near as possible to two-dimensional. By this means the tip regions, which cause trailing vortices, will be restricted to as small as possible a proportion of the whole wing area, and it will have the lowest possible induced drag at any given speed. In practice this is achieved by having as high an aspect ratio as possible.

The aspect ratio of a rectangular wing is defined as span/chord (span being the distance from wing-tip to wing-tip). Most aircraft wings are tapered in some way and so do not have a constant chord length, and so it is convenient to define a mean chord c where $c =$ (Wing area)/(span), the wing area being the same as the S in our definition of force coefficients. Substituting this mean chord for the chord in the above definition of aspect ratio gives rise to the more useful and commonplace definition:

Aspect Ratio = $(\text{Span})^2 / (\text{Area})$

(Notations for aspect ratio vary from A through AR to a sort of diphthong $A\!R$)

High aspect ratios are seen especially in commercial transport aircraft such as airliners, where drag must be minimised in the cruise in order to keep fuel costs as low as possible. Lower fuel consumption also allows for a greater payload, since the weight of the fuel no longer required may be replaced by extra passengers or cargo. There is always this double pay-off resulting from reductions in drag, which shows why such great efforts are made these days to reduce aircraft drag by even small percentage values.

In Chapter 11 we saw how the use of advanced supercritical aerofoils on modern airliners enabled the aircraft to fly at higher Mach numbers without incurring additional drag. We also saw how these aerofoils allowed for higher wing loadings and hence smaller wings to be used. Whether or not they in themselves reduce the profile drag of the aerofoil section, they do provide the opportunity of designing aircraft with substantially higher aspect ratios and hence lower induced drag. Previously the use of thin wings and sweep-back to raise the critical Mach number implied the need for very strong and hence heavy wing structural members to resist the large twisting and cantilever stresses imposed. But the increased thickness of a supercritical aerofoil section allows the same cantilever strength to be achieved with a much lighter structure. Furthermore, the requirement for sweep-back is reduced, since it is no longer necessary to keep the air flow subsonic over the upper wing surface, and this results in lower twisting forces which again permits a lighter structure. The pay-off available from these increases in structural efficiency is that the aspect ratio can be substantially increased, with great benefit. A dramatic example of this effect is seen in the evolution of the European Airbus series A300, A310, A320 and A340, especially if compared with an early jet airliner such as the Boeing 707 of four decades ago. From the first to the last, through improvements in aerofoil design, there has been a small progressive reduction in sweep-back angle, accompanied by a very substantial increase in aspect ratio and (for the same aircraft weight) a reduction in wing area. A comparison between the plan-views of such aircraft illustrates this quite dramatically.

More strikingly, and perhaps more surprisingly, very much higher aspect ratios than on airliners are to be found on high-performance sailplanes. Clearly for a glider it is important to minimise all component parts of total drag for the sake of achieving good range characteristics. However, it is interesting to note why there appears to be this obsession with minimising induced, i.e. lift-dependent, drag on an aircraft which might at first glance be thought not to have very great lift requirements. The reason is that a glider repeatedly requires to gain height by flying in a thermal rising air current. Such thermals are often very small, frequently with a radius not much greater than the aircraft's wingspan. In order to remain within the thermal, the pilot must fly in extremely tight circles. To achieve this, the aircraft must be banked steeply and set at a high C_L value (i.e. angle of attack), so that the lift will provide a large inward (centripetal) force component whilst maintaining a vertical component equal to the aircraft's weight, as was discussed in Chapter 2. If this high-lift configuration were to impose excessive additional drag on the aircraft, it would be necessary to adopt a flight path sloping steeply downwards in order to maintain the required speed, since there is no engine to provide the required extra thrust. Thus the process of ascending in a thermal would of itself imply a rapid rate of descent relative to the surrounding air, negating some, or perhaps all, of the benefit of the thermal.

The low drag benefits of high aspect ratio are very important. It is therefore surprising to note that many subsonic combat aircraft, and probably all supersonic aircraft, have very low aspect ratios. The reason in the subsonic case is almost entirely because of structural demands, (although the requirements of a high roll rate also make a low aspect ratio desirable). It is simply not possible to build light thin wings of high aspect ratio capable of providing lift of up to nine or ten times the weight of the aircraft (i.e. 9 or 10 'g', as discussed in Chapter 2), and so a high degree of manoeuvrability can only be obtained at the expense of low aspect ratio and high induced drag.

This same feature also accounts for the fact that a combat aircraft's *maximum sustained turn rate* will often be substantially lower than its *maximum instantaneous turn rate*. A very tight turn produces so much additional induced drag that there may be insufficient engine thrust available to maintain the aircraft's speed. The sustained turn rate is that at which the total drag equals the maximum available thrust, so that a sustained speed can be maintained.

There is in fact another feature occurring in this context, with both favourable and unfavourable consequences. It will be shown in Chapter 14 that the lift curve slope of an aircraft depends amongst other things on its aspect ratio. A low aspect ratio implies a low lift curve slope, and thus the need for a very much higher angle of attack than might be expected to achieve the high C_L value required for a tight turn. This being the case, the jet exhausts in a turn are angled substantially outwards, so that the thrust direction is equally inclined inwards. There is then a significant component of the thrust acting towards the centre of the turn, assisting the wing lift in providing the necessary centripetal force and thus helping to tighten the turn. It is through this so-called 'vectored thrust' technique that missiles are able to augment the aerodynamic lift force available from their wings and achieve very tight turn rates and high 'g' values, where there is no limit artificially imposed by the physiology of the pilot, since there is no pilot. But, in both aircraft and missile, the thrust is no longer all available for overcoming drag in the direction of flight, and this effect is likely to reduce further the sustained turn rate available.

It is clear from this why fighter pilots frequently apply reheat during tight manoeuvres. As military flying display organisers and pilots know well, there can be few more dramatic sights than that of a fast jet fighter on a cold damp day performing tight manoeuvres at speed near the ground. In addition to the bright white glow from the tailpipes seen by the observer as the aircraft swings away from him, he is likely to see a distinct, sharp-edged cloud of vapour over the top surfaces of the aircraft wings, as the moisture from the air condenses in the very low pressure region there causing the immense lifting force. And trailing strongly from the wing-tips are two short-lived vapour trails clearly indicating the low-pressure cores of the wing-tip vortices. The astute observer will also notice the very substantial angle between the direction of these wing-tip vapour trails and the axis of the aircraft (approximately the chord line of the wing), revealing the high angle of attack being applied, whilst the casual observer will form the impression that the aircraft is 'skidding' outwards.

It is not commonly appreciated that an aircraft such as the Tornado, with variable sweep, probably obtains as much performance benefit from the variation available in aspect ratio when sweeping the wings forward or back (from about eight to one or two) as it does from that available through the angle of wing sweep. In subsonic flight it is its high aspect ratio with wings unswept that enables it to have such good range and endurance characteristics, allowing it to loiter in battle zones for long periods (reinforced by air-to-air refuelling), whilst all the time ready for combat action.

SPEED STABILITY

In Chapter 9, when discussing the situations in which it is desirable to increase rather than reduce the drag of an aircraft, we mentioned that there was an additional reason for doing so which we would leave until later to discuss. Having expanded our ideas of drag to include induced drag, we can pick up this point again now. We will base our

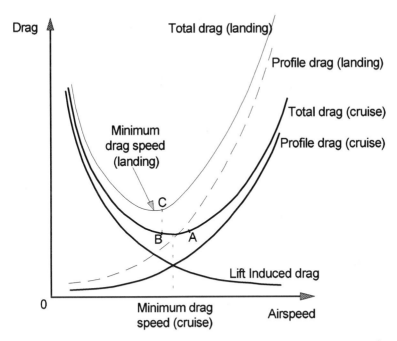

Figure 12.6   Minimum Drag Speed and Speed Stability

discussion on Figure 12.5, which is reproduced here as Figure 12.6 so that some additional points can be added to it.

Figure 12.6 demonstrates that the pilot of an aircraft has a substantial choice over how much drag his aircraft experiences, simply by flying at different speeds, and furthermore that there are two possible speeds corresponding to every drag value in the normal operational range. Before we had introduced the idea of induced drag, there was only the profile drag, which we have seen varies with the dynamic pressure and hence with the square of the speed, and so the slower one went the less drag there would be. But with the introduction of induced drag, that picture was changed, and the graph showing total drag first of all falls to a minimum value as the airspeed increases, before eventually rising again. To fly with minimum drag, the pilot must adjust his controls so that the aircraft is operating at the lowest point of the total drag curve, at the speed called the minimum drag speed.

Now on the face of it it would appear obvious that the minimum drag speed would be the most efficient speed to fly at. In fact, it can be shown that to fly for the greatest *specific air range* (which means the greatest distance on a given amount of fuel), the best point to operate at is actually slightly to the right of the minimum drag speed point. (It is actually at the point where a tangent from the origin meets the total drag curve, since at this point the ratio of drag:airspeed is minimum.) If, however, the pilot wishes to fly for maximum *endurance*, so as to stay airborne for as long a time as possible without necessarily getting anywhere at all, then the minimum drag point is the best theoretical point for him to operate at.

In practice, however, the pilot will normally choose to fly a little to the right of the minimum drag point, whichever type of objective he has, since it is far less hard work for him (and hence safer) than operating at the bottom or to the left. To see why this is, let us assume that the pilot is cruising straight and level at a steady speed (so that the thrust equals the drag), and that he is operating at point *A* on the cruising total drag graph (a little to the right of the minimum drag point). Let us now suppose that a temporary small disturbance occurs in the atmosphere – a gust of wind – such that the aircraft's speed is briefly reduced by a little bit. As a result, the aircraft's operating point moves down the graph to the left just a little (towards the minimum drag point), and so the drag reduces by a small amount. Now if the pilot takes no action with his controls, the thrust of the engines remains unchanged, so that the thrust is slightly greater than the drag, and the aircraft will consequently accelerate back up to its original speed, the drag will recover to its original value, and the cruising equilibrium will be restored. If on the other hand the disturbance in the air had caused a temporary increase in speed, the drag would have increased a little making it greater than thrust, the aircraft would have been decelerated, and its speed would once again have been restored automatically to the *status quo*. Therefore operating at point *A* has the great advantage that the aircraft possesses *speed stability*, so that with no interference from the pilot the aircraft will always automatically settle back to its undisturbed speed following a disturbance.

Now let us see what transpires if the pilot elects to cruise at point *B*, just to the left of the minimum drag point on the cruising total drag curve. If a disturbance causes a small increase in speed, this will be accompanied by a small *reduction* in drag, so that (with no movement of the thrust control) thrust is now greater than drag, and the aircraft will accelerate away from its original speed. The speed will continue to increase (unless the pilot intervenes by throttling back) until the minimum drag speed is exceeded, and then the speed will become stable as it was at *A*. On the other hand, if from point *B* the speed temporarily decreases by a little, the drag will increase and will exceed the thrust, and so the speed will continue to fall. In order not to lose lift and thus height, the pilot will have to pull back on the pitch control, thus increasing the angle of attack of the wings, and hence the lift coefficient. This causes an increase in the lift induced drag as we have seen, and so the progress up the left-hand limb of the total drag curve continues. The top left end of the total drag curve corresponds to the stall point, and so ultimately if no thrust correction is made the aircraft will stall.

A pilot can fly 'hands-off' in a condition of speed stability such as at point *A*, but at a point such as *B* with speed instability it is only possible to fly by making constant adjustments to the thrust control, which is very demanding of the pilot's time and concentration, and may lead to an inadvertent stall if the pilot's attention is distracted.

In order to bring a fast aircraft safely in to land, we have already seen that the speed will require to be lowered, and for an aircraft cruising at point *A* of Figure 12.6 this might typically involve moving left along the curve to point *B,* which is undesirable since the speed is unstable. However, if it is possible to increase the profile drag of the aircraft by use of flaps, undercarriage and/or air brakes, then the profile drag curve will be moved up to the dashed curve, resulting in a new modified total drag curve shown by the fine continuous line. Instead of operating at the unstable point *B* on the cruising total drag curve, the aircraft is now flying at point C of the landing configuration total drag curve, and *C* is to the right of the minimum drag point on this curve and is hence stable. So increasing the aircraft's drag for landing has not only enabled a steeper approach to be used without excessive speed, but has also enabled the pilot to be flying in the more desirable speed-stable regime, even though the speed is below the aircraft's normal minimum drag speed.

WINGLETS AND WING-TIP SAILS

The quest for a means of reducing aircraft induced drag has led to a variety of ideas, such as an aircraft with a continuous circular or oval wing (as viewed from the front) with tips meeting above the fuselage; or a twin-fuselage aircraft with a single wing joining the two hulls, which would act as end plates thus ameliorating the effect of the wing-tip vortices as they are formed. However, the only idea to have gained real commercial acceptance is that of winglets, small aerofoil devices attached to wing-tips, usually inclined upwards. We will examine these in conjunction with a similar idea investigated in the early 1980s by Professor John Spillman (amongst others) at Cranfield Institute of Technology, that of wing-tip sails. These are effectively arrays of nearly horizontal winglets, the idea being inspired by the wing-tip feathers of soaring birds such as the Eagle and Condor.

The large aerofoil in Figure 12.7 is a view of a wing-tip from out-

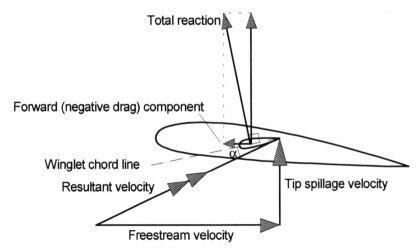

Figure 12.7   The Winglet Principle

board of the tip. The horizontal arrow is the free-stream velocity vector, and the vertical arrow is the (very localised) flow velocity due to the spillage from lower to upper surface. The resultant is shown with two arrow heads. As before, all angles have been exaggerated in order to make things clearer. A small aerofoil is placed such that it is at a positive angle of attack to this local resultant velocity. The total reaction on this small aerofoil has a horizontal component acting forward, producing negative drag, or thrust. Wing-tip sails consist of an array of such aerofoils distributed along the tip as in Figure 12.8, being displaced vertically from each other in order to avoid being too much in the downwash of the one ahead.

One disadvantage of such wing-tip sails is that the larger component of the total reaction on each sail is upwards. This component produces no thrust, but being at the wing-tip it does produce a marked increase in wing bending moment. Consequently it is often not possible to add these devices to existing aircraft since the wing roots have not been

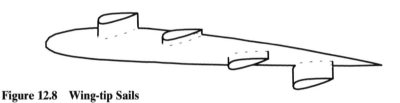

Figure 12.8   Wing-tip Sails

designed to be sufficiently strong for the increased bending loads, and to incorporate wing-tip sails at the design stage might involve an unacceptable increase in wing structural weight.

This disadvantage is today overcome on a substantial and increasing number of large and small transport aircraft by the use of a vertically mounted winglet on the wing-tip. This produces negative drag in exactly the same way as a wing-tip sail, but the major force component is now horizontal, towards the wing root, and thus produces a far smaller moment at the wing root. It is essentially trying to squeeze the wing length-wise rather than bend it.

There is one other major disadvantage in the use of wing-tip sails, which carries over to winglets. This is that, as was pointed out when discussing Figure 12.7 above, the vertical velocity due to wing-tip spillage is very localised. Its magnitude depends strongly not only on its precise position but particularly on the aircraft's lift coefficient, since as we have seen this determines the strength of the wing-tip vortex. Furthermore, the free stream velocity can also vary substantially. Consequently it is only possible to position the winglets to have optimum effectiveness for one particular flight condition. At any other flight condition, it is likely that the benefits will disappear and even that additional drag might result. Thus winglets are proving their usefulness on transport aircraft, which are strongly optimised around a constant speed cruise design point, but are not likely to find their way into the more versatile combat aircraft. The use of a control system to adjust and optimise the incidence of such devices, although a possibility, is very unlikely to be cost-effective on balance.

THREE-DIMENSIONAL CONSIDERATIONS FOR SUPERSONIC WINGS.

In incompressible flow we have seen that wing lift falls off towards the tips due to tip spillage, and so high aspect ratio wings are most efficient, producing good spanwise lift distribution and low induced drag. Do these advantages carry over into supersonic aircraft?

To answer this question, consider any point on the surface of a finite straight supersonic wing such as the double-wedge wing shown on the left of Figure 12.9. This point is only aware of what is happening inside its upstream Mach cone (shown with hair-lines), and so it only 'sees' a continuous leading edge, and thus 'thinks' that the wing is two-dimensional. (The 'flat-earth' syndrome!) Exactly the same will be true all the way out to very near the wing-tip; in fact, everywhere inboard of the shaded area, which is the region demarked by the Mach line from the extreme end of the leading edge. Thus 3-D effects and consequent downgrading of aerodynamic efficiency can only occur in the shaded

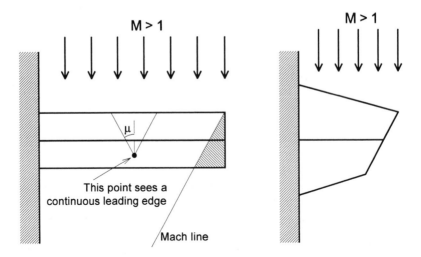

Figure 12.9   Aspect Ratio Considerations for a Supersonic Wing

area. All the rest of the wing behaves in all respects just as if it were infinitely long, or two-dimensional. The logical conclusion is to cut off the less efficient tip region, or 'crop' it. Having done this, clearly the aspect ratio of what is left is of no concern aerodynamically, since the wing now behaves entirely as if it were two-dimensional, and so the structural designer of, say, a missile is free to have as low an aspect ratio as he wishes without compromise. This leads to the familiar planform of many supersonic missile wings, as shown on the right of Figure 12.9. It is usually referred to as a 'cropped delta', since if not cropped, the wing would have a triangular shape. Since the leading edge is not swept back as steeply as the Mach line, it is not primarily swept back for aerodynamic reasons but in order to provide taper, for structural reasons.

For supersonic flight, wings may thus have as low an aspect ratio as is required for structural reasons. One other reason why supersonic aircraft invariably have low aspect ratios is so that the required wing area may be accommodated within a very small frontal area, in order to achieve a high fineness ratio (roughly, the inverse of thickness:chord ratio). By this means the wave drag due to thickness is kept to a minimum.

It should be pointed out, however, that cropping a supersonic wing does not eliminate lift-dependent drag. We have already seen in Chapter 10 that inviscid supersonic lift is inclined backwards producing lift-dependent wave drag, and this is exactly equivalent to the induced drag discussed above for subsonic wings. Wave drag due to lift is related to downwash (by Newton's Third Law) just as is induced drag, but it is given a different name.

INDUCED DRAG IN NATURE

Just as inside a subsonic aircraft's horseshoe vortex there is down-wash, so outside the wing-tip vortices there is a region of upwash. Since an aircraft has to spend all its flying time struggling 'up-hill' against the downwash it is producing, it is intriguing to speculate whether any configuration could be devised which would allow the aircraft to fly in its upwash region instead, so 'planing' down-hill (like the boat having climbed over the hump of its bow-wave) and experiencing some 'induced thrust'. Aircraft would not appear to be able to fly outside their own downwash region in this way, yet migrating birds do seem to have solved the riddle. By flying in echelon formation, each bird (except for the leader) does fly in the upthrust region of the bird diagonally ahead of it, and so gains a substantial drag advantage. An ornithologist would tell you how smart the lead birds are, and how frequently they politely make way for another leader, since it is extra hard work being the leading bird. Military aircraft flying in formation also obtain a significant performance advantage by this means, although the reason for formation flying is chiefly operational. One wonders whether we will ever see flocks of airliners crossing the Atlantic in tight echelon formation!

CHAPTER 13
Wing Planform Considerations

INTRODUCTION

The core of *Flightwise*, right from the start of Chapter 1, has been its search for an understanding of how the *shapes* of aircraft have come about and have evolved. We have broken this question down into stages, starting by considering an aerofoil shape as if it were a slice taken at random from an infinitely long two-dimensional object. Having firmed up on our ideas of aerofoils, we extended our thinking in Chapter 12 to include the effect that wing-tips have on air flow, and found that long, slender wings were best for minimising undesirable wing-tip losses and induced drag. Now that we have reached the penultimate chapter in this volume, we will add to this survey by examining the question of what wing planform shapes are best or worst for aircraft design, and what advantages and disadvantages different shapes offer.

Reference books of aircraft commonly present, for each aircraft, one or more photographs and a set of three silhouette drawings showing the aircraft as it appears viewed from three mutually perpendicular directions. A browse through such a book illustrates dramatically what a very large range of variations on the basic theme of fuselage, wings and tail have been thought of and tried out. In *Flightwise: Aircraft Stability and Control* we will be looking in detail at many of the features that emerge from such a set of drawings, since they reveal most of the things that one needs to know in order to understand how an aircraft actually behaves dynamically during flight. But for now we are going to concentrate purely on the largest of the three drawings, the plan view.

We have already introduced two very important features of wing design, namely the aspect ratio of the wings and the use of sweep-back, and of course we have also taken account of the overall size of the wings in terms of the plan area S in our lift and drag formulae. But we can now ask additional questions such as: Is it best for the leading and trailing edges of a wing to be straight or curved? If curved, what shape curve should they follow? Should wings be tapered towards their tips, or should they have the same chord throughout their length? Or perhaps, like a few strange-looking aircraft of yesterday, wings should get wider towards their tips. What influence do such considerations have on the use of sweep-back and high aspect ratio? What compromises must the designer bear in mind between aerodynamic and structural considerations? Furthermore, do such considerations have any bearing on the flight handling characteristics of the aircraft, and of its safety?

If we can add to our previous understanding of flight answers to all of these questions in this chapter, we will have a very much deeper understanding of the physiology of aeroplanes. Key to answering these questions is the more fundamental question, on what basis can the designer make decisions about which wing shape to use? Before we can tackle this in earnest, we must extend some of our earlier modelling work, since some of the assumptions and simplifications made previously will now let us down.

Although there are many important considerations to be taken into account when discussing the design of an aircraft, for our present purposes we will home-in on one aspect only of the plan view of the aircraft, and that is the shape of the wings. We will simplify our thinking and our diagrams by representing the aircraft fuselage simply as a straight line of symmetry between two symmetrical halves of the wing, and will ignore the fuselage's width. The diagrams will be somewhat stylised, but this is the mathematician's stock in trade, to extract from a situation just those aspects of the problem that are pertinent to the question in hand, and to dismiss everything else in the interests of clear thinking.

EXTENDING THE HORSESHOE VORTEX MODEL

In Chapter 12 we saw that the lines representing the wing lifting vortex (which we called the bound vortex) and of the wing's two trailing vortices formed an open square shape that is referred to as a horseshoe vortex system. In this simple model we assumed that the lift across the entire wing span was uniform, and that it instantaneously fell to zero at the extreme wing-tips. In practice, however, the pressures above and below the wing do not change suddenly but gradually over the outer region of the wing, so that the lift falls off smoothly as the wing-tips are approached. In order to model this mathematically, the single bound lifting vortex of the horseshoe model must be replaced by a bundle of vortices of smaller magnitude, each representing some small arbitrary unit of lift. Then as the lift diminishes towards the tip, so gradually one at a time these unit vortices will stop producing lift at different spanwise positions.

Previously the trailing vortices were considered to emanate just from the wing-tips, and their vortex strength was found to be the same as that of the single bound vortex. But now, the small unit vortices must peel off one at a time all along the trailing edge. If this is a true picture of what is happening, it implies that the trailing vortex is not in fact shed from just the tip, but from the entire trailing edge.

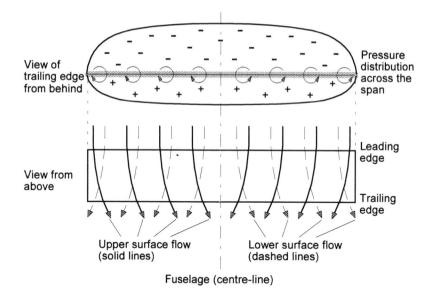

View of
trailing edge
from behind

Pressure
distribution
across the
span

View from
above

Leading
edge

Trailing
edge

Upper surface flow
(solid lines)

Lower surface flow
(dashed lines)

Fuselage (centre-line)

Figure 13.1 Pressure Distribution and Flow Directions Over a Rectangular Wing

Figure 13.1 shows the flow pattern resulting from the pressure distribution across the wing span. There will be an outward flow on the
lower surface and an inward flow on the upper surface. When viewed
from the rear, this will constitute a circulatory flow around each wing,
and it is convenient to think of this flow as if it consisted of lots of little separate vortices. In practice, each vortex of this vortex sheet, as it
is called, very quickly wraps itself up with all the others, to form one
large vortex a short distance downstream, which is effectively the
wing-tip vortex of the horseshoe vortex model. Whilst the simple
horseshoe vortex provides a useful model for an overview of the wing,
for an examination of the flow behaviour over the different regions of
the wing it is necessary to consider the distribution of the elemental
vortices.

Figure 13.2 shows how we may interpret Figure 13.1. The graph at
the top of Figure 13.2 corresponds to the pressure distribution diagram at the top of Figure 13.1. The horizontal axis matches up exactly
with the span of the wing, and the vertical axis represents values of *lift
per-unit-span*. The shape of the curve corresponds exactly with the
shape that would be produced in the pressure distribution diagram of
Figure 13.1 if the lower surface contribution (which is a positive
pressure pushing upwards) were added at each point to the upper surface contribution (which is a negative pressure pulling upwards). If
you are concerned at how we have jumped from units of pressure (in

Figure 13.1) to units of lift per-unit-span (in Figure 13.2), it is easiest to understand this by working backwards as follows, remembering that lift is a force:

$$\text{Lift per unit span} = \frac{\text{Force}}{\text{Span}} = \frac{\text{Force}}{\text{Area}} \times \frac{\text{Area}}{\text{Span}}$$

$$= \frac{\text{Force}}{\text{Area}} \times \frac{\text{Span} \times \text{Mean chord}}{\text{Span}} = \text{Pressure} \times \text{Mean chord}$$

So the 'lift per-unit-span' magnitudes are directly proportional to the 'pressure' magnitudes which produce the lift, (i.e. top effect plus bottom effect), and the 'mean chord' is the constant of proportionality. The heights, or vertical axis values, of the new graph in Figure 13.2 (presented in arbitrary units) are thus directly proportional to the total heights of the pressure distribution diagram in Figure 13.1. Using lift per-unit-span as the vertical axis measurement enables us to think of each cross-section of the wing as if it were a two-dimensional aerofoil with its own value of lift per-unit-span; but of course the value now changes from section to section.

Starting from a series of points evenly spaced up the vertical axis of

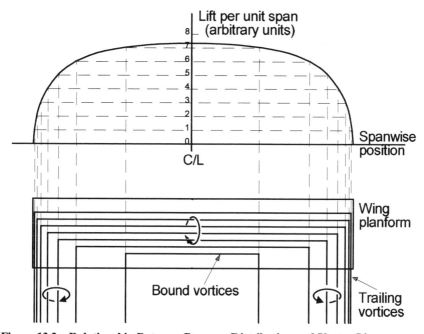

Figure 13.2 **Relationship Between Pressure Distribution and Vortex Line Distribution**

the graph, horizontal dashed lines have been drawn outwards until they meet the curve on both sides. From these points of intersection, the dashed lines have been continued vertically downwards, where they strike a plan-view drawing of the wing itself. As you go outwards from the centre of the wing, each time you come to one of these vertical dashed lines (after passing the first) it means that the lift per-unit-span has fallen by one full unit of measurement. The maximum lift, which is found in the centre span region, is just over seven units, and so we can represent the lift in this region (rounding down to the nearest whole unit) by a bundle of seven bound vortex lines along this part of the span. Each time the vortex lines meet a vertical dashed line, the lifting strength has reduced by one unit and one vortex line from the bundle peels off and streams out to the rear of the wing as a trailing vortex.

A tremendous amount can be learned from this diagram. It illustrates exactly the basis on which serious analysis of wing planforms is carried out, using a mathematical process known as Fourier Analysis. In that process, the starting point is the bottom diagram, and the output of the method is an actual mathematical equation of the lift curve, the graph of the top diagram. More usefully for our own purposes, the figure provides us with a very powerful means of getting to grips with the questions we have posed about planforms. By applying a little logic to the question of how the distribution of the vortex lines in the diagram varies for different planform wings, we will be able to visualise how the flow pattern varies from root to tip of an aircraft's wing, and thus how the aerodynamic forces behave, with what consequences.

The basis of the approach is to determine the *downwash* behind the wing at each section along the span. In Chapter 12 we found that the simple horseshoe vortex model was sufficiently accurate for our purposes at that time. In that model we assumed the downwash behind a wing to be constant everywhere, and this enabled us to gain an understanding of induced drag. Now, however, we need to find out how the downwash varies from section to section along the wing. In the horseshoe vortex model the downwash was contributed to by exactly three and only three vortices, the bound vortex and two trailing vortices. Now we have to consider the contribution made by a very much more complex arrangement of bound and trailing vortices. The length of the bound vortices varies, and so does the spacing of the trailing vortices.

The mathematical task is indeed a large one, although as we have said we can serve our own purposes very well by the application of logic to Figure 13.2. But before we do that, we will deviate briefly to try to penetrate the mind of the mathematician, and see how this problem is tackled. In doing so, we will come across a fascinating link between aerodynamics and electricity.

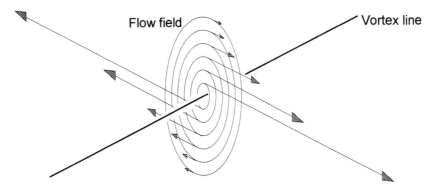

Figure 13.3   The Flow Field Around a Vortex Line

BIOT-SAVART LAW

Our requirement is to find a way of calculating the downwash velocity of the airflow at any point on the wing. This downwash is produced by a multifarious set of vortices at varying distances away. As usual we must strip down this complicated picture until we can identify the simple essential core of what is happening, and then try to model that by using just simple mathematical relationships. In this case, the core of what is happening is a single vortex. We already know that the velocity of vortex flow is in concentric circles around the vortex axis line, and that the magnitude of the velocity on each of these circles is inversely proportional to the radius of that circle. In Figure 13.3 we illustrate a vortex line and the velocity distribution around it at just one plane of intersection normal to the vortex line. The straight arrows represent the velocities, the greatest magnitudes occurring where the radii are smallest, and *vice versa*. Bear in mind that a velocity distribution such as this exists on *every* plane normal to the vortex line, so that the velocity rings are in fact cylinders.

We can make the approximation that the bound vortex and the trailing vortex lines of the wing system are all in the same plane (which is horizontal in level flight), and so conveniently all the velocity vectors representing contributions to downwash in this plane (which is all we are interested in) will be vertical. We therefore do not need to worry at all about the directions of the velocity vectors, since we know them already, and so we only need to attend to their magnitudes.

When the pioneers of aeronautical aerodynamics faced the question of how to work out mathematically the flow velocity at a point in the vicinity of one or more vortices, they conveniently did not have to tackle the problem from scratch. In 1820 two French physicists Jean Baptiste Biot and Félix Savart, working on the link between electrical and mechanical power, had solved what turned out later to be an identical problem, that of calculating the magnetic field strength at a point in the vicinity of electrical conductors. If in Figure 13.3 the vortex line is thought of as being a wire carrying an electric current from bottom left of the figure towards top right, then the magnetic lines of force behave exactly like the vortex flow streamlines shown, appearing as clockwise circles in planes normal to the current-carrying conductor. The magnetic field strength on each circle is inversely proportional to the radius of that circle, just like the flow velocities around the vortex line, and the only difference (mathematically) between the two situations is the constant of proportionality.

In 1804 (about 100 years before the Wright brothers' first powered flight), Biot had accompanied Gay-Lussac, chemist, physicist and father of meteorology, on the first French balloon ascent undertaken for scientific purposes, during which they rose to a height of over 13,000 feet and examined the nature of the Earth's magnetic field and the composition of the atmospheric air. However, undoubtedly it was Biot's (and Savart's) law of electromagnetic induction that proved eventually to be of far more value to the world of aeronautics than any scientific results achieved on that aerial adventure!

Let us by-pass the electrical background to the Biot-Savart law, and home in directly on its application to aerodynamics. Consider a single vortex of strength (or circulation) Γ with its axis line lying in the plane shown in Figure 13.4, and a point P which is also in the plane but not on the vortex line. Every little bit of the vortex, such as the short length labelled[1] dx at a distance r from P, makes a small contribution to the downwash velocity at the point P, its contribution being the short vertical velocity arrow labelled dv, which is proportional to the vortex strength Γ and inversely proportional to the distance r, and so dv can be expressed by a very simple mathematical expression. Now

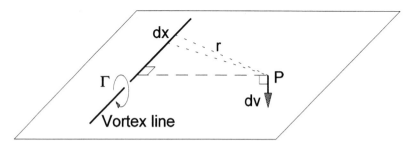

Figure 13.4 Derivation of the Biot-Savart Law

---

[1]Remember from Chapter 6 when introducing 'Rates of Change' that the notation dx (or dv) should simply be interpreted as 'a little bit of x (or v)'.

the total downwash at P consists of the sum of all the dv's contributed by all the dx's which make up the entire length of the vortex line, all the way from where the vortex starts at one end (which may be at infinity or at a finite point) to where it finishes at the other end. It is here that the branch of mathematics called integral calculus comes into its own, since it has been developed especially for the purpose of obtaining formulae which result from processes of adding, or summation, such as this. The Biot-Savart Law is simply the formula which results from this process; it allows us to work out the downwash velocity at any point P near a vortex in terms of the vortex circulation Γ and the perpendicular distance of the point P from the vortex line. We do not need to know what the actual formula is for our purposes.

Although the Biot-Savart law in its basic form stops at this point, we can now apply the idea again, going one level deeper into the real problem that we wish to solve. Let us suppose that the vortex of Figure 13.4 is accompanied by a whole family of additional vortices, each of the same strength as the first and lying parallel to the first in the plane. They are all represented just by their vortex lines like an array of thin spaghetti sticks lying side by side on a table. Point P is still there, and it doesn't matter whether P gets covered up or not. Now, the total downwash velocity at P due to this entire array of vortices (which is what we are finally after) receives a contribution from the full length of each of the vortex lines in the plane. Just as we integrated (the name given to the process of summation in integral calculus) in order to add the contributions of all the little dx segments of the single vortex, so now we merely integrate again, not over all the little lengths but over all the individual vortices, to find the sum of all of their downwash effects at P. We have now integrated twice to achieve the final answer, and so the process is known as a double integral.

We can now go back to our aeroplane situation as shown in Figure 13.2 and apply this Biot-Savart theory. In the figure we have shown the plan view of the wing (in the lower part of the figure) as a rectangle for the sake of showing how the bundle of small vortices peel off at different points along the span. However, it will now be more useful to think of all these bound vortices being bound tightly together again, and lying along a single lifting line, the line by which we now represent the wing in place of the rectangle. If now we wish to work out the downwash at any one spanwise position on the wing, the bound vortices spanning the wing will have no effect since the point is on their centre line, but there will be a contribution from each of the two flat arrays of trailing vortices, one array from each wing. The situation exactly matches the double integral method we have just outlined for calculating the downwash due to an array of vortices, and so it is possible to use the Biot-Savart result to give us the downwash at this point on the wing. The process can then be repeated for every other point on the wing, so that it is possible to obtain the complete down-wash distribution.

But where, you may be asking, does knowing the downwash distribution lead us? Certainly we used its existence to predict induced drag, but how can it help us when considering the equally important topic of wing lift? The answer to this is quite simply that, as shown in Figure 12.3, downwash alters the direction of the air flow as it arrives at the wing, and thus changes the effective angle of attack of the wing, and hence its lift coefficient. The more downwash there is at a wing cross-section, the smaller will be the effective angle of attack α_{eff}, and hence the smaller will be the lift coefficient produced by that section. So it will be important to bear in mind (when we get our minds working on a number of mental tongue-twisters in a few minutes) that *downwash and lifting effect are inversely related to each other*.

LOOKING AT PLANFORMS

We will structure our guided tour through the characteristics of various aircraft wing planforms by presenting a set of three diagrams for each planform. Each of Figures 13.5 to 13.9 is arranged according to this system, which we will outline here as applying to all of them. The left-hand drawing of each set shows the shape of just one of the pair of wings, with a hatched line on its left indicating the aircraft centreline. (For simplicity we will ignore the fuselage.) Thus the length of these drawings is the semi-span of the aircraft, and this has been chosen to be the same for each plan view considered.

The other two drawings are graphs showing two aspects of the behaviour of the planforms. For the moment ignore the actual shapes of the curves, while we explain the axes and scales that have been used. Each point on the horizontal axis of each graph corresponds with the position of an aerofoil section in the plan view, and these axes have been labelled with *C/L* (for 'centre-line') and *TIP* for wing-tip.

The first of the two graphs, the central drawing, shows us how much lift force each aerofoil cross-section of the wing is producing, or to be more precise, how much lift force would be produced by one length unit (e.g. one metre) of span if the aerofoil were constant at this size and angle of attack along the span. The values on the vertical axis have been simplified by a process known as *normalisation*, which means that each graph height (i.e. each value of lift per-unit-span) has been divided by [the overall wing lift divided by the total wing span], a quantity which has the same units as the sectional lift per-unit-span, and so the final quantity is dimensionless. If the lift per-unit-span were the same over the entire semi-span, then the plotted quantity [lift per-unit-span] ÷ [overall lift per-unit-span] would be exactly one over the entire semi-span, and the graph would be a rectangle of height one. A glance at the graph therefore gives an immediate indication as to whether the lift produced by any cross-section is more or less than average, (i.e. the graph is higher or lower than one), without having to get embroiled in the actual numerical values of lift per-unit-span. For simplicity and convenience we will in fact refer to this first graph in each case as the lift curve or the lift distribution. Remember that it is effectively a lift *force* distribution. Apart from the vertical scaling due to the normalisation process, this graph corresponds with the top part of Figure 13.2.

Turning now to the second graph, the right-hand drawing of each set of three, we have a rather similar looking set of graphs again plotted over the semi-span. The difference in this case is that it is not the lift *force* that is being plotted at each section but the lift *coefficient*. Of course, if the aerofoil section and chord length were the same over the entire wing semi-span, then (at the same flight conditions of speed and air density) the lift coefficient graph would behave in exactly the same way as the lift force graph we have just been looking at. However, two of these factors are now not necessarily the same. Firstly, the chord length may not be the same over the entire semi-span, if, for example, the wing is tapered. Secondly, and most significantly (as we have already discussed), we have now got to take account of varying *downwash* at different spanwise positions of the wing, which is where the Biot-Savart analysis comes in. Different downwash speeds imply different angles of attack and thus different coefficients of lift.

Once again you will see the number one by each vertical axis, since a similar process of normalisation has been used. This time we have divided by the overall lift coefficient. Of course, lift coefficients are already dimensionless, so that it was not necessary to normalise in order to make the values dimensionless. The reason for normalising in this case is simply to provide that convenient average reference value of unity for all of our graphs, making instant comparison very easy. These right-hand graphs we will generally refer to simply as the lift coefficient distribution or the angle of attack distribution – they may be thought of in either way – and you should always bear in mind, as we said at the end of the previous section, that the angle of attack, and hence the lift coefficient, is *inversely* related to the downwash.

Elliptical Wing

We have previously considered the effect that the slenderness of a wing (as measured by its aspect ratio) has on its drag. A very obvious question for the designer that we have not yet asked ourselves is, does the planform shape of the wing have any effect on the induced drag[2] of the wing? If so, then what is the best shape? We know that the induced drag cannot be zero since there must be wing-tips, but we would like to know how to minimise the induced drag that does occur.

Our mathematical colleagues can tackle this question by means of working out a formula for the induced drag based on the mathematical approach that we have outlined, and then finding the minimum value of that formula by resorting once again to the methods of calculus, but we can get close to the answer just by the application of logical thinking, as follows. If the drag of the wing is to be minimised, it is a reasonable assumption that every cross-section of the wing should be 'working' as hard as it is able, and that no one section should be working more or less hard than the others. An analogy might be a large team of slaves all hauling on ropes to raise or move a heavy piece of stone, whilst building the pyramids. Clearly if any one slave is working harder than, or is not working quite as hard as, all the rest, then the effort is not being applied quite as efficiently as would be possible if they all worked equally hard.

In aerodynamics terms, therefore, we require every section of the wing to be working as hard as every other. This means that each section should be operating at the same angle of attack, and thus the same coefficient of lift, as all the others. The lift per-unit-span thus produced by different sections may not be the same, since the aerofoil chord, and hence area per-unit-span, may not be the same. Likewise, if all the slaves apply the same effort to pulling the ropes, bigger slaves will usually produce a greater force than smaller ones.

Now if a wing is to have exactly the same coefficient of lift at all points across its semi-span, it means that its C_L-distribution graph will be constant at one over the entire semi-span. If you look now at Figure 13.5, and pretend for the time being that the left and centre parts of the figure are concealed from your view, this is exactly what you see in the right-hand graph. We will assume that all the cross-sections of all the wings we consider have identical aerofoil shape, and furthermore, that the wings are not twisted, so that if there were no down-wash all sections would be acting at the same angle of attack, and hence coefficient of lift. Thus the only thing left which can alter the sectional coefficient of lift is the downwash, and so in the present case we want constant downwash over the entire semi-span. To achieve this, the solution that emerges from a mathematical analysis based upon the Biot-Savart law is that the wing should be shaped in

---

[2]Remember that profile drag cannot be predicted by theory, and so it is only induced drag that we are considering here.

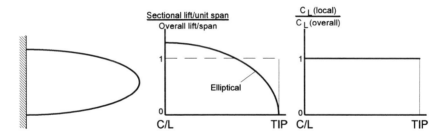

Figure 13.5 Elliptical Planform Wing

the form of an ellipse, a rather special oval shape which has a nice simple mathematical equation. Based on this mathematical result, a semi-span planform of an elliptical wing is shown in the left-hand drawing of Figure 13.5.

You may now mentally uncover the remaining, central drawing of Figure 13.5 which shows the lift distribution. How has this been obtained? To answer this, we must take a moment to consider how the two graphs, the C_L distribution and the lift distribution, are related to each other. Based on the facts that

$$L = C_L(\tfrac{1}{2}\rho V^2)S \text{ and } \frac{L}{\text{Span}} = C_L(\tfrac{1}{2}\rho V^2)c$$

where we are using L to mean total lift and c as the wing mean chord, without getting bogged down in the mathematical details it can be shown that, at any corresponding spanwise position on the two graphs,

[The lift-graph value] = [The C_L-graph value] $\times$ c

Now in the present case, the C_L distribution is constant, equalling one at all points, but the chord length c is distributed elliptically over the span. (That is just a way, in words, of describing the planform drawing on the left.) Consequently, since $c \times 1 = c$, the lift graph will, like the planform drawing, be elliptically distributed.

So much for the graphs, but what does it all mean? What are the practical implications of these two graphs? For each planform that we look at we are going to consider how an aerodynamicist's proposals for an aircraft designed with this wing planform might be received by two very important parties who will be strongly affected by the design decisions made. First of all we will think about those members of the design team who are going to have to design the structural aspects of the aircraft and will be responsible for minimising structural weight, producing an aircraft that is structurally sound and will not break or distort unduly, and achieving efficient and economical production methods. Then we will turn to the interests of the pilot who, whilst priding himself on his skill and professionalism, must be provided with an aircraft that is fundamentally very safe to fly and will not have any flying characteristics that would cause him or his passengers undue concern.

Returning to the elliptical wing, we recall that this shape emerged in response to the question 'what is the best shape for minimising induced drag?' So if the minimisation of drag is a prime design consideration for a particular aircraft (as it often is), we might think that we should choose an elliptical wing. A wing is a cantilever, and so if we can put more of the load towards the root and less towards the tip, this allows for a more efficient cantilever and thus a lighter wing structure. Looking at the elliptical shape of the lift distribution in Figure 13.5, this would certainly seem to be a reasonably satisfactory way to load a wing, and so structurally the elliptical wing would be very acceptable.

But there is a snag, which emerges when you begin to consider the factors affecting aircraft production. To make a wing of an elliptical shape is complicated in a number of ways. First of all, the skin of the wing has to be curved in two directions, which means that the material used to cover the wing has to be sufficiently elastic to stretch to the right shape. If using a metal skin it will necessitate very expensive tooling to press out or cut out the complicated shapes. Secondly, many of the important members, such as leading and trailing edge and wing-tip components, must be curved rather than straight, once again making very much greater demands on the manufacturing plant than would straight components. And thirdly, there will be scarcely any commonality between different components. The wing ribs (its aerofoil-shaped formers) will probably each be different in size from all the others, and so at most only two of each rib (one for each wing) will be required, but there will be a very large number of different components and ribs to design for all wing sections.

One classic and often quoted example of an aircraft whose wings were designed with elliptical variation of chord over the span is the Spitfire, and indeed it did have very low drag. In war-time conditions, production costs were not a major consideration, and the lack of commonality of components was not such a problem since such very large numbers of Spitfires were being built that single components could be mass-produced. However, we have not seen many aircraft built with elliptical wings since the Spitfire, and this is because, as we will see shortly, almost as good induced drag figures can be obtained with very much easier-to-build structures, so that there is no justification for the additional cost and complication of elliptical wings.

What do pilots think about elliptical wings? Certainly the Second World War Spitfire pilots were immensely proud of their excellent air-

craft, but was it because of, or despite, the characteristics of the elliptical wing? To investigate this question, look again at the C_L-distribu-
tion diagram of Figure 13.5 in which the C_L value is constant
everywhere over the span. Now the occasions during flight at which a
pilot is most concerned about aerodynamics are when he is flying
somewhere near to one or other limit, and most particularly as the
maximum angle of attack of the wings and hence the stall is
approached. With an elliptical wing, every point along the entire wing
span approaches the stalling angle of attack simultaneously, and so
when the stall occurs it occurs over the entire wing almost at once.
This means that the usual (and desirable) warnings of an impending
stall such as buffet on the tailplane and fuselage will not occur until
the whole wing has stalled, when it is too late to avoid the stall. This is
the price the pilot has to pay to fly an aircraft that has been optimised
for minimum induced drag, and such flight characteristics are very far
from being desirable.

Rectangular Wing

A rectangular wing would seem to be a very attractive proposition
from the consideration of production costs, since it is much simpler to
build than other shapes. Is it a good solution? Certainly it will not
achieve as low a value of induced drag as the elliptical planform, but
maybe this will be a price worth paying in terms of the benefits of simplicity and hence cheapness of production, and the commonality of
components such as aerofoil ribs. Let us start by examining the rectangular planform in terms of its structural desirability. To do so, we will
look at the lift distribution of Figure 13.6.

If we compare the planform shape of the rectangular wing (Figure
13.6 left) with that of the elliptical wing (Figure 13.5 left), then assuming that they are of the same total area, this area is concentrated much
more towards the centre-line in the elliptical wing and is spread more
outboard in the rectangular wing. Hence the wing loading of the rectangular wing would be expected to be greater towards the tip than

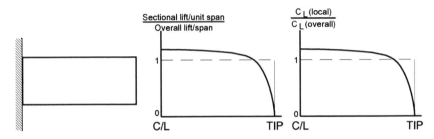

Figure 13.6   Rectangular Planform Wing

that of the elliptical wing. This is borne out by the rectangular wing lift distribution (obtained from the theory) in the centre of Figure 13.6, which is more pushed out in the top right-hand corner than is the elliptical distribution, and is more flattened in the inner region. Incidentally, the area under each curve (in both lift and C_L graphs) must be the same as that under the rectangle of height one, and so the area of the region above the one-line towards the root must exactly equal the area of the region beneath the one-line towards the tip.

This means that, structurally, the rectangular wing provides a somewhat worse cantilever loading, the load more being biased towards the tip region, so that it produces a larger moment trying to bend the wing, necessitating a thicker and stronger, and hence heavier, wing root structure. However, despite this drawback, rectangular wings are sometimes used on cheap and simple aircraft such as basic trainers where they may be preferred because of their ease of manufacture and commonality of parts.

If such a wing shape is likely to be used in the design of basic trainers, it is worth considering what effects this choice may have on the handling characteristics of an aircraft that will frequently be flown by pilots with very limited experience and skill. As before, this requires us to examine the C_L distribution. The chord c of the rectangular wing is constant over the entire semi-span, and so dividing the lift distribution values by this constant c results in exactly the same graph for the C_L distribution, as shown in Figure 13.6 (right). Thus because of the variation of downwash the angles of attack and C_L values are greatest in the root region. This means that if the aircraft approaches the stalling condition, the root region of the wing will reach the stall a little earlier than the outer region. This is the safest place for the stall to start for several reasons. Firstly, the turbulent air from the stalled root is likely to strike the tail of the aircraft and cause buffeting, which serves as a natural stall warning to the pilot. Secondly, the wing-tips will remain unstalled until last, so that there will not be a tendency for one of the wings to drop as the stall is approached. Thirdly, if the ailerons are in the conventional place near the wing-tips, they will continue to be effective right up to the stall since the angle of attack is less there. Fourthly, the loss of lift at the root region will lead to a reduction of downwash in the air flow reaching the tailplane, and so there will be a reduction in the downward force on the tailplane[3]. This will allow the aircraft automatically to pitch, or tip, nose downwards,

---

[3]There is usually a downward force on the tailplane of a conventional aircraft with its tail at the rear. This is because of stability and control considerations that will be explained in *Flightwise: Aircraft Stability and Control*.

which is exactly the right action to encourage recovery from the impending stall.

For all of these reasons, it is quite likely that, if the pilot takes no action at all, the aircraft will tend to recover unaided from the stall. If the stall were occurring in level flight, it is likely that the aircraft would re-configure itself automatically into a descending flight path, so that the forward component of gravity will raise the speed, increasing the lift and reducing the need for such a large angle of attack. A very safe design – but on the other hand, perhaps the pilot under instruction needs to be brought face to face with the realities of a wing stall, and being cocooned from its possible effects will not provide the best overall training to the new pilot.

Highly Tapered Wing

Just as the rectangular wing was more loaded towards the tip than the elliptical one because of its area distribution, so for the corresponding reason the highly tapered wing is more loaded towards its root, giving rise to a very steeply falling lift distribution as shown in the centre drawing of Figure 13.7. The strong bias of the load inboard produces a very much smaller moment at the wing root than previously, allowing very light wing structures to be used. The American U2 reconnaissance aircraft, besides having a high aspect ratio as we saw earlier, also has highly tapered wings in order to minimise the structural weight, and this allows for a larger fuel load to be carried, so that the aircraft can stay airborne for long periods of time.

The induced drag characteristics of the tapered wing are not as good as those of the elliptical wing, since the lift distribution of the latter is the optimal elliptical shape, and the lift distribution in the present case is far from elliptical. However, analysis shows that a *moderately* tapered wing, where the wing-tip chord length is about one third of the root chord length, has an induced drag which is almost as

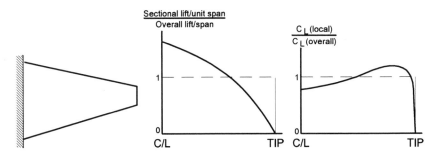

Figure 13.7   Highly Tapered Planform Wing

low as that of the elliptical wing. Consequently a tapered wing of these approximate proportions is highly favoured because of its very advantageous drag characteristics whilst at the same time offering a very practical straight-membered shape for economic manufacture. In the present section, however, we are primarily considering a more highly tapered planform than this, in order to accentuate the lessons to be learned.

If we try to derive the general shape of the C_L distribution of the tapered planform by the method used previously, which was to divide the lift distribution values by the chord lengths, we are let down. This is because, as we approach the tip, we are dividing a quantity (the lift value) which approaches zero by another quantity (the chord length) which also approaches zero, and the trend as to which one has the greatest effect is not obvious.

To resolve this difficulty, whilst keeping Figure 13.7 in front of us, we must cast our eyes and minds back to the lifting line model of Figure 13.2. By comparison with the lift distributions of the elliptical and rectangular wing planforms considered earlier, it would not be unreasonable to approximate the tapered planform lift curve of Figure 13.7 (centre) by a straight line. Thus the lift is falling off towards the tip in fairly even steps over the entire semi-span. This means that the shed trailing vortices are no longer bunched together into the wing-tip region as they were in the rectangular or elliptical type of distribution illustrated in Figure 13.2 but are very much more uniformly spread over the entire semi-span.

Imagine yourself standing behind the tapered wing of Figure 13.7 (left), about two thirds of the way out from the root to the tip, and facing upstream towards its trailing edge, with the trailing vortices streaming off past you. Since the trailing vortices are now fairly uniformly distributed, there are substantially fewer trailing vortices close by to the right of you, in the wing-tip region, than was the case with the trailing vortex distribution of Figure 13.2 in which they are crowded together in this region. In fact, quite a few of these vortices which were in the tip region bunch have effectively moved across to your left and are now inboard of your observation point. The flow of all the vortices as viewed is anticlockwise, and so many vortices that were previously to your right and creating a downwash at your observation point are now to your left and creating an upwash at the same point instead. The net effect of this is a substantial increase in upwash on the middle-to-outer region of the semi-span, and a corresponding increase of angle of attack and thus lift coefficient on this outer region.

The result of carrying out this type of analysis at all points along the wing is a C_L distribution of the form shown on the right of Figure 13.7. The curve is different from anything we have met before, so let us investigate its implications for the pilot in handling the aircraft, especially when approaching the stall. Despite the very great structural advantages and reasonably good drag characteristics, wings which are very highly tapered down to virtually a point at the wing-tips, as seen on a few of the passenger aircraft of yester-year, are never used today because of the very dangerous handling characteristics which they possess. Since the angle of attack is greatest in the wing-tip regions, the stall will start there, and this is undesirable for all of the reasons that made the stall starting at the wing root desirable. The turbulent wake from the stalled wing-tips will miss the tailplane and fuselage altogether, so that there will be no natural stall warning by buffeting. The ailerons, being near to the tips, are not only ineffective at controlling the aircraft in roll once a stall has commenced, but may actually be counter-productive. This is because the down-going aileron, which is trying to provide extra lift to prevent a stalled wing-tip from dropping, actually plunges its wing-tip deeper into the stall which has already commenced there, so that the lift falls off rather than increasing. When the aircraft first starts to stall, it is unlikely that both wing-tips will stall at exactly the same instant. If one wing stalls first, then as it descends its effective angle of attack will be increased even further because of the upward relative airflow, and this will put it more deeply into the stall. At the same time, the other wing-tip goes upwards, so that its effective angle of attack will be reduced, and thus it will remove itself from the risk of stalling. The resulting rolling motion will be uncontrollable and may be catastrophic.

Swept-back Wing

In Chapter 11 we saw the benefits that sweeping a wing, either forwards or backwards, could have in reducing the effective speed of the air flow over the aerofoil sections normal to the wing's axis, and hence allowing higher subsonic or transonic design speeds to be used. At that time we hinted at the structural problems that accompanied the use of swept wings, but now that we have expanded the lifting line

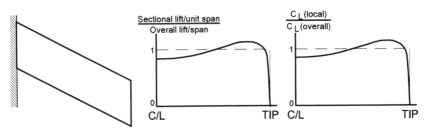

Figure 13.8   Swept-back (untapered) Planform Wing

theory we can consider the situation in rather more detail. We will limit ourselves here to considerations of just swept-back wings, as forward-swept wings are very rare, but we will close the chapter with a look at the intriguing use of forward-swept wings.

The planform drawing of Figure 13.8 represents a swept-back wing that is developed by taking the rectangular planform of Figure 13.6 and shearing it backwards. This means that none of the aerofoil cross-sections of the wing have been rotated from their positions in the rectangular wing, but have simply been slid past each other backwards to their new positions. The area and the chord at every section are thus the same as those of the rectangular wing, which means that the aspect ratio is also unchanged.

The line of the bound vortices (the lifting line) is now swept back along with the wing. This means that the trailing vortices that are shed from the wing no longer start from a line that is normal to the free stream air flow. Those that are shed from the region nearer to the wing root start substantially further upstream than those that are shed from the region nearer to the wing-tip. The flow from the trailing vortices from the root region will therefore have a much greater effect on the tip region than the tip region vortices will have on the root region. If this is not immediately clear, think where you would have to place an object to gain the maximum heating benefit from a single electric heater bar that was completely exposed with no reflector behind it. The best heating effect will obviously be gained alongside the bar, at points between the two planes normal to the bar and through its ends; outside this region, beyond the ends of the bar, the heating effect will fall away.

Remembering that the vortices flow anticlockwise from our viewpoint behind the starboard wing, the strongest consequence of this is that the upwash effect on the tip region caused by the vortices shed from the root region will be substantially more than it would be on an unswept wing. At the same time, there will be very little downwash effect from the tip region vortices on the root region. Hence, for a very different reason, we obtain a very similar C_L distribution for the swept wing as we obtained for the highly tapered wing, as shown on the right of Figure 13.8. We will come back to look at the implications of this in a moment.

Remembering that we can develop the lift distribution by multiplying each value of the C_L distribution by the chord at that point, and that the chord of the swept wing is constant, it follows that the lift distribution will be exactly the same shape as the C_L distribution, as is shown in the centre of Figure 13.8. The lift distribution is thus a long way removed from the minimum drag elliptical load distribution, and so the induced drag of this wing will be high.

Let us look first of all at the structural implications of using this swept-back wing. The large proportion of lift outboard will cause very large moments at the wing root. Furthermore, this concentration of load is now well aft of the wing root, introducing a substantial twisting effect to the wing, a phenomenon we have not come across with any of the previous planforms, and this must be resisted by additional structural members to provide the wing with sufficient torsional strength. For both of these reasons the structural designer is likely to throw up his hands in horror, as it seems to him that a swept wing must represent the worst possible scenario, and must inherently be very heavy and structurally inefficient.

Leaving the structural designer for a moment, let us see what the pilot thinks of this kind of wing. The high values of C_L in the tip region will again make the aircraft strongly prone to tip stalling which, as we have already seen, is dangerous in terms of wing drop and lack of roll control or stall warning. But now an additional danger arises, because the stalling wing-tips, being swept back, find themselves well behind the centre of gravity of the aircraft. As the tips stall and lift is lost aft of the centre of gravity, the unstalled root region ahead of the centre of gravity retains its lift, and so the aircraft tends to pitch nose up. This in itself aggravates the stall, but it is not the end of the story. Since the wing-tips have stalled, the wing-tip vortices (the twisting together of the trailing vortices a little way downstream of the wing) move in towards the remaining strong lift of the root region, and they consequently produce a downwash region and subsequent increased download on the tailplane, further enhancing the tendency of the aircraft to pitch up into a deeper stall. If the aircraft has a long slender nose protruding ahead of the wing, then these in-board 'wing-tip' vortices will be added to by the vortices that are shed from the fuselage that we referred to in Chapter 9 when discussing the danger of a high tailplane aircraft getting into a deep stall. Clearly long fuselages, high tailplanes and swept-back wings tend to aggravate the disadvantages of each other. But even without these additional problems, it is clear that the penalties of swept-back wings in terms of safe aircraft handling are very grave, and the pilot will be every bit as unhappy as the structural designer with the prospect of designing an aircraft with swept-back wings.

Swept-back and Tapered Wing

The reason for sweeping back a wing was to increase the cruise speed without incurring undue additional wave drag, but induced drag characteristics were not good. So the designer, still with his eye on the economic 'bottom line', looks for a design which combines achieving a high M_{div} (drag divergence or drag rise Mach number) with low

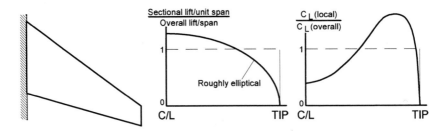

Figure 13.9 Swept-back and Tapered Planform Wing

induced drag. The natural development from our foregoing discussion is to try the idea of combining sweep-back with taper, since we recall that moderately tapered wings have very low induced drag. On the left of Figure 13.9 we show such a swept, tapered planform.

There are no new features to be taken into account when considering the swept-back and tapered planform, and the characteristics discussed in the case of the tapered wing and of the swept wing are merely combined, reinforcing or cancelling each other as appropriate. The lift and C_L distributions are as shown on the centre and right of Figure 13.9.

Looking once again at the structural implications of this composite design first, we see that the form of the lift distribution has now reverted more or less to our desired elliptical distribution. As we have seen, this is very good news for the sake of low induced drag, and also the load distribution being biased inboard allows for an efficient cantilever structure to be designed. Furthermore, although this is not apparent from Figure 13.9 alone, we no longer have the large twisting force on the wing that the high load at the tip region produced in the case of the swept (untapered) wing, and so the torsion-resisting structure can be made less hefty. Both economist and structural designer are therefore delighted with the idea of a swept, moderately tapered wing.

Unfortunately the good news ends there. By combining the bad characteristics of the C_L distributions of both the swept wing and the tapered wing, we have come up with a planform which has the worst possible stalling characteristics, since the C_L peak in the tip region has become even more pronounced. The pilot will rightly throw up his hands in horror at the prospect of flying an aircraft with stalling characteristics as bad as this aircraft promises to have, and furthermore all those who are concerned primarily with flight safety will realise that they have a very substantial problem on their hands. But the economics of long-range airliner design says quite clearly that this is the best shape to go for, and so the aerodynamicists are forced into the situation of having to come up with suitable devices or practices to overcome all the problems that it raises.

We have by no means over-stated the problem here. Actually the opposite is the case, as there are one or two additional problems which arise from the use of swept wings. In the first place, because of the sweep-back there is a component of the air flow whose direction is span-wise (i.e. from root to tip) rather than chord-wise. This is easiest to grasp if you imagine a very highly swept wing, at say 80° back from the normal to the fuselage. Clearly the flow over such a wing would be almost entirely span-wise and only a tiny component would be chord-wise. With a moderately (less than 45°) swept wing the spanwise component is the smaller of the two, but is still appreciable. This spanwise flow naturally creates a spanwise boundary layer, which has got the entire semi-span of the wing (rather than just the chord) over which to form and grow thicker. Thus the overall thickness of the combined boundary layer (i.e. chord-wise plus span-wise) becomes greater towards the wing-tips, which means that more air is being slowed down and is sacrificing energy to the surface. Consequently the wing-tip stalling tendency of a swept wing which has been referred to already is aggravated.

This spanwise flow over swept wings has another very significant effect which, although a nuisance in the present context, has provided aerodynamicists with a completely new set of answers to a large range of problems, and that is the phenomenon of leading edge vortices. But before we can properly understand these, it will be useful to step back a little and look at a feature which sometimes occurs in two-dimensional aerofoil stalling.

We have talked earlier about a leading edge stall, explaining how it occurs because of the very rapid deceleration and accompanying adverse pressure gradient following immediately behind the relatively sharp leading edge of an aerofoil. Looking a little more closely at the phenomenon, what often occurs in practice is that, as the angle of

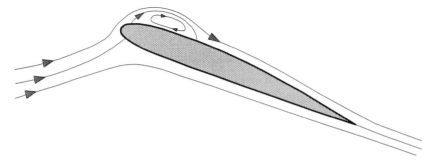

Figure 13.10   Boundary Layer Separation Bubble

attack is increased towards the stalling value, the boundary layer first of all separates as explained before immediately behind the trailing edge, but even after separating it benefits from the high-speed flow above it and actually re-attaches itself to the surface just a little way further downstream, as illustrated in Figure 13.10. Underneath this short jump away from the surface there occurs a rotating eddy current featuring reverse flow close to the wing surface which is (not very accurately) referred to as a boundary layer separation 'bubble'. Of course on an infinitely long wing of this cross-section the bubble takes the form of a long cylinder of rotating flow parallel to and behind the leading edge. When the angle of attack increases through the bubble-forming phase, the separation bubble cylinder grows from starting as a line with zero diameter, into a larger and larger cylinder of flow until the reattachment at the rear of it suddenly fails to occur any more, and this is the moment at which the fully developed leading edge stall occurs.

Now let us envisage exactly the same phenomenon occurring on a swept wing. The long cylinder of re-circulating flow behind the relatively sharp leading edge now has an additional flow, the spanwise component of the free stream flow that we discussed above, superimposed on it. This has the effect of strengthening every cross-section of the bubble flow by adding to it some of the bubble flow from positions further upstream along the leading edge. In a swept-*back* wing this means that the more inboard flow adds progressively to the further outboard flow, so that the diameter of the bubble 'cylinder' progres-

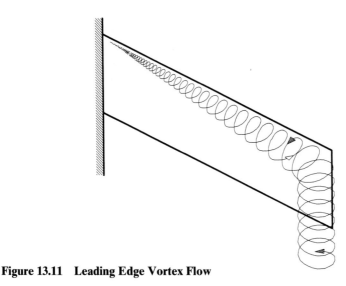

Figure 13.11   Leading Edge Vortex Flow

sively increases towards the wing-tips. This of course means that the flow no longer has the shape of a cylinder, but has developed into a conical shape, within which the flow has both a circulatory component in a plane normal to the wing axis and also an axial component parallel to the wing axis. The flow is thus a combination of spiral and helical in form, as shown in Figure 13.11, and is called a leading edge vortex.

In the early days this leading edge vortex was sometimes referred to as a ram's horn vortex, but this phrase is not commonplace today. It is clear from Figure 13.11 that it also gives rise to a trailing vortex from the wing-tip, since it cannot just end there. Although this is being formed as a result of different circumstances from the usual wing-tip vortex or trailing vortex sheet, it is all grist to the mill in the resulting trailing vortex flow region behind the aircraft, and of course contributes to the downwash effect that we have already considered in this and the previous chapter.

It is not, however, the contribution to downwash which is now our chief concern, since anyway the main strength of the vortex is not felt until the vortex is already downstream of the wing. Rather, the problem is the propensity that this vortex has for becoming detached. Just as the boundary layer separation bubble on the two-dimensional wing grows and eventually 'bursts', allowing the boundary layer to become separated and the wing stalled, so in a somewhat similar manner the leading edge vortex is also prone to causing separation as it grows large, so that the wing-tip region stalls. Thus for yet another reason the tip regions of swept-back wings are very prone to stalling, and so it is clearly becoming urgent to see if anything can be done to prevent or delay the problem.

SOLUTIONS TO TIP-STALLING PROBLEM

If we observe that the tip stalling phenomenon is only going to be a problem at high coefficients of lift and high angles of attack, then perhaps we should start our search for a solution by considering high angle of attack flight only at first, and see where that leads us. If you will forgive the absurdities involved, the simplest way to explain one important solution is by asking you to exercise your mind with a little bit of mental high jinks while we fly straight and level in a swept, tapered-wing aircraft. The pilot steadily reduces power to the engines but maintains the aircraft in level flight by lowering the tail with elevator and consequently increasing the angle of attack and lift coefficient. He continues this process until the aircraft is on the very point of stalling, flying as slowly as possible without losing height, and he then holds all the controls steady in that situation. Now for the interesting bit. You and I climb out of the aircraft, get hold of one of the wings and pull it off the fuselage, being careful not to change its orientation to the fuselage (i.e. the angle between the wing chord plane and the longitudinal axis of the aircraft), so that the aircraft can continue to fly undisturbed on the point of stalling. Now, with you holding the wing-tip and me holding the root, we will *twist* the entire length of the wing, not haphazardly, but making certain that the overall coefficient of lift of the entire wing remains unaltered all the time, so that the total wing lift remains the same and the aircraft continues in level flight. Our purpose in twisting the wing is to reduce the angle of attack at your end (the tip), so that we move away from the threatened stall there. You must therefore twist your tip end nose-down, and I against you will twist the root end nose-up, thus increasing the angle of attack at the root and all inboard parts of the wing to compensate. We keep twisting until the root end is on the point of stalling, which is where we would much prefer the stall to begin. This is called applying *washout* to the wing.

Now we simply re-attach the wing in its new configuration and ori-entation back onto the fuselage, dash round to the other side and repeat the process on that wing, and then resume our seats in the cabin and allow the pilot to recover to normal level flight from the point of stall, not by diving but by opening up the throttles and thus increasing speed. We have greatly improved the stalling characteristics of the aircraft by adding wash-out. But at what cost?

In order to answer this question, let us follow the same process through on the set of graphs shown in Figure 13.12, which are similar to the lift coefficient distributions on the right of Figures 13.5 to 13.9,

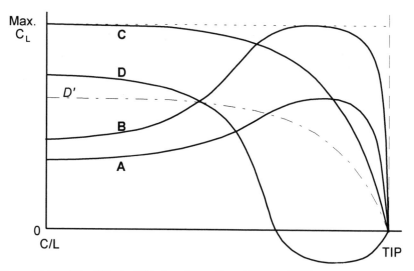

Figure 13.12   The Effect of Wash-out on a Swept Tapered Wing

but this time showing actual C_L values on the vertical axis. We start from the cruising C_L distribution shown as graph A, which is of the form we have already come to expect for this shape wing with no twist applied. When the pilot has slowed down and settled at the point of stalling, the distribution has taken up the curve marked B. As we twist the wing, the peak of the curve moves along from the tip region to the root, remaining at the aerofoil maximum value, and so we arrive at curve C, still flying on the point of stalling.

Now as we recover to normal speed in level flight with our newly washed out wings, we would hope and might reasonable expect that the C_L distribution curve would come back down in a tidy proportional fashion, so that we would finish up with a curve something like the dashed-and-dotted curve shown as D', which would be very acceptable. Unfortunately, however, life is not quite so kind to us. If you look back at the way curve A was altered to change into curve B, you will see that, because of the effects of the downwash distribution and following the Biot-Savart analysis, the increase in C_L in the tip region is very much greater than in the root region during the process of increasing the overall C_L of the aircraft. Likewise, when reducing the overall C_L value, it happens that the reduction in C_L is much greater in the tip region than in the root region, so that we do not arrive at curve D' but at the very much less advantageous curve D.

Curve D shows that the tip region of the wing, now that the aircraft is back in the cruise, is actually achieving a downward force because there is a negative angle of attack there. If you think through logically what has occurred, this is not a bit surprising. Before applying any twist the wing in the cruise was everywhere at a fairly small angle of attack. Now that the wing is twisted, the angle of attack at the root end will be greater than at the tip just because of the twist, irrespective of any downwash effect, and thus to obtain an overall C_L value the same as before, the root will have to operate at a higher angle of attack and the tip at a lower one. If the reduction in the tip angle of attack is more than its actual angle of attack before twisting, then it will now be negative and will be producing a downward force.

This downward force is bad news to the bottom-line-driven aircraft designer for two reasons. Firstly, of course, one has to produce that much dead lift from the rest of the wing surface just to compensate for the download, which means that much less load (passengers or cargo or fuel) can be carried. Secondly, we now have effectively a lower aspect ratio wing with all the useful lift being produced over a limited portion of the span which excludes the tip regions. This inner region consequently produces more induced drag, which being lift dependent means once again that the load carried by the aircraft must be further limited to compensate. In practice most swept tapered-wing aircraft do have a certain amount of wash-out designed into the wing, but this has to be severely limited on account of economic considerations.

One sophisticated solution which is available to this problem is to use what is called a *mission adaptive wing*, by which the actual shape of the aerofoil sections at different spanwise positions can be adapted in flight, by mechanically moving flexible or hinged members. This is an extension of the lift augmentation system idea, but takes the concept far further, in that it is conceived of as a system for full-time operation during all stages of flight, especially when the mission calls for a variety of different flight conditions to be optimised at different times, as the name suggests. Theoretically with a computerised system – the pilot has enough to think about without having to work out optimum settings for his wings at all phases of flight – it should be possible to design the perfect wing for all flight conditions. The reasons that this has not to date been used other than in experimental aircraft is that the systems are too costly in terms of weight and system complexity to make them economically worthwhile.

Let us turn our attention now to trying to reduce the aggravating effects of the wing spanwise flow and of the leading edge vortex on wing-tip stalling. A number of devices have been used to cure these problems, but very often in the past these devices have been added as fixes after problems have come to light in flight trials or in operational service. A very common such fix is the use of *vortex generators*, small usually rectangular sharp blades protruding from the wing surface, spaced out along the span in front of the region where separation is prone to occur. They are set at an angle to the flow, so that each will stir up a vortex in the flow, thus entraining the high speed air from above the boundary layer into that layer to re-invigorate it and thus ensure that it remains attached. Very effective in flight, they can be an absolute menace and a very serious hazard to fitters and mechanics handling or climbing over the aircraft on the ground. These, along with other devices mentioned below, are illustrated in Figure 13.13. In this figure all the devices have unrealistically been shown on the same swept wing, whereas normally one or at most two of the devices would be used on a wing.

The growth of the leading edge vortex can be stemmed in a couple of ways. A notch cut into the leading edge at around mid-span is sometimes used to generate and to locate a special small vortex of its own. This is effective both by means of re-invigorating the boundary layer and also by enticing the leading edge vortex to peel off the wing at this point rather than going out to the tip. The latter ploy can also be achieved by means of a small thin plate attached to the leading edge of the wing, set with its plane vertical and parallel to the free stream air flow, which forces the growing leading edge vortex to be

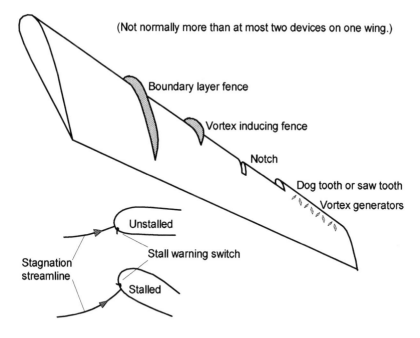

(Not normally more than at most two devices on one wing.)

Boundary layer fence

Vortex inducing fence

Notch

Dog tooth or saw tooth

Vortex generators

Unstalled

Stall warning switch

Stagnation
streamline

Stalled

Figure 13.13   Various Tip Stalling Prevention Devices

shed. If another one grows outboard of this point, it will have reached a very much smaller size by the time it reaches the tip.

Sometimes this small plate may be extended backwards so that it extends over a significant portion of the wing chord. This is done in order to provide a physical barrier to the spanwise flow component with its troublesome spanwise boundary layer, thus removing another source of early tip region separation.

Occasionally the tip regions of wings have actually been substantially modified in order to improve their flying characteristics. The leading edge of the wing-tip region is sometimes extended forwards, incorporating some droop, and thus providing an easier path for the air over the leading edge. This can also have the effect of increasing the lift coefficient in this region by dint of the extra camber and area, thus increasing the overall C_L of the wing at less overall angle of attack. However, the load distribution and wing root bending moment will both suffer as a result; but, as we said, this is a post-design fix rather than a deliberate design ploy. This approach has the additional benefit of producing a discontinuity (a saw-tooth or dog-tooth) on the leading edge, which as with the leading edge notch and fence will shed a vortex and disrupt the growth of the leading edge vortex.

All sorts of other devices have been used at various times as a result of the ingenuity of aerodynamicists, but the underlying problem remains. Since flight safety, especially in passenger aircraft, must always carry very high priority, the system most often used in transport aircraft is to ensure that the stall is totally avoided at all costs. Triggered by an aerodynamic sensor, various warning devices such as bells, lights, klaxons and stick (control column) shakers are activated. The sensor may be a small flap switch carefully located at the wing leading edge, as shown in Figure 13.13, which directly senses whether the stagnation point is above it (not stalled) or below it (on the point of stalling), but in practice it is more common to use an angle of attack measuring sensor at some other point on the aircraft which is also used for other purposes, and to get it to trigger the stall warning system at the appropriate angle of attack. As a last resort, the warning may be reinforced by a stick pusher which forcibly pushes the pitch control forward to make quite sure that it is not possible for a pilot to overlook or to disregard the warning of an imminent stall. However, the use of stick pushers has become unfashionable today, in view of the need for the pilot to retain ultimate authority over the aircraft.

LEADING EDGE VORTICES – THE PLUS SIDE

Aerodynamicists have developed something of a love-hate relationship with leading edge vortices. We have seen above that they can be extremely treacherous for high angle of attack flight in swept tapered-wing aircraft. But they have also been put to extremely good use in the aerodynamicist's aid, sometimes producing effects and making concepts possible that without leading edge vortices would probably never have been conceived. The significant feature of these vortices is that, as with all vortices, there is a very high speed associated with the flow near to the vortex core, which in turn carries with it a long, dependable region of low pressure, which can be used to great advantage by dint of careful design.

Leading edge vortices are sometimes used to produce lift, either in substitution for or as well as conventional aerofoil lift. Perhaps the best known example of this technique being used is in the Concorde supersonic airliner. This aircraft has highly swept-back leading edges, so that its leading edges can operate subsonically at all speeds up to its cruise Mach number. Not only the plan view of Concorde shows that the leading edge of Concorde's wing is very curved, but this is the case whichever direction the wing is viewed from, being a highly complex aerodynamic form. Measurement of the plan view with a protractor quickly shows that most of it is swept back by 60° or more, in line with our thinking at the end of Chapter 10 for Mach 2 flight. Thus the wing can accept a rounded leading edge, although in the case of Concorde it is actually fairly sharp but cambered to compensate, and at high subsonic speed it can fly conventionally at low angles of attack.

The lift augmentation problem of obtaining high lift coefficients at low speeds is not so easy to solve by conventional means on a wing of Concorde's shape, partly because the total wing area and aspect ratio are small and partly because the trailing edge is the only place to put all lift augmentation and other control surfaces, be they ailerons, elevators or high lift flaps, and their purposes conflict with each other.

This problem was tackled from the very earliest stages of conceptualising the design of Concorde, and a low-speed delta wing aircraft was built especially for the purpose of testing out what was then a new idea, that of achieving major aircraft lift by means of generating leading edge vortices. Concerns over whether these vortices would burst or become unstable under critical conditions were totally dispelled by tests on this aircraft, so that today the idea is taken for granted as an everyday phenomenon. When it is landing and taking off, Concorde will be observed to have a very much greater angle of attack than conventional aircraft, so much so that, if it were relying on conventional aerofoil lift it would already be fully stalled. It is for this reason that the 'droop snoot' is necessary, so that the flight crew may have an adequate view ahead. At this angle of attack large leading edge vortices form along the entire wing leading edges and roll up to a large diameter over the top of the wings, providing the strong low pressure region required to generate the lift needed.

It has been shown that the large suction region produced in the leading edge vortices has moved backwards and upwards from just in front of the leading edge where it occurs in conventional aerofoil flow. Just above the stagnation point on the leading edge of an aerofoil operating conventionally at positive angle of attack, the air accelerating up and over the leading edge causes a very low pressure in this region, which pulls forwards on the aerofoil and is effectively what keeps the drag of the aerofoil down close to the d'Alembert's Paradox ideal of no drag. However, when the flow is persuaded to separate at high angle of attack and to roll up into a lifting vortex on the top surface, this leading edge suction is sacrificed to lift, so that there is a corresponding substantial increase in drag. For an aircraft on the approach to land this is welcome, but during take-off it is undesirable since it has to be overcome by engine thrust.

Vortex lift is also used in a variety of other ways. Some combat aircraft wings are given a highly swept inboard portion whilst having a much less swept outer region, and by this means they can take advantage of greatly enhanced lift at high angles of attack, whilst also benefiting from the advantage of high aspect ratio. Such devices are called leading edge root extensions, shortened to LERX. Similar devices are sometimes used at the foot of the leading edge of the fin of an aircraft, in order to ensure that the fin has a sufficiently large side force to maintain the aircraft's directional stability in the presence of an air-flow coming from a substantial side angle. An example of this is the Nimrod maritime reconnaissance aircraft based on the Comet air liner. This aircraft was found to have somewhat too small a fin when modified for the new rôle, in particular because of the ventral fin de-stabilising effect of the large bomb bay pannier doors beneath the fuselage. A highly-swept root extension was added to the front of the tail fin to provide more side force at large sideslip angles. However, when during the Falklands campaign the Nimrods were equipped with in-flight refuelling probes protruding forward of the nose, once again their directional stability became inadequate, and required enhancing. Since the swept root extension had already been used, the solution adopted was to add small vertical fins to the tips of the horizontal tailplane.

When vortex lift is used to enhance conventional lift on combat air-craft, tremendous beneficial changes can be achieved to the shape of the lift curve. This has made it possible to design aircraft which do not stall in the accepted manner, but can fly with still increasing lift coefficients at very large angles of attack, and substantial advantage is now-a-days taken of this ability to improve the combat manoeuvrability of these aircraft.

FORWARD-SWEPT WINGS

Sweep-back has become a familiar and conventional design feature of most high-speed aircraft, although many of the arguments for its use apply equally well to forward sweep, which is by no means as com-monplace. The main reason why forward sweep has never been very seriously considered as a viable alternative is that it possesses an intrinsic structural disadvantage, that of wing divergence or structural instability. If you extend your arm forward out of a car window with palm flat, and raise it a little, it tends to be lifted further and becomes hard to hold in place, whereas if you extend it backwards from the window the aerodynamic force on your palm always tends to restore it to the horizontal position when raised or lowered. In the same way a swept wing experiences a twisting moment, and this bends the wing-tip, modifying the angle of attack of the tip and hence its lift coeffi-cient. If the sweep is forward, this distortion has the effect of increasing the wing-tip's angle of attack and so accentuating the twist-ing moment, effectively trying to tear the wing-tip off the wing. If however the wing is swept aft, the distortion results in a reduced angle of attack, thus reducing the twisting load and actually taking the strain off the wing-tip.

Using traditional constructional methods and materials, the weight

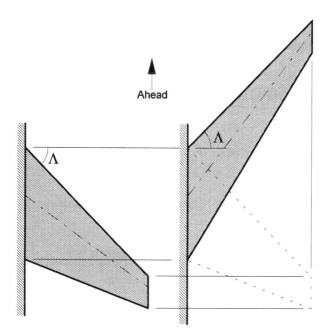

Figure 13.14   Comparison of Forward Sweep and Sweep-back for Supersonic Wings

penalty imposed by building a forward-swept wing strong enough to resist this structural instability safely has always been so great as to outweigh any possible aerodynamic advantage there might be. However, with the use of modern composite materials incorporating carbon fibres and a constructional technique called aeroelastic tailoring the weight penalty can now be made minimal, and so it becomes worthwhile to examine whether there are any aerodynamic benefits to be gained by using forward sweep. It is the aerodynamic rather than the structural features which we wish to look at here.

As we have seen, sweep serves different purposes in supersonic, subsonic and transonic wing design, and so we must investigate each of these separately. First of all we will show that for a supersonic wing forward sweep has a substantial disadvantage over aft sweep. At the end of Chapter 10 we saw that it is the sweep of the *leading edge* of the wing that is significant for supersonic purposes. Figure 13.14 depicts two supersonic wings each with the same root chord and tip chord and hence taper ratio, and also each with the same span. Both have an equal leading edge sweep angle of Λ (defined as the angle from the straight out, unswept position) being designed for flight at the same Mach number. Despite having the same leading edge sweep as demanded by supersonic considerations, it is immediately apparent

that, because of taper, there is much more overall sweep in the forward-swept wing than in the aft-swept one. Let us examine a bit more
closely what we mean here by overall sweep.

When a wing gets twisted along its length, the front parts near the
leading edge get bent one way and the rear parts towards the trailing
edge get bent the other way. It is reasonable to suppose that, somewhere between the leading and trailing edge, there could be a line
drawn that does not get bent in either direction, but just gets twisted
like a straight piece of wire. The dashed-and-dotted chain lines represent these lines, which we will refer to as the structural axes of the
wings. From a structural point of view, the length of these lines is a
better indication of cantilever length than is the aerodynamic semi-
span measured normal to the fuselage, and therefore we will loosely
refer to the length of the structural axes as the structural spans of the
two wing forms.

Looking at the figure, it is clear that the sweep angle of the structural axis of the forward-swept wing is greater than that of the aft-swept
wing. Also the structural span of the forward-swept wing is clearly
greater than that of the aft-swept wing, and both of these facts can
readily be confirmed by measuring with a protractor and a ruler. Both
of these facts magnify the already unfavourable structural characteristics of swept, tapered wings that we considered earlier in this chapter,
and this is in addition to the inherent structural instability of the forward-swept wing that we have already pointed out at the start of this
section. If designing an aircraft mainly for supersonic flight, then, a
forward-swept wing would be a far worse choice than the equivalent
aft-swept wing.

On the other hand, we have seen that sweep can also be used to
advantage in the design of high subsonic speed wings. Do the same
disadvantages of forward sweep apply there? Let us examine this
question. The first thing we need to clarify is how far back on the
aerofoil chord of the wing we should measure the sweep angle. Just
now we recalled that for a supersonic wing the sweep must be measured at the leading edge, since it is at the leading edge that we wish to
control whether the flow is effectively subsonic or supersonic.
However, when using sweep to raise the critical Mach number of a
wing, a different consideration must be applied. It is at the point of
maximum thickness of the aerofoil section that the greatest flow speed
is achieved, and at which Mach 1 is first reached, and so it is reasonable that it should be the locus of such points that should be used as
the reference line for measuring the wing sweep, and not the leading
edge. The position of this point on the aerofoil depends on the aerofoil section shape. It might typically be at about 35% of the chord
from the leading edge, and so it roughly coincides with the structural

axis of the wing. Consequently forward sweep for high subsonic purposes has virtually no effect on the structural span as compared with aft sweep, and so it is not ruled out on these grounds, but neither does it achieve any advantage.

Chapter 11 was given over completely to studying transonic flow, and at the end of the chapter a major outcome of the transonic research was seen to be the adoption for virtually all high-speed transport aircraft of the supercritical aerofoil, and the acceptance of operating within the transonic regime, with a shock wave present on the upper surface of the wing towards the trailing edge. Some American research in 1976 revealed that the transonic drag rise of a wing is in fact related to the sweep angle of the shock wave line, and not to the line of points of greatest flow speed as it is for high subsonic design.

Now a supercritical aerofoil is designed so that the shock is as near to the trailing edge as possible, and in practice this may be typically 70% of the chord length back from the leading edge. This best line for measuring the sweep angle is thus substantially behind the structural axis which we estimated to be at around the 35% chord position, so that sweeping the wing forward rather than aft, using the shock line as reference, will have the advantage of reducing the sweep angle of the structural axis, and of reducing its length, the structural span. Figure 13.15 illustrates this phenomenon. On the left is the identical swept tapered planform that we started from in Figure 13.14, showing the structural axis as before but with the addition of the shock wave line, at about the 70% chord position. The sweep angle Λ has been redefined now as the sweep angle of the shock wave line. The right-hand drawing shows the effect of shearing the wing forward so that root, tip

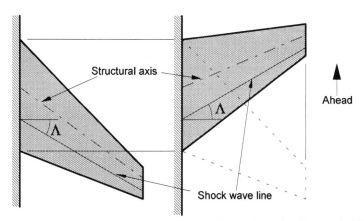

Figure 13.15   Comparison of Forward Sweep and Sweep-back for Transonic Wings

and semi-span lengths and hence aspect ratio all remain unchanged and the shock line sweeps forward by Λ rather than aft. The result is a wing with exactly the same aerodynamic sweep but less overall sweep and a much sturdier, squatter profile, in which the wing structural span is shorter for the same aerodynamic span. Overall then, the swept forward transonic wing would be structurally superior for the same aerodynamic sweep, if it were not for the wing-tip divergence problem.

One of the primary aims of aircraft design is to minimise drag, and when considering planform shapes we are concerned especially with the minimisation of induced drag. How does the direction of sweep (fore or aft) bear on the induced drag? Earlier in this chapter we looked at the two major factors which contribute to the creation of a large C_L peak in the wing-tip region of a swept, tapered wing. Such a distribution is unfavourable for producing low induced drag since we ideally require the C_L value to be constant over the entire span. In both cases the excess upwash in the tip region was produced by the vortices being shed from further inboard, but the reasons for the effect being strong were different in each case. The choice as to whether the wing should be swept forward or backward cannot have any influence on the effect of taper since the taper ratio is not affected and we have deliberately considered taper and sweep separately from each other. However, the tip region upwash due to sweep-back was produced by the fact that the root region was upstream of the tip region and hence had a stronger effect on the tip region than the tip region had on the root region. Since the trailing vortices are anticlockwise (on the starboard wing viewed from behind), the root region produced strong upwash at the tip region. Now if the wing is swept forwards instead of backwards, it is the tip region that will have the stronger effect on the root region, which means that there will now be a preponderance of downwash over the inner regions of the wing. But apart from making necessary an overall higher angle of attack to achieve the total wing lift coefficient required, this does not have any clear implications on the relative upwash and downwash on tip region and root region. There is still more upwash or less downwash (whichever way you prefer to look at it) in the tip region than in the root region, so no conclusion jumps out at us. However, in the forward-swept wing there will be some improvement in C_L distribution due to sweep and a consequent reduction in induced drag. This is because, for the sake of calculating induced drag (by the Biot-Savart approach) we must take our lifting line as being at the 25% chord point, whereas we have already seen that for designing a transonic wing we should measure the sweep angle at the 70% chord point. If (as in Figure 13.15) the 70% line is swept forward by the same angle Λ as that by which it was previously swept back, then the 25% line is less swept than it was before. (If this is not obvious, it can be checked from the figure by sketching in the 25% line and using a protractor.) Thus on the lifting line we have less sweep, and hence less of the tip region upwash effect, than on the equivalent transonic swept-back wing. In conclusion, forward sweep may be expected to have a favourable effect on the induced drag of the transonic aircraft. It will also bring the initial stall zone away from the wing-tip and towards the root, bringing with it improvements to the aircraft's stalling characteristics.

In the next chapter on gust response we will explain the fact, which for brevity we will merely state here, that the lift curve slope of a wing decreases as the sweep increases. This is a true result for an infinitely long wing, and so it is not a finite wing downwash phenomenon. Consequently it makes no difference whether the wing is swept forward or aft, since no distinction can be made between the two 'ends' of an infinitely long wing. This swept wing is of uniform cross-section, and so the leading edge, the trailing edge and other reference lines (such as the line of aerodynamic centres at 25% chord) are all parallel to each other. Therefore we do not need to specify at which line we measure the sweep angle. However, in the case of our tapered swept wing, we will once again use the theoretical lifting line, the line joining the 25% chord points. As we saw in the previous paragraph, for the same amount of sweep at the 70% chord line, the 25% chord line will be somewhat less swept on a forward-swept wing than on an aft-swept one. Thus the transonic forward-swept wing, being overall less swept, has a larger lift curve slope or a steeper lift curve than the equivalent aft-swept wing. During manoeuvring this is a substantial advantage for combat aircraft, since a small increase in angle of attack (produced by pushing the tailplane down using the elevators) produces a larger increase in lift coefficient than would be the case on the equivalent aft-swept wing aircraft, and so changes in wing lift are more quickly achieved, and the aircraft is more manoeuvrable.

There is another feature of the forward-swept wing which also contributes to this manoeuvrability advantage, and it lies in the flexible nature of the wing-tips. When the wings of an aft-swept aircraft are producing a large amount of lift such as, for example, during a turn, the upward bending of the wing-tips makes the angle of attack in that region get smaller, so that the lift falls off there, with the result that even more overall angle of attack is required to compensate for this and produce the same total lift force. If the wings are swept forward, however, then the bending up of the wing-tips increases the angle of attack in that region, so that the lift actually increases more rapidly than would be the case without the flexing of the wing. If this is not clear, it can very easily be demonstrated by once again putting your arm out of a car window, palm extended flat, first in the 'forward-

'swept' and then in the 'aft-swept' position, and experimenting by inclining the arm slightly upwards. This means that the structural flexibility of the wing, which lies behind the main objection to the use of forward-swept wings, actually turns out to provide a major benefit for combat aircraft, so long as the structural strength requirements can be met.

Structural strength, weight and aerodynamic factors are not the only considerations that an aircraft designer has to take into account, and forward-swept wings may sometimes offer solutions to other problems related to the lay-out of components. For example, an aft-swept wing allows the wing main spar to cross the fuselage[4] further aft, thus releasing more unobstructed space further forward. It may also offer the opportunity for much better downward visibility, as in the case of a Swedish light observation aircraft, the MFI 15B, and the tandem-seat all-aluminium Blanik glider. In both cases forward sweep is very moderate, and is certainly not provided for achieving a high critical Mach number! In the case of the German forward-swept Hansa executive jet, all cabin windows are ahead of the wing.

The undercarriage of an aircraft must be placed slightly behind the centre of gravity, which often necessitates stowing it in the thinnest part of a swept-back wing. Another major layout benefit of the forward-swept wing is that its root will be further back relative to the centre of gravity than the root of an aft-swept wing, so that the undercarriage may be stowed in the forward part of the wing, which is deeper and provides more stowage space. The Hansa referred to above provides a good example of this effect.

We have seen on a number of occasions that one design feature may be favourable for a certain flight condition but undesirable for another, so that an aircraft cannot be optimised for all flight conditions. This is the case with the use of a forward-swept wing on combat aircraft which are designed for both transonic and supersonic operations. If the forward-swept wing is optimised for transonic flight so that the forward sweep angle is measured at the 70% chord line, then the leading edge sweep angle will be less than that of the corresponding aft-swept wing. The aircraft will therefore be limited to a lower maximum supersonic Mach number if the leading edge is to operate subsonically.

---

[4]A wing main spar is the chief structural member that extends from wing-tip to wing-tip. Almost always it extends across the fuselage as a single member shared by both wings, since this provides greatest strength at the wing roots where the bending effect is greatest. If two separate wing spars were to be attached to the fuselage, the fuselage itself would have to be designed to withstand the very large bending loads at the roots, and this would make for a very inefficient fuselage structural design.

There are other aerodynamic factors which make a forward-swept wing behave somewhat differently from its equivalent aft-swept wing, and these features (as they apply to combat aircraft at least) have been thoroughly investigated by the American experimental forward-swept wing aircraft, the Grumman X29. The scene is further complicated in this case by the fact that the aircraft also possesses the unconventional feature of canard foreplanes rather than a tail at the back, so that to a casual observer the aircraft looks as if it were a fairly normal swept-wing aircraft with a conventional tail, flying backwards! Furthermore, it was designed to be thoroughly unstable, which means that it would not naturally fly forwards but would turn around and over, and so it can only be flown at all with the assistance of sophisticated computer technology operating the controls. It has so many unconventional features that it is difficult to extract the effect of any one feature (such as forward sweep) in isolation. We will be considering canard foreplanes at some depth in *Flightwise: Aircraft Stability and Control*.

From this discussion about forward-swept wings, we can conclude that it is highly unlikely that we will ever see any predominantly supersonic aircraft designed with forward-swept wings. Transonic transport aircraft will only use forward sweep if there are decisive benefits in this concept on other grounds, which appears on the whole unlikely. But for future combat aircraft optimised for manoeuvring in the transonic regime, the benefits available make the use of forward sweep appear somewhat more promising, although its adoption will ultimately depend on the overall balance of favourable and unfavourable characteristics.

CHAPTER 14
Gust Response

We have travelled a very long way from the beginning of this book in our quest for a deeper understanding of the principles of aircraft flight. A glance back at the first few chapters will convince you that you are very much more 'flightwise' now than when launching into this escapade of discovery. Our language has matured and our speed of assimilating new material has greatly increased when comparing the latter chapters with the earlier ones.

We have now essentially finished studying the physiological features of the aeroplane, and are ready to build upon our understanding by studying the equally intriguing topics in *Flightwise: Aircraft Stability and Control*. The book's coverage has been wide-ranging and has demanded deep concentration, so that right up to the end of the previous chapter there has been no sense of having reached a summit and of descending triumphantly to the foot-hills. Perhaps a little winding down is in order now before we close this volume.

It is for this reason that this final chapter on gust response has been included. The ideas covered in it are not essential for a general understanding of aircraft flight, and indeed you will not find them dealt with explicitly in many aerodynamics text books. But they enable us to expand and reinforce a number of the important ideas covered thus far, whilst at the same time extending our understanding of the pro's and con's of certain choices of design configuration. Regard it, if you like, as the cherry on the cake, or the bright student's reward for reaching the end of the course.

What do we mean by this rather technical-sounding phrase 'gust response'? We have been led to believe so far that the air flow over an aircraft in flight can safely be assumed to be steady and uniform. We might therefore be forgiven for thinking that gusts are the province of objects on the ground, where the wind velocities over them may be strongly affected by the turbulence generated in the wind as it passes over and around obstacles and is affected by meteorological features. But aircraft, we feel, are usually (literally) above all that.

For aircraft whose prime mission is to carry a load from A to B efficiently, this is fortunately quite true for most of the flying time. At the height at which modern jet transport aircraft fly, usually the only weather considerations of concern are the overall steady speed and direction of the wind, which alter the aircraft's progress relative to the ground but have no effect on its flight performance relative to the air in which it is moving.

However, just as supersonic aircraft must fly subsonically and transonically to reach supersonic speed, so high-altitude aircraft must pass through low altitudes at the beginning and end of every flight, and it is with that phase of flight that we are now concerned. But this is not the whole, or even the most important part, of the story. In today's scenario of high-speed, high-altitude, ultra complex aviation, some of the greatest demands on sophistication and ingenuity come from the military tacticians, who now require combat aircraft to fly very fast, extremely low, and for great distances, in order that they can be protected from observation on ground based radar tracking installations by intervening ground features such as hills, trees and buildings. Although 250 feet altitude is the lowest height allowed over populated ground during training in the United Kingdom, military pilots are trained and required to fly at high speed as low as possible, down typically to fifty feet above the ground, when the chips are down.

It requires very little imagination to appreciate how demanding, both of pilot skills and technically, such intensive low-flying must be. Not only must the pilot cling closely to all the undulations of the hilly terrain and avoid trees (sometimes using them for radar shelter), church spires, pylons, tall chimneys and even larger houses, but he must also take account of the ubiquitous cobweb of high-voltage electricity cables, which are difficult to see and avoid when flying at hundreds of miles per hour. On top of these problems is the fact that the air at this height above the ground is no longer smooth-flowing and turbulence free, but is saturated with eddies and general turbulence caused by the wind flowing around all the irregular ground features. The aircraft is flying deep within the earth's own turbulent boundary layer.

We are not concerned in this book with the ingenious and sophisticated electronic aids which are provided to render the low-flying task possible for the pilot with reasonable safety, but we are interested in investigating what effect the turbulent gusts of air may have on the flying and handling qualities of aircraft of differing designs in this turbulent air near to the ground, and what the structural design implications may be. This is what is meant by gust response.

The effect of gusts is that they provide a bumpy ride. In a few minutes we must investigate this statement a little more carefully and try to identify exactly what it means, but for the moment let us accept intuitively that we know what we mean. If you have ever been out on a choppy sea in a small fast motor boat, you will know that every time the boat's prow comes down on top of a wave there is a very pronounced 'bang' and the impact feels as if it is as solid as a hammer on a nail – there seems to be no resilience at all. This sort of ride can be physically stressful for passengers, imposing perhaps large and uncomfortable impact loads through the seat (if hard) and up the spine. Clearly it is not likely to do the boat itself any good either, and the wear and tear on the boat's hull can be substantial. A larger boat, or a different design of boat of the same size, may well ride the same waves with far less bumpiness, providing a much more comfortable ride to crew and passenger and necessitating less maintenance work.

The situation for the low-flying aeroplane is directly comparable with that of the motor boat. The pilot of a single-seat combat aircraft flying into a battle zone at extremely low level clearly has a very high work load. The aircraft must be controlled vertically and horizontally with rapid control movements to avoid obstructions and to take advantage of ground cover, which requires most of the pilot's visual and mental attention and physical effort. Furthermore he has to be constantly checking on his route to the target, looking for and spotting landmarks, which may be less precisely identified in advance in enemy territory than in his familiar training grounds. In particular he must be systematically on the look-out for unknown hazards such as electrical power lines. All of these demanding tasks of observation and control will be made very much more difficult if not impossible if the aircraft is bumping along in a hard and uncomfortable manner.

Moreover, the fatigue load on the pilot may be so great on a rough ride that he will be too tired and shaken up by the time he reaches his target area to perform at top efficiency. On reaching the target, the aircraft has to serve as a weapon platform. If you imagine the difficulty of trying to aim an air rifle to shoot at a buoy from the speed-boat on the choppy sea, you will immediately appreciate the need for the aircraft weapon platform to be flying steadily if there is to be any chance of hitting the target. Of course the aircraft and weapon are fitted with a number of sophisticated aids to assist the pilot with many of these tasks, but the pilot must remain fully in charge at all times.

Turning now to think about an airliner flying through turbulent air at low levels, at a first glance it may appear that there is no similar need for concern. The very much greater size, and the flexibility of the wings, would be expected to dampen out the worst of the roughness of the ride. But there is a different problem to contend with in this case, and it arises largely from the fact that the structure of the transport aircraft is designed using a different criterion from that of the combat aircraft. The combat aircraft's wing may be designed to withstand a load factor of perhaps eight or nine, as discussed in Chapter 2 at the end of the section entitled 'Forces in Curved Motion', whereas to save on unnecessary structural weight the wings of an airliner may be designed to accept no more than about twice the weight of the aircraft. Each gust bump, therefore, will take the airliner wing structure very much nearer to its design load limit than a corresponding bump will take the relatively stronger combat aircraft's wing. It is therefore far more critical for structural reasons to anticipate carefully and allow for the magnitude of bumps when designing an airliner, than it is when designing the stronger combat aircraft.

There is an additional feature that the structural designer has to take carefully into account and understand thoroughly, not mentioned at all so far in this book, and that is the problem of *fatigue*. If you bend or stretch an object within what is called its elastic limit, when the bending or stretching force is removed the object reverts to its undistorted shape, without any obvious effect on the object. However, a small permanent change to the internal structure of the material of the object has in fact occurred, and if you repeat this bending (or stretching) and releasing process a large number of times, the material will eventually be weakened so much that it will crack and break. This phenomenon of fatigue is most easily demonstrated by bending a wire paper clip or coat hanger backwards and forwards at the same point a number of times until it breaks. (Actually in both of these examples the bending is done beyond the elastic limit of the material, and so the failure occurs after far fewer loadings and unloadings than in the case of a deformation within the elastic limit. But the principle is well illustrated.)

Now all structural parts of an aircraft are subjected, during the life of the aircraft, to a very large number of loading and unloading 'cycles', as they are called, and this means that, although the damage is hidden inside the material, they are becoming weakened and may eventually fail. If the loads are very small, then the components can take extremely large numbers of loading cycles with scarcely any effect. But if the magnitude of the loading is somewhere approaching the elastic limit of the material (which means that a relatively small amount of additional load would take the member beyond its elastic limit), then the number of cycles before failure will be very much lower. Although fatigue failure was not unknown at the time, the first dramatic evidence of its impact on aviation came by way of the series of high-altitude explosions that occurred on a number of Comet airliners not long after their introduction in the 1950s. There was a concentration of stress at the corners of the window holes in the fuselage, so great that only a relatively low number of loading cycles was necessary to cause failure. The loading that produced these cycles was the pressurising and de-pressurising of the passenger cabin, which occurs once per flight, and after a while the fuselages started exploding catastrophically at high-altitude. Fortunately, just before the flying public finally lost all faith in the safety of aircraft flight, the problem was identified and rectified.

Today all components have to be 'lifed' in terms of the number of loading cycles that they can be subjected to, and the actual loading cycles on highly stressed members such as wings have to be counted and meticulously logged. Now cabin pressurisation and de-pressurisation occurs once per flight, but wing structural members undergo a loading and unloading cycle every time they fly through a turbulent gust which creates a bump in the ride. Since airliner wings are typically designed for a load factor of only about 2, any load greater than the weight produces stresses in the wing not very far removed from the design maximum, and hence from the elastic limit. Consequently designers have to take gust loading of wings very carefully into account when designing the wing structure.

MODELLING A GUST

How can we talk about the effects of gusts in a way that can be modelled and analysed by a precise (mathematical) approach, rather than just referring to a 'bumpy' ride? It will be useful to try and interpret what is going on in terms of *cause* and *effect*, in the way that so many physical relationships are expressed, as we discussed at length in Chapter 6 in the section headed 'Viscosity'. As in that section, if we are lucky we may discover that we have nice tidy proportional relationships to deal with. We will start off by stating unequivocally that the cause is the gust, and the effect is the resulting bump in the ride. How can we express these two items in terms of measurable quantities that we can give numbers to?

Let us first of all answer this for the effect, the bump. From the foregoing discussion, it is clear that the bumpiness of ride of an aircraft is very closely related to the temporary additional amount of lift that occurs on the wings as a result of going through a gust. Lift is a force, and a force causes a mass to accelerate. If the lift on the wings of the aircraft (for instance during a banked turn) is twice the weight, then using the symbol n for the load factor we say that $n = 2$. Alternatively, in terms of the acceleration produced, we say that the aircraft is 'pulling $2g$', which means that it is experiencing an acceleration (resulting from the total lift force) equal to twice the acceleration that would be produced by the weight of the aircraft acting alone on its mass, since the latter is exactly what g stands for.

Now a bump constitutes a bit of additional lift, but probably not normally of the same order of magnitude as the additional lift required for a banked turn. (It may feel more, but that is because it happens suddenly.) In normal straight level flight the load factor n of an aircraft is equal to one, (since lift equals weight), and so we will simply define the size of the additional bit of lift that we call a bump as Δn, which (as in Chapter 6 page 126) we read as 'delta n' or 'a little bit of n'. Remember that the Δ is not a number multiplying by n, but that whenever the two symbols appear together like this they have the above meaning. So to summarise, the bump, the effect of a gust, has magnitude Δn where n is the aircraft load factor.

Let us now turn to think about the cause. This on the face of it is rather more tricky, since the cause is an element of turbulence in the air, and by its very definition turbulence implies random motion. So we are going to have to stylise our random turbulent eddy of air, in order that it can represent most closely what actually causes the bump. First of all let us assume that our turbulent eddy is a cylindrical flow with its axis parallel to the lifting line of the wing, so that the entire wing of the aircraft is uniformly and symmetrically affected by the gust. Alternatively, if that sounds too far fetched, you may assume that the aircraft is so small relative to the gust that the whole of the aircraft may be regarded as a point. This may not be a very accurate picture of the reality, but it is sufficient for us to build a model which will enable us to find out about the dependencies that we are looking for.

Next, we think of this cylindrical gust as consisting of four major portions of air flow in the four directions relative to the aircraft's flight: rearwards, downwards, forwards and upwards consecutively (or they could equally well be in the opposite order). Now the rearwards and forwards parts of the eddy simply produce small changes in the aircraft's speed, which change the lift, but by such a tiny amount that we can conveniently ignore them. So we are left with the downwards and upwards portions, which are positive and negative vertical velocities. It is these that are of interest to us, because a downward velocity here is very much like the downwash (and *vice versa*) that we were considering in Chapters 12 and 13, and it affects the angle of attack and hence the lift coefficient. The main difference is that this vertical velocity is now transient rather than permanent.

As in our previous thinking about downwash and upwash, so now, it is convenient to think directly of the change that is produced to the wing angle of attack rather than considering the horizontal and vertical velocity components of the air flow separately. Therefore we will say that our stylised gust is identified by the fact that it produces a temporary increase in angle of attack that we will call $\Delta \alpha$, 'delta alpha' or 'a little bit of alpha'. This $\Delta \alpha$, then, is the cause, and its effect is a bump of magnitude Δn.

We are now ready to establish a relationship between $\Delta \alpha$ and Δn. To do so, we will start by developing a relationship between α and n based on a formula with which we are already familiar, and will then see how it can be adapted to serve our purpose. The related equation with which we are already familiar is our old friend the lift formula:

$$L = C_L \cdot \tfrac{1}{2}\rho V^2 S$$

We are not going to need to separate out the bits of $\tfrac{1}{2}\rho V^2$, and so we will give it a single letter name. Since it is a pressure, the dynamic pressure, and since p is usually used for static pressure, we will use the next letter q to stand for the dynamic pressure $\frac{1}{2}\rho V^2$ from now on. This is very common practice in aviation circles, and the letter 'q' is frequently used in speech to mean 'dynamic pressure'. If, for instance, you hear a pilot referring to 'q-feel', you will know roughly what he is talking about. The formula now reads

$$L = C_L\, qS$$

Now in this formula we have the lift coefficient C_L appearing, but for our purposes we require instead to see the angle of attack, and so we need to know the relationship between them. Although we will lose a little bit of generality, let us assume for simplicity that the wing of the aircraft has a symmetrical aerofoil section, so that the lift curve (the graph of C_L against α) goes through the origin. Furthermore, we will assume that the graph is a straight line and C_L is proportional to α. The relationship between C_L and α is thus

$$C_L = a\alpha$$

where a is the slope of the lift curve, the constant of proportionality. (It is common practice to use the letter a for this purpose.) Substituting this in the lift formula gives

$$L = a\alpha qS$$

Another change that we must make to the formula is to introduce the load factor n. Now n is defined as Lift $\div$ Weight (or L/W), and so in place of L in the formula we can write nW. In doing so, note that we have replaced one variable quantity L by another variable quantity n, the weight W being a constant. We thus have

$$nW = a\alpha qS$$

There is a useful quantity called the aircraft's 'wing loading', which is defined as the total weight divided by the wing plan area, (W/S). Very often when talking about aeroplanes and their wings, wishing to compare like with like, one is not quite sure whether one should be comparing aircraft of the same weight W, or aircraft of the same approximate size as represented by the wing plan area S. Often what we are really interested in is neither of these two quantities, but rather the relationship between them, the amount of weight distributed over each unit of area of the wing, or in other words the wing loading W/S. We will therefore divide both sides of the formula by S, and then bracket together the expression (W/S) and keep it as one term from now on:

$$n(W/S) = a\alpha q$$

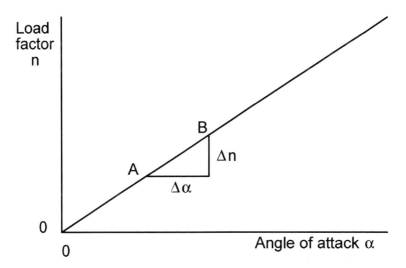

Figure 14.1 Relationship of Gust and Effect to Graph of Load Factor Against Angle of Attack

Finally, we would like the formula in a form which will allow us to extract the nature of the relationship between the effect of a gust Δn and the cause $\Delta \alpha$. To do this we will isolate n on the left-hand side by dividing both sides by the bracket (W/S), thus expressing n as a function of α:

$$n = \left(\frac{aq}{(W/S)} \right) \alpha$$

Very gratifyingly, we see from this formula that, for a given aircraft (which fixes W and S) flying at a given speed and height (which fixes the dynamic pressure q) and with a fixed lift curve slope a (which for the moment, but not for much longer, we can regard as constant at about 2π, as we saw in Chapter 9 under the heading 'Aerofoil Characteristics'), all the contents of the large brackets in the formula, and hence the value of the bracket itself, are constant. Thus the load factor n is directly proportional to the angle of attack α, and the overall quantity in the large brackets is the constant of proportionality.

This makes the final stage in the development of the required formula very simple. In Figure 14.1, which shows a proportional relationship between load factor and angle of attack for our aircraft, let us assume that the aircraft has been flying steadily at the point A on the graph, when it suddenly flies through a gust. As a result the angle of attack increases by $\Delta\alpha$, the load factor increases by Δn, and the aircraft is now flying (just for the duration of the gust) at point B on the graph. Now the slope of the graph line between A and B is the same as that of the whole graph, and so we can use exactly the same constant of proportionality to express the desired relationship between $\Delta\alpha$ and Δn as we had in the α -n relationship. Thus our final required formula is

$$\Delta n = \left(\frac{aq}{(W/S)} \right)\Delta\alpha$$

So far we have thought of this formula as showing us how the Δn effect of the gust varies with the size of the gust $\Delta\alpha$, all other things remaining constant. What we now want to do is to imagine that the aircraft flies through a 'standard', fixed-sized gust, and see how the various quantities inside the large bracket impinge on Δn and thus how each of them affects the hardness of the aircraft's ride. In other words, we are now going to let $\Delta\alpha$ remain constant, and, one at a time, we will allow the other quantities on the right-hand side of the equation to vary, and we will examine what effect this has on Δn, the ride hardness.

FACTORS AFFECTING RIDE HARDNESS

A few paragraphs back we were reminded of the fact that the lift curve slope of an aerofoil is about 2π, a little over 6. But this was a result that emerged from the ideal flow theory applied to a two-dimensional aerofoil, and we have not reconsidered this result at all since we began in Chapter 12 to look at more realistic three-dimensional wings with wing-tips. This we must now do. We will not need to use the sophisticated lifting line model that we developed in Chapter 13, but instead can go back to using the simpler horseshoe model that we introduced in Chapter 12. In that chapter we explained that, because of the existence of wing-tips and hence wing-tip vortices, there is always a downwash everywhere on and behind the wings of an aircraft, and that this affects both the lift and also the drag produced by the wing. Whereas our attention in that chapter was directed from that point onwards firmly along the drag branch, our task now is to consider the effect of downwash on the lift of the wing. We will want to refer to Figure 12.3 once or twice, and so it will be useful to have a finger in its page.

To refresh our memory, the aerofoil shape in Figure 12.3 represents the mean section of the wing of an aircraft in level flight. The effective air flow at the wing itself is assumed to have the average of the 'before' and 'after' free stream directions, and consequently it is inclined downwards by an angle that is half-way between the horizontal free stream ahead and the downstream free stream direction behind the wing. The angle between the downstream flow direction and the upstream free stream direction is arbitrarily given the value of 2ε, and so the effective free stream direction at the wing itself is inclined at an angle ε, called the downwash angle, to the upstream free stream direction.

At our previous encounter with this diagram, the point of note was that the lift force direction was inclined backwards from the normal to the upstream free stream direction, so that it possessed a drag component. On the present occasion, however, it is not so much the direction of the lift force that exercises us, but its magnitude. The figure does not show us how much less overall lift force is being produced than would be the case if there were no downwash, but we know that (assuming the aerofoil to be symmetrical for simplicity) the lift force is proportional to the angle of attack, and that this has been reduced by ε, or in other words by a fraction ε/α of its two-dimensional value. In the illustrative Figure 12.3 the proportion appears to be round about 1/3 of the two-dimensional value, and so we would appear to be talking about a substantial short-fall of lift.

Since the downwash, and hence the short-fall in lift, increases in proportion to the angle of attack, it follows that the entire lift curve is modified to a new proportional line at a lower lift curve slope, as shown in Figure 14.2. It is clear that the lift coefficient at any given angle of attack (e.g. on the dashed line) is substantially lower for the finite wing, and so the lift curve slope (a in the gust formula) is considerably reduced. To achieve any required increase in lift coefficient along the flatter lift curve, it will be necessary to increase the angle of attack, and hence pitch up the nose of the aircraft, considerably more than would be the case if the wing were infinitely long.

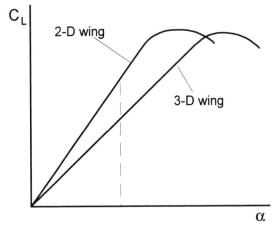

Figure 14.2   Comparison Between Two-dimensional and Three-dimensional Lift Curves

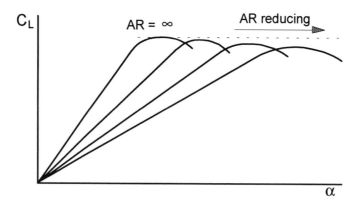

Figure 14.3   Variation of Lift Curve Slope with Aspect Ratio

If an aircraft has a high aspect ratio, a large proportion of the wing is so far removed from the tips that it scarcely feels the downwash effects of the small wing-tip vortices, and so it approximates to a two-dimensional wing. As the aspect ratio reduces, however, the proportion of the wing close to the tips and strongly influenced by them increases, so that at very low aspect ratios the downwash field is very strong over the whole wing. Thus a substantially greater increase in angle of attack is needed on a very low aspect ratio aircraft to produce a certain required increase in lift coefficient, than is required for a high aspect ratio aircraft. As shown in Figure 14.3, this implies that the lift curve slope reduces as the aspect ratio increases. Notice also that as the aspect ratio increases the maximum C_L value remains substantially unaltered but reduces a little, as shown by the dotted line.

Aspect ratio is not the only feature of a wing's planform that affects the lift curve slope. Similar behaviour occurs as a result of sweeping a wing. When an infinitely long wing is swept by shearing through an angle Λ (as in Figure 11.8) various components of the lift formula are affected in various ways, and a detailed analysis is by no means straightforward. However, the overall effect is that the lift curve slope decreases as the sweep increases, as shown in Figure 14.4. Furthermore, as our reading of Chapter 13 will have led us to expect, the maximum C_L value available at higher angles of wing sweep drops off quite markedly as the spanwise component of the flow strengthens with sweep, the boundary layer thickens and the tip region shows signs of stalling.

This restricted range of lift coefficient values would appear to limit the usefulness of a swept wing. In practice, however, the lift is often strongly augmented by vortex lift produced by highly swept leading edge root extensions or by the swept leading edge itself. Consequently lift curve slopes resembling Figure 14.5 may be obtained. Thus mod-

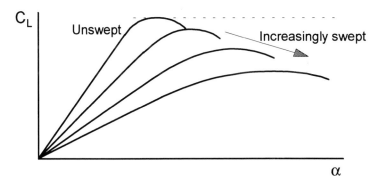

Figure 14.4   Variation of Lift Curve Slope with Angle of Sweep

ern fighters often operate at extremely large angles of attack, appearing to an observer as if they ought to be stalled, but actually producing very strong wing lift.

The effects of sweep and of low aspect ratio on the lift curve slope have a profound effect on the handling qualities of the aircraft as experienced by the pilot. Pilots transferring from relatively straight winged, high aspect ratio aircraft to aircraft with this type of planform are immediately struck by the very much greater degree of nose-up pitch that is required to execute a pull-up or a turn. More change in angle of attack is required to achieve the same change in lift coefficient, because of the reduced lift curve slope. But it is the corollary of

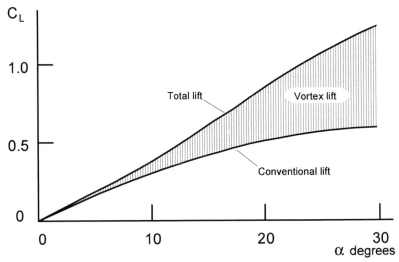

Figure 14.5   Conventional and Vortex Lift Contributions to Lift of a Delta Wing

this, that for the same increase in angle of attack there is a smaller increase in lift coefficient, that provides for a smoother ride, as we shall see in the next paragraph. The handling characteristics of the swept-wing aircraft are also very greatly influenced by the ubiquitous presence (particularly at higher lift coefficient values) of the ram's horn vortex discussed in Chapter 13. One of the first things taught to pilots progressing from flying straight-winged aircraft to swept-winged combat aircraft is to be able to distinguish between a stall and the presence of a leading edge vortex. At typical 'circuit' speeds, (i.e. when flying slowly in the vicinity of an airport whilst preparing to land) the high angle of attack demanded means that the pilot of the swept-wing aircraft is continuously flying with turbulence generated by a ram's horn vortex, and this he finds strange since in all of his straight-wing flying he was taught emphatically to avoid buffet, which signified an incipient stall.

We have seen that the lift curve slope a in the gust formula depends on the aspect ratio and the sweep of the aircraft's wing. An aircraft with highly swept or short stocky wings (or both) has a much lower lift curve slope, and hence a lower value of Δn for a given gust, than one with unswept slender wings. Therefore typical high-speed rugged fighter aircraft are well shaped to provide a much smoother and less bumpy ride than straight slender winged aircraft. For this reason, even flying at a subsonic speed well below the critical Mach number, the pilot of a variable sweep combat aircraft such as a Tornado or an F-111 flying at low level towards a combat zone will usually select wings swept back in order to provide a smoother ride than with unswept wings. Not only does this increase the wing sweep, but it also very substantially reduces the aspect ratio, providing a double benefit.

Having looked at sweep and aspect ratio, there is another feature of the planform which also has a bearing on the aircraft's gust response, and that is the wing loading (W/S). Since this appears on the bottom of the fraction in the large brackets, it implies that a larger value of wing loading will give a smaller value of Δn and a smoother ride. With today's greatly improved aerofoils it is becoming possible to have more and more weight supported by each unit of area of wing surface, giving improved gust response, and this is beneficial both to low-flying combat aircraft and also in designing airliners, where fatigue considerations are somewhat less demanding than with the lower wing loadings of the past.

But there is no such thing as a free meal, and high wing loading brings a penalty with it. It can be shown simply by manipulating the lift formula that the speed at which an aircraft in level flight stalls is proportional to the square root of the aircraft's wing loading. This has meant that the trend towards increased wing loading has brought with it the need for higher take-off and landing speeds. This is particularly noticeable in modern fighter aircraft, which seem to have smaller and smaller wings, carry heavier and heavier loads, and land and take-off ever faster.

We have seen that there are a number of features of the planform of an aircraft that will have a direct and substantial effect on the aircraft's response to gusts. The one final piece of information that we can obtain from the gust formula relates not to the design of the aircraft but rather to the way in which it is being flown. It tells us that the hardness of ride is directly proportional to q, the dynamic pressure. Now the dynamic pressure is given by $\frac{1}{2}\rho V^2$, and so it is clear that flying at high speed, and flying at low level in high-density air, are both things that will produce a large value of q and hence a bumpy ride. This is unfortunate, since this is exactly where the combat aircraft pilot on a low-level mission has to operate. Furthermore, it is down here that the air is most turbulent because of the wind passing over ground obstructions, so that the $\Delta\alpha$ term is also larger than it would be at a greater height. It appears that the military tacticians' insistence on flying fast and low make it inevitable that the pilot and aircraft will have to endure a rough ride.

Index